Glencoe McGraw-Hill

Teacher Edition

Mastering the ISTEP+

Practice and Assessment for the Indiana Statewide Testing for Educational Progress-Plus

Grade 6

The McGraw·Hill Companies

 Glencoe

Send all inquiries to:
Glencoe/McGraw-Hill
8787 Orion Place
Columbus, OH 43240-4027

ISBN: 978-0-07-893997-6
MHID: 0-07-893997-6

Mastering the ISTEP, Grade 6 TE

Printed in the United States of America.

1 2 3 4 5 6 7 8 9 10 009 17 16 15 14 13 12 11 10 09

Contents

To the Student

Indiana's Academic Standards describe what mathematics you should learn this school year. Your textbook, *Math Connects, Course 1*, is one of the main tools you will use to learn this math. If you master the mathematics, you should be able to do well on the ISTEP+ test in the spring.

This workbook, ***Mastering the ISTEP+***, is another tool to help you review the mathematics you will need for performing well on the test this year. It is actually two workbooks in one.

This side of the workbook contains tools to help you determine which of the standards you know well and which ones you still need to practice. The questions are similar to those you might see on the ISTEP+ test.

- The **Reference Sheet** on the next page lists some of the formulas that you should be familiar with in order to solve problems more quickly.
- A **Prerequisite Skills Check** tests the standards from last year, which are tools you'll need for this year's mathematics.
- The **Diagnostic Test** assesses the math skills you will learn this year.
- The **Practice by Standard** section contains worksheets that focus on each standard individually. These also can be used to practice types of questions you may have answered incorrectly on the Diagnostic Test.
- In the **Problem Solving** section, you will learn how to read word problems and find the best ways to solve them.
- **Practice Tests** are included to help determine how much you have learned this year.

If you flip this workbook over, you will find the ***Study Guide and Intervention and Practice Workbook, Course 1*** that goes along with your student edition textbook. There are two pages of practice for each lesson in your textbook. These pages review the math being taught in the lesson and give you practice problems for that math.

Remember that the most important thing is to concentrate on learning the mathematics. When you know the math, you have the power to do well on the test.

Mathematics Reference Sheet

Figure		Formulas for Area (A) and Circumferences (C)	
Triangle		$A = \frac{1}{2}bh$	Area = $\frac{1}{2}$ × base × height
Rectangle		$A = \ell w$	Area = length × width
Trapezoid		$A = \frac{1}{2}h(b_1 + b_2)$	Area = $\frac{1}{2}$ × height × sum of bases
Parallelogram		$A = bh$	Area = base × height
Square		$A = s^2$	Area = side × side
Circle		$A = \pi r^2$ $C = 2\pi r$	Area = π × square of radius Circumference = 2 × π × radius $\pi \approx 3.14$ or $\frac{22}{7}$

Figure		Formulas for Volume (V) and Surface Area (SA)	
Rectangular Prism		$V = \ell wh$ $SA = 2\ell w + 2hw + 2\ell h$	Volume = length × width × height Surface Area = 2(length × width) + 2(height × width) + 2(length × height)
Cylinder		$V = \pi r^2 h$ $SA = 2\pi r^2 + 2\pi rh$	Volume = π × square of radius × height Surface Area = 2 × π × square of radius + 2 × π × radius × height

Conversions

1 foot = 12 inches
1 yard = 3 feet
1 mile = 5,280 feet
1 mile = 1,760 yards

1 pound = 16 ounces
1 ton = 2,000 pounds

1 minute = 60 seconds
1 hour = 60 minutes
1 day = 24 hours

1 cup = 8 fluid ounces
1 pint = 2 cups
1 quart = 2 pints
1 gallon = 4 quarts

1 meter = 1000 millimeters
1 meter = 100 centimeters
1 kilometer = 1000 meters

1 gram = 1000 milligrams
1 kilogram = 1000 grams

1 liter = 1000 cubic centimeters
1 liter = 1000 milliliters

How To Use This Book

This workbook is a combination of two workbooks, ***Mastering the ISTEP+, Grade 6*** and ***Math Connects Course 1 Study Guide and Intervention and Practice Workbook.***

Mastering the ISTEP+

This side of the workbook includes various practice opportunities to help students master the mathematics needed to do well on the ISTEP+. The questions included in this workbook are similar to those that students might encounter on the ISTEP+, but are not released or actual test questions that students would encounter when being assessed. The questions are annotated in the Teacher Edition with the standard assessed, the DOK level, the lesson from *Math Connects, Course 1* that most closely addresses the standard, and the correct answer.

- The **Problem Solving** section (pages IN1-IN16) provides instruction on a problem solving plan, focusing on how to attack the types of problems that might appear in Constructed-Response or Extended-Response questions. Students progress from a step-by-step approach of leading questions to a guided approach with hints and then onto independent problem solving.

- **Prerequisite Skills Check** (pages IN17-IN24) is an assessment of the standard indicators from the previous grade level. This test can be used at the beginning of the school year to evaluate your students' mastery of the Grade 5 Mathematics Content Standards. All questions are in multiple-choice format. The Prerequisite Skills Check Answer Key and Item Analysis (pages INxxv-INxxix) in the Teacher Edition of this workbook includes not only the correct answer but also the Grade 5 standard assessed by each question and an item analysis of wrong answers. This information can be used to determine which topics need to be reinforced before attempting the standards for Grade 6.

- Use the **Diagnostic Test** (pages IN25-IN34) to evaluate your students' understanding of the Grade 6 Mathematics Standard Indicators. You may wish to give this test all at once or break it up into smaller assessment sessions sometime after mid-year. All questions are in multiple-choice format. The Data-Driven Decision Making table (pages INxv-INxxiv) provides correct answers, an item analysis for incorrect answers, and resources in this workbook and in *Glencoe Math Connects, Course 1* to reinforce skills for any standard(s) not mastered.

How To Use This Book (continued)

- **Practice by Standard** (pages IN35-IN58) includes one page of practice problems for each of the Grade 6 standard indicators. Problems in this section include multiple-choice and constructed-response formats. You may wish to assign specific pages for each student based on their performance on the Diagnostic Test. You can also use these pages as a general review of the Grade 6 standards before students take the Practice Tests. Each question is referenced with the lesson from *Math Connects* that corresponds to the topic being assessed.

- There are several **Practice Tests** (pages IN59-IN79) included in this workbook.
  - The first Practice Test is labeled Applied Skills and contains open-ended questions that are similar to constructed-response and extended-response questions that students might experience in the early spring (March) ISTEP+ testing. Students use their problem solving skills to show all their work and answer the question. You may wish to have students complete the Problem Solving section prior to giving this test. Scoring rubrics can be found on pages INxxxi and INxxxii.
  - Practice Test, Sessions 1 and 2, contain the multiple-choice questions similar to those on the ISTEP+ in the late spring (May) testing. These can be given at the same time or given on separate days.

Math Connects, Course 1 Study Guide and Intervention and Practice Workbook

Flip this book and you will access the other workbook, *Study Guide and Intervention and Practice Workbook* that accompanies the *Glencoe Math Connects, Course 1.* This provides additional instruction and practice for each lesson in the student textbook.

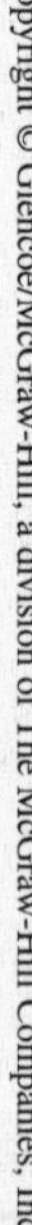

Indiana's Academic Standards

Grade 6 Mathematics

Indiana's Academic Standards for Mathematics are composed of three areas of emphasis: the Core Standards, the Process Standards, and the Content Standards.

Grade 6 CORE STANDARDS
Core Standard 1: Number Sense and Computation
1. Positive and Negative Numbers Understand and apply the concept of positive and negative numbers. Add, subtract, multiply and divide positive and negative integers. Represent negative numbers, and computation with negative numbers, on a number line. *[Standard Indicators: 6.1.1, 6.1.5]*
2. Percent Representations Use percents to represent parts of a whole. Represent numbers as fractions, decimals and percents. *[Standard Indicators: 6.1.3, 6.1.4]*
3. Multiplication and Division of Fractions and Decimals Understand and perform multiplication and division with positive decimals and fractions. *[Standard Indicator: 6.1.6]*
4. Ratio and Rate Solve simple ratio and rate problems using multiplication and division. *[Standard Indicator: 6.1.7, 6.1.9]*
Core Standard 2: Geometry and Measurement
1. Angles and Polygons Use properties of complementary, supplementary and vertical angles, and properties of triangles and quadrilaterals, to find missing angles. *[Standard Indicators: 6.3.1, 6.3.2]*
2. Shapes and Solids Find and use the circumference and area of circles and the surface area of right prisms and cylinders. *[Standard Indicators: 6.3.3, 6.3.5]*
Core Standard 3: Algebra and Functions
1. Linear Equation Write and solve one-step equations and inequalities in one variable. *[Standard Indicators: 6.2.1, 6.2.3]*
2. Linear Equations Use equations and graphs of linear functions to represent a given situation. *[Standard Indicators: 6.2.4, 6.2.5]*

Indiana's Academic Standards

Grade 6 Mathematics (continued)

PROCESS STANDARDS
Process Standard 1: Problem Solving
• Build new mathematical knowledge through problem solving. • Solve problems that arise in mathematics and in other contexts. • Apply and adapt a variety of appropriate strategies to solve problems. • Monitor and reflect on the process of mathematical problem solving.
Process Standard 2: Reasoning and Proof
• Recognize reasoning and proof as fundamental aspects of mathematics. • Make and investigate mathematical conjectures. • Develop and evaluate mathematical arguments and proofs. • Select and use various types of reasoning and methods of proof.
Process Standard 3: Communication
• Organize and consolidate their mathematical thinking through communication. • Communicate their mathematical thinking coherently and clearly to peers, teachers, and others. • Analyze and evaluate the mathematical thinking and strategies of others. • Use the language of mathematics to express mathematical ideas precisely.
Process Standard 4: Connections
• Recognize and use connections among mathematical ideas. • Understand how mathematical ideas interconnect and build on one another to produce a coherent whole. • Recognize and apply mathematics in contexts outside of mathematics.
Process Standard 5: Representation
• Create and use representations to organize, record, and communicate mathematical ideas. • Select, apply, and translate among mathematical representations to solve problems. • Use representations to model and interpret physical, social, and mathematical phenomena.
Process Standard 6: Estimation and Mental Computation
• Know and apply appropriate methods for estimating the results of computations. • Round numbers to a specified place value. • Use estimation to decide whether answers are reasonable. • Decide when estimation is an appropriate strategy for solving a problem. • Determine appropriate accuracy and precision of measurements in problem situations. • Use properties of numbers and operations to perform mental computation. • Recognize when the numbers involved in a computation allow for a mental computation strategy.

Indiana's Academic Standards

Grade 6 Mathematics (continued)

PROCESS STANDARDS (continued)
Process Standard 7: Technology

• Technology should be used as a tool in mathematics education to support and extend the mathematics curriculum.
• Technology can contribute to concept development, simulation, representation, communication, and problem solving.
• The challenge is to ensure that technology supports-but is not a substitute for-the development of skills with basic operations, quantitative reasoning, and problem solving skills.
  ○ Elementary students should learn how to perform thoroughly the basic arithmetic operations independent of the use of a calculator.
  ○ Graphing calculators should be used to enhance middle school and high school students' understanding and skills.
  ○ The focus must be on learning mathematics, using technology as a tool rather than as an end in itself.

Indiana's Academic Standards

Grade 6 Mathematics (continued)

This diagram shows what each part of the standard code represents.

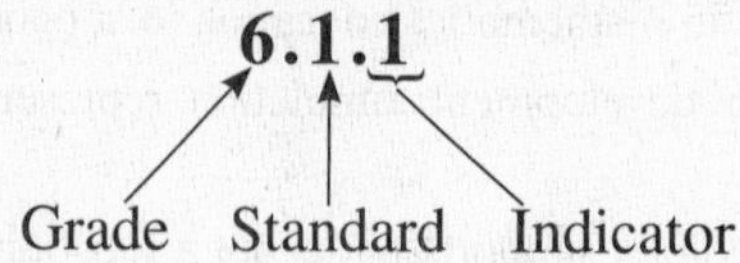

Grade 6 ACADEMIC STANDARDS AND STANDARD INDICATORS	
Standard 1: Number Sequence and Computation	
6.1.1	Compare, order, and represent on a number line positive and negative integers, fractions, decimals (to hundredths), and mixed numbers.
6.1.2	Interpret the absolute value of a number as the distance from zero on a number line, find the absolute value of real numbers, and know that the distance between two numbers on the number line is the absolute value of their difference.
6.1.3	Use percents to represent parts of a whole and find the percentage part of a whole.
6.1.4	Recognize commonly used fractions, decimals, and percents and their equivalents and convert between any two representations of any non-negative rational number without the use of a calculator.
6.1.5	Solve problems involving addition, subtraction, multiplication and division of integers and represent computation with integers on a number line. Describe the effect of operations with numbers less than zero.
6.1.6	Solve problems involving addition, subtraction, multiplication and division of positive fractions and decimals and explain why a particular operation was used for a given situation.
6.1.7	Interpret ratios, model ratios, and use ratios to show the relative sizes of two quantities. • Use the notations: a/b, a to b and a:b. • Write equivalent ratios, • Express a ratio in its simplest form. • Find the ratio of two given quantities.
6.1.8	Recognize proportional relationships and solve problems involving proportional relationships. Find the missing term in a pair of equivalent ratios and find one quantity given the other quantity and their ratio.
6.1.9	Solve simple percent, ratio and proportion problems, including problems involving discounts at sales, interest earned and tips.

Indiana's Academic Standards

Grade 6 Mathematics (continued)

Grade 6 ACADEMIC STANDARDS AND STANDARD INDICATORS (continued)
Standard 2: Algebra and Functions
6.2.1 Write and solve one-step linear equations and inequalities in one variable.
6.2.2 Write and use formulas with up to three variables to solve problems.
6.2.3 Apply the correct order of operations and the properties of real numbers [identity, inverse, commutative, associative and distributive properties] to evaluate numerical expressions, including those that use grouping symbols such as parentheses. Justify each step in the process.
6.2.4 Identify and graph ordered pairs in all four quadrants of the coordinate plane.
6.2.5 Solve problems involving linear functions with integer values. Create a table and graph the resulting ordered pairs of integers on a grid. Look for patterns in how a change in one variable relates to a change in the second variable and write the equation.
Standard 3: Geometry and Measurement
6.3.1 Identify, draw and use the properties of vertical, adjacent, complementary, and supplementary angles, and properties of triangles and quadrilaterals, to solve problems involving a missing angle.
6.3.2 Recognize that the sum of the interior angles of any triangle is 180° and that the sum of the interior angles of any quadrilateral is 360°. Use this information to solve problems.
6.3.3 Develop and use the formulas for the circumference and area of a circle.
6.3.4 Recognize that real-world measurements are approximations. Identify appropriate instruments and units for a given measurement situation, taking into account the precision of the measurement desired.
6.3.5 Develop and use the formulas for the surface area and volume of a cylinder and find the surface area and volume of three-dimensional objects built from rectangular solids and cylinders.
Standard 4: Data Analysis and Probability
6.4.1 Construct and analyze circle graphs and stem-and-leaf plots.
6.4.2 Choose the appropriate display for a single variable set of data from bar graphs, line graphs, circle graphs and stem-and-leaf plots. Justify the choice of data display.
6.4.3 Compare the mean, median and mode for a set of data and explain which measure is most appropriate in a given context.
6.4.4 Solve problems involving probability as a measure of chance and verify that the probabilities computed are reasonable.
6.4.5 Recognize and represent probabilities as ratios, measures of relative frequency, decimals between 0 and 1, and percentages between 0 and 100.

Name Date

Diagnostic Test

Data-Driven Decision Making

Item	Academic Standard (DOK)	What's the Math	Item Analysis	*Math Connects, Grade 6*	Practice in This Workbook
1	6.3.1 (DOK1)	find a missing angle	A, B, D: did not subtract 75 from 180 to find the supplementary angle. C: CORRECT	**SE:** Lesson 9–3	p. IN51
2	6.1.1 (DOK2)	order positive and negative fractions and decimals	F: ordered the fractions first, then the decimals G: ordered the decimals first, then the fractions H: CORRECT J: overlooked the negative sign	**SE:** Lesson 4–6	p. IN37
3	6.1.5 (DOK1)	solve problems involving addition of integers	A: CORRECT B: started at 0 and added 16 C: added incorrectly D: added 3 and 16 instead of −3 and 16	**SE:** Lesson 11–2	p. IN41
4	6.1.9 (DOK2)	solve simple percent problems, including problems involving tips	F: calculated the tip correctly but did not add this to the dinner amount G: calculated the tip correctly but subtracted this from the dinner amount H: did not calcutate the tip properly; added $2 to the dinner amount J: CORRECT	**SE:** Lesson IN2	p. IN45
5	6.2.1 (DOK1)	write one-step linear equations with one variable	A, C, D: did not use an equation with division B: CORRECT	**SE:** Lesson 1–8	p. IN46
6	6.1.6 (DOK1)	solve problems involving addition of positive fractions	F: added the numerators and denominators G: used 48 as the common denominator and did not find the correct equivalent fractions H: used 18 as the common denominator and calculated incorrectly J: CORRECT	**SE:** Lesson 5–4	p. IN42

Name Date

Diagnostic Test

Data-Driven Decision Making (continued)

Item	Academic Standard (DOK)	What's the Math	Item Analysis	*Math Connects, Grade 6*	Practice in This Workbook
7	6.3.3 (DOK1)	use the formula for the circumference of a circle	A: CORRECT B: multiplied the radius instead of the diameter C: used the formula for area instead of circumference D: used the diameter as the radius and multiplied it by 2	**SE:** Lesson 10–2	p. IN53
8	6.2.1 (DOK1)	write one-step linear expressions with one variable	F: CORRECT G, H, J: did not use an expression with multiplication	**SE:** Lesson 1–8	p. IN46
9	6.1.8 (DOK1)	solve problems involving proportional relationships	A: CORRECT B: divided miles by hours C: multiplied the hours by the miles hiked in the ratio D: multiplied the number of hours to hike 5 miles by the total number of miles	**SE:** Lesson 6–3	p. IN44
10	6.1.1 (DOK1)	represent decimals on a number line	F: located 0.8 G: located 1.2 H: CORRECT J: located 2.8	**SE:** Lesson 3–1	p. IN37
11	6.2.3 (DOK1)	apply the correct order of operations to evaluate numerical expressions	A: did the operations in order instead of adding last B: added first, then multiplied and divided C: CORRECT D: did the operations in wrong order	**SE:** Lesson 1–4	p. IN48
12	6.2.1 (DOK1)	solve one-step linear equations	F: added 48 + 32 and used incorrect sign G: CORRECT H: switched sign J: added 48 + 32	**SE:** Lesson 12–3	p. IN46

Name Date

Diagnostic Test

Data-Driven Decision Making (continued)

Item	Academic Standard (DOK)	What's the Math	Item Analysis	*Math Connects, Grade 6*	Practice in This Workbook
13	6.3.2 (DOK1)	recognize that the sum of the interior angles of a triangle is 180°; use this to find the value of a third angle	A, B, D: did not use the fact that the sum of the angles in a triangle equals 180° C: CORRECT	**SE:** Lesson 9–4	p. IN52
14	6.1.7 (DOK2)	express a ratio in simplest form	F: reduced the ratio incorrectly G: reduced the ratio incorrectly H: switched the order of terms in the ratio J: CORRECT	**SE:** Lesson 6–1	p. IN43
15	6.4.4 (DOK1)	find probability of an event happening	A: found probability of choosing a nonrookie card B: simplified the fraction incorrectly C: CORRECT D: simplified the fraction incorrectly	**SE:** Lesson 7–4	p. IN59
16	6.4.3 (DOK2)	compare mean and median for a set of data	F: did not realize that adding or taking away data changes the mean G: did not realize it changes the median only slightly H: CORRECT J: did not realize that adding data usually changes the median	**SE:** Lesson 2–7	p. IN58
17	6.2.2 (DOK1)	write and use formulas with up to three variables to solve problems	A: CORRECT B: did not understand 2% as 0.02 and did not multiply C: multiplied by 0.2 instead of 0.02 D: calculated the final account balance rather than just the interest	**SE:** Lesson IN3	p. IN47

Name Date

Diagnostic Test

Data-Driven Decision Making (continued)

Item	Academic Standard (DOK)	What's the Math	Item Analysis	*Math Connects, Grade 6*	Practice in This Workbook
18	6.1.4 (DOK1)	convert between a commonly used fraction and its percent	F: did not know how to convert between a fraction and a decimal G: found the fraction that is equivalent to 70% H: switched the numerator and denominator of the fraction J: CORRECT	**SE:** Lesson 7–1	p. IN40
19	6.4.5 (DOK2)	represent probabilities as decimals	A, B, D: did not calculate the probability correctly C: CORRECT	**SE:** Lesson 7–4	p. IN60
20	6.4.1 (DOK2)	analyze and construct circle graphs	F: selected a graph that shows that Jacob and Emily each raised about the same percent of the money G: selected a graph that shows each person raised the same percent of the money H: CORRECT J: selected a graph that shows that Jacob and Emily each raised about the same percent of the money	**SE:** Lesson 7–2	p. IN56
21	6.1.2 (DOK2)	interpret the absolute value of the difference between two numbers	A: added the absolute value of both temperatures B: CORRECT C: found the difference of the temperatures D: added the absolute value of both temperatures and then used a minus sign	**SE:** Lesson IN1	p. IN38
22	6.1.3 (DOK1)	use percents to represent parts of a whole	F: named a figure that is 80% shaded G: named a figure that is 60% shaded H: CORRECT J: named a figure that is 75% shaded	**SE:** Lesson 7–3	p. IN39

Name Date

Diagnostic Test

Data-Driven Decision Making (continued)

Item	Academic Standard (DOK)	What's the Math	Item Analysis	*Math Connects, Grade 6*	Practice in This Workbook
23	6.2.4 (DOK1)	identify ordered pairs in all four quadrants of the coordinate plane	A: CORRECT B: identified the ordered pair (3, 4) C: identified the ordered pair (−3, −2) D: identified the ordered pair (5, −4)	**SE:** Lesson 11–7	p. IN49
24	6.1.6 (DOK1)	divide positive fractions	F: CORRECT G: added the numerators and denominators H: used the correct reciprocal but then added the numerators and denominators J: multiplied the numerators and denominators	**SE:** Lesson 5–9	p. IN42
25	6.2.5 (DOK2)	solve problems involving linear functions with integer values; use tables and graphs	A: read the graph incorrectly B: read the *x*-axis incorrectly C: reversed the *x* and *y* values D: CORRECT	**SE:** Lesson 4–9	p. IN50
26	6.3.4 (DOK1)	identify appropriate units for a given measurement situation	F: chose a unit that is too small for the measurement situation G: CORRECT H: chose a unit that is too large for the measurement situation J: chose a unit that is too large for the measurement situation	**SE:** Lesson 8–3	p. IN54
27	6.3.5 (DOK2)	find the surface area of a cylinder	A: found the surface area of the bases only B: found the surface area of the sides only C: found the surface area of the sides and one of the bases D: CORRECT	**SE:** Lesson IN5	p. IN55

Name Date

Diagnostic Test

Data-Driven Decision Making (continued)

Item	Academic Standard (DOK)	What's the Math	Item Analysis	*Math Connects, Grade 6*	Practice in This Workbook
28	6.4.5 (DOK1)	represent probability as a ratio	F: CORRECT G: reduced the ratio incorrectly H: used the difference of 100 and 45 as the denominator J: reversed the numerator and denominator	**SE:** Lesson 7–4	p. IN60
29	6.1.4 (DOK1)	express a commonly used percent as a decimal	A: misplaced the decimal point B: named the decimal for 75% C: CORRECT D: misplaced the decimal point	**SE:** Lesson 7–3	p. IN40
30	6.3.3 (DOK1)	use the fomula for the area of a circle	F: multiplied the radius by π G: squared the radius only H: CORRECT J: squared the diameter, instead of the radius, and then multiplied by π	**SE:** Lesson IN4	p. IN53
31	6.2.3 (DOK1)	apply the order of operations to evaluate numerical expressions, including those that use parentheses	A: CORRECT B: did the operations in order instead of multiplying first C: added 6 instead of subtracted 6 D: multiplied last	**SE:** Lesson 1–4	p. IN48
32	6.3.1 (DOK2)	use the properties of triangles and supplementary angles to solve problems involving a missing angle	F: found the measure of $\angle ACB$ rather than the measure of $\angle ACD$ G: may have found the measure of $\angle ACB$ correctly, but subtracted it from 90° rather than from 180° H: made errors in computation J: CORRECT	**SE:** Lesson 9–4	p. IN51

Name Date

Diagnostic Test

Data-Driven Decision Making (continued)

Item	Academic Standard (DOK)	What's the Math	Item Analysis	*Math Connects, Grade 6*	Practice in This Workbook
33	6.1.9 (DOK2)	solve simple percent problems, including problems involving discounts at sales	A: found the correct discount but did not subtract this from the original price B: subtracted $30 instead of calculating 30% C: CORRECT D: found the correct discount but added it to the original price	**SE:** Lesson IN2	p. IN45
34	6.3.5 (DOK1)	find the volume of a cylinder	F: used diameter in formula instead of radius squared G: used diameter times 2 in formula instead of radius squared H: CORRECT J: squared diameter instead of radius in formula	**SE:** Lesson IN5	p. IN55
35	6.4.2 (DOK2)	select most appropriate type of display for a given data set	A: CORRECT B: chose a display used for illustrating the relationship of parts to a whole C: chose a display used for categorical data D: chose a display that illustrates the shape and distribution of a data set	**SE:** Lesson 2–8	p. IN57
36	6.1.8 (DOK1)	find the missing term in a pair of equivalent ratios	F: CORRECT G: added the difference between the denominators to the numerator 2 H: cross-multiplied but did not place the decimal correctly J: cross-multiplied but subtracted 15 instead of dividing by 15	**SE:** Lesson 6–7	p. IN44

Name Date

Diagnostic Test

Data-Driven Decision Making (continued)

Item	Academic Standard (DOK)	What's the Math	Item Analysis	*Math Connects, Grade 6*	Practice in This Workbook
37	6.4.2 (DOK1)	choose the appropriate display for a single variable set of data	A: CORRECT B: chose a display used for showing data collected over a period time C: chose a display that illustrates the shape and distribution of a data set D: chose a display used for illustrating the relationship of parts to a whole	**SE:** Lesson 2–8	p. IN57
38	6.4.3 (DOK2)	compare the mean, median, and mode for a set of data	F, G, J: did not recognize that the mean, median, and mode are equal for this set of data H: CORRECT	**SE:** Lesson 2–7	p. IN58
39	6.4.4 (DOK2)	solve problems involving probability	A: used the same percentage as the number of hamsters B: CORRECT C: divided 30 by 6 and changed it to 50% D: used 6 out of 10 instead of 6 out of 30	**SE:** Lesson 7–4	p. IN59
40	6.1.1 (DOK1)	order decimals	F, G, J: did not order decimals correctly H: CORRECT	**SE:** Lesson 3–2	p. IN37
41	6.1.2 (DOK1)	find the absolute value of real numbers	A: kept the minus sign B: added the digits and kept the minus sign C: added the digits and ignored the minus sign D: CORRECT	**SE:** Lesson IN1	p. IN38
42	6.1.3 (DOK2)	find the percentage part of a whole	F: subtracted 60% of 18,345 from 18,345 G: CORRECT H: added 60 to 18,345 J: added 60% of 18,345 to 18,345	**SE:** Lesson 7–1	p. IN39

Name Date

Diagnostic Test

Data-Driven Decision Making (continued)

Item	Academic Standard (DOK)	What's the Math	Item Analysis	*Math Connects, Grade 6*	Practice in This Workbook
43	6.1.5 (DOK1)	divide integers	A: CORRECT B: divided incorrectly C: used the incorrect sign D: subtracted 3 from 18 instead of dividing	**SE:** Lesson 11–6	p. IN41
44	6.1.7 (DOK1)	use ratios to show the relative sizes of two quantities	F: did not simplify the ratio G: simplified incorrectly H: CORRECT J: reversed the values in the ratio	**SE:** Lesson 6–1	p. IN43
45	6.3.2 (DOK2)	recognize that the sum of the interior angles of any quadrilateral is 360° and use this information to solve problems	A: CORRECT B: found the difference of 122 and 58 C: named the measure of one of the other angles D: found the sum of 58 and 122	**SE:** Lesson 9–5	p. IN52
46	6.3.4 (DOK1)	identify appropriate units for a given measurement situation	F: selected a unit that is too small G: CORRECT H, J: selected units that are too large	**SE:** Lesson 8–3	p. IN54
47	6.1.8 (DOK1)	solve problems involving proportional relationships	A: did not set up the proportion correctly and divided by 12 B. CORRECT C. divided 42 by 3 incorrectly D. did not set up the proportion correctly and multiplied 3 by 42	**SE:** Lesson 6–7	p. IN44

Name Date

Diagnostic Test

Data-Driven Decision Making (continued)

Item	Academic Standard (DOK)	What's the Math	Item Analysis	*Math Connects, Grade 6*	Practice in This Workbook
48	6.3.1 (DOK1)	use the properties of complementary angles to solve problems involving a missing angle	F: estimated rather than calculated the answer G: CORRECT H: subtracted incorrectly J: subtracted 44° from 180° instead of 44° from 90°	**SE:** Lesson 9–3	p. IN51
49	6.4.1 (DOK2)	analyze stem-and-leaf plots	A, B, D: did not read the stem-and-leaf plot correctly C: CORRECT	**SE:** Lesson 2–4	p. IN56

Name Date

Prerequisite Skills Check

Answer Key and Item Analysis

Item	Academic Standard (DOK)	What's the Math	Item Analysis
1	5.1.5 (DOK1)	solve problems involving multiplication	A: subtracted the numbers instead of multiplying B: added the numbers instead of multiplying C: did not regroup correctly when multiplying D: CORRECT
2	5.1.2 (DOK2)	compare fractions with unlike denominators	A, B: did not choose the correct symbol to compare the fractions C: did not correctly find a fraction equivalent to $\frac{1}{3}$ with a denominator of 12 D: CORRECT
3	5.1.1 (DOK1)	write a decimal in word form	A: chose the word form of 9 B: chose the word form of 0.9 C: CORRECT D: chose the word form of 0.009
4	5.1.9 (DOK3)	predict the chance of future events based on data collected from an experiment	A: did not correctly compare the number of red marbles to the total number of marbles B: CORRECT C: chose the bag with the greatest number of red marbles drawn D: chose the bag with the greatest number of marbles
5	5.3.3 (DOK1)	identify a triangular pyramid based on its number of vertices and edges	A: chose a figure that has exactly 5 vertices and 8 edges B: CORRECT C: chose a figure that has exactly 8 vertices and 12 edges D: chose a figure that has no vertices and 2 edges
6	5.3.1 (DOK2)	estimate the measure of an angle	A: chose a measure greater than the measure of the given angle B: CORRECT C, D: chose a measure less than the measure of the given angle
7	5.1.2 (DOK2)	order fractions with unlike denominators from greatest to least	A: ordered the fractions from least to greatest B, C: did not correctly write equivalent fractions with like denominators or did not correctly order the equivalent fractions D: CORRECT
8	5.3.4 (DOK1)	identify a translation	A: CORRECT B, C, D: does not understand transformations
9	5.3.2 (DOK1)	identify an obtuse triangle	A: chose a triangle with a 90° angle B: chose a triangle with 3 equal sides C: CORRECT D: chose a triangle with all acute angles.

Name Date

Prerequisite Skills Check

Answer Key and Item Analysis (continued)

Item	Academic Standard (DOK)	What's the Math	Item Analysis
10	5.2.1 (DOK1)	evaluate an algebraic expression	A: substituted 16 for the variable B: CORRECT C: subtracted instead of multiplying D: divided instead of multiplying
11	5.1.6 (DOK2)	add fractions with unlike denominators	A: subtracted the fractions B: added the numerators and used the GCF as the denominator, but did not make equivalent fractions C: added the numerators and the denominators D: CORRECT
12	5.2.1 (DOK2)	write an algebraic expression	A: added *n* to the product of 2 times 4 B: added 2 to the sum of 4 and *n* C: added $\frac{1}{2}$ to the product of 4 times *n* D: CORRECT
13	5.1.7 (DOK2)	multiply fractions	A: added the numerators and the denominators B: multiplied the numerators and added the denominators C: CORRECT D: divided the fractions
14	5.2.1 (DOK1)	write an algebraic expression	A: chose the expression that represents 12 times *x* B: chose the expression that represents *x* divided by 12 C: chose the expression that represents 1 divided by the product of 12 times *x* D: CORRECT
15	5.1.3 (DOK2)	identify the prime factors of a composite number	A, D: does not understand composite numbers B: used addends as prime factors C: CORRECT
16	5.3.2 (DOK1)	identify a scalene triangle	A: chose an isosceles triangle B: chose an equilateral triangle C: CORRECT D: chose a right isosceles triangle
17	5.2.2 (DOK1)	identify a point that falls on a line on a coordinate grid	A: CORRECT B: transposed the *x*- and *y*-coordinates C, D: did not choose coordinates of points that fall on the line
18	5.3.4 (DOK1)	identify a reflection	A: CORRECT B, C, D: does not understand transformations
19	5.1.5 (DOK1)	multiply a 1-digit whole number by a 3-digit whole number	A, B, C: did not regroup correctly when multiplying D: CORRECT

Name Date

Prerequisite Skills Check

Answer Key and Item Analysis (continued)

Item	Academic Standard (DOK)	What's the Math	Item Analysis
20	5.3.5 (DOK2)	find the area of a parallelogram	A: used the formula for area of a triangle B: multiplied the height by the length of a side C: CORRECT D: multiplied the base by the length of a side
21	5.3.5 (DOK2)	find the perimeter of a parallelogram	A: found the sum of side A and side B B: found the sum of side A, side B, and the height C: multiplied 2 by the sum of side A and the height D: CORRECT
22	5.1.3 (DOK1)	identify a composite number	A, C, D: does not understand composite numbers B: CORRECT
23	5.1.6 (DOK2)	subtract mixed numbers with unlike denominators	A: subtracted the whole number parts of the mixed numbers but did not subtract the fractions B: CORRECT C: subtracted the whole number parts of the mixed numbers but added the fractions D: added instead of subtracting
24	5.1.8 (DOK2)	analyze a double bar graph	A: CORRECT B: used the bars for adults, not students C: chose the number of students who attended on Sunday D: found the total number of students who attended on Friday and Sunday
25	5.1.3 (DOK1)	use a factor tree to find the prime factors of a number	B: CORRECT A, C, D: chose factor pairs that are not both prime numbers.
26	5.1.4 (DOK1)	write a decimal in standard form	A: CORRECT B: chose seventy-three hundredths C: chose seven and three tenths D: chose seventy-three thousand
27	5.3.1 (DOK1)	use a protractor to measure an angle	A, B: used the inside scale of the protractor C: CORRECT D: did not read the degree marks between 155° and 160°
28	5.1.5 (DOK2)	interpret the remainder in division	A: dropped the remainder rather than increasing the quotient by 1 B: CORRECT C: used the remainder to increase the quotient by 2, not 1 D: chose a number in the problem

Name Date

Prerequisite Skills Check

Answer Key and Item Analysis (continued)

Item	Academic Standard (DOK)	What's the Math	Item Analysis
29	5.2.2 (DOK2)	identify a point that falls on a line on a coordinate grid	A, D: chose coordinates that do not fall on the line B: transposed the *x*- and *y*-coordinates C: CORRECT
30	5.3.3 (DOK1)	identify the shape of the base of a cylinder	A: chose the base of a cube B: chose the base of a rectangular prism C: CORRECT D: chose the base of a triangular prism
31	5.1.7 (DOK2)	multiply fractions	A: multiplied the numerators and added the denominators B: added the numerators and multiplied the denominators C: CORRECT D: added the numerators and the denominators
32	5.3.6 (DOK2)	find the volume of a rectangular prism	A: CORRECT B: multiplied only the length and height C: multiplied only the length and width D: added the length, width, and height
33	5.3.6 (DOK2)	find the surface area of a rectangular prism	A: used the product of $2lh$ as an addend two times and did not use the product of $2wh$ as an addend B: used the product of $2lw$ as an addend two times and did not use the product of $2wh$ as an addend C: CORRECT D: used the product of $2wh$ as an addend two times and did not use the product of $2lw$ as an addend
34	5.1.8 (DOK2)	analyze a line graph	A: transposed the meaning of the *x*- and *y*-values of the ordered pair B: CORRECT C: transposed the meaning of the *x*- and *y*-values of the ordered pair and used the *y*-value as the number of customers in all 5 hours rather than the number of customers in the fourth hour alone D: used the *y*-value of the ordered pair as the number of customers in the first 4 hours rather than the number of customers in the fourth hour alone
35	5.1.4 (DOK1)	identify the place of a digit in number	A: chose a number with 4 in the ones place B: chose a number with 4 in the tenths place C: CORRECT D: chose a number with 4 in the hundredths place

Name Date

Prerequisite Skills Check

Answer Key and Item Analysis (continued)

Item	Academic Standard (DOK)	What's the Math	Item Analysis
36	5.1.6 (DOK1)	add decimals	A: subtracted the numbers B: did not align the numbers using the decimal points and place value C: did not regroup correctly when adding D: CORRECT
37	5.1.9 (DOK3)	predict the chance of future events based on data collected from an experiment	A: chose the same number for 40 students as 20 students B: chose a number only 1 greater than the number for 20 students C: CORRECT D: chose a number for 40 students that is much less than the number for 20 students
38	5.1.4 (DOK1)	write the expanded form of a decimal	A: transposed the value of the digits in the tenths and hundredths places B: wrote the digits in the tenths and hundredths places as whole numbers C: CORRECT D: wrote the value of the digit in the hundredths places as tenths
39	5.1.1 (DOK1)	locate a decimal on a number line	A: chose a point that represents the location of 3 B: chose a point that represents the location of 3.5 C: CORRECT D: chose a point that represents the location of 5
40	5.1.2 (DOK2)	order decimals from greatest to least	A, C: did not order the numbers correctly B: CORRECT D: ordered the numbers from least to greatest

Constructed-Response Rubric

	CONTENT RUBRIC
2	A score of two indicates a **thorough understanding** of the mathematical concepts embodied in the task. The response • shows algorithms, computations, and other content related work executed correctly and completely.
1	A score of one indicates a **partial understanding** of the mathematical concepts embodied in the task. The response • contains errors in the execution of algorithms, computations, and/or other content related work.
0	A score of zero indicates **limited or no understanding** of the mathematical concepts embodied in the task.

	PROBLEM-SOLVING RUBRIC
2	A score of two indicates a **thorough understanding** of the problem-solving concepts embodied in the task. The response • shows an appropriate strategy to solve the problem, and the strategy is executed correctly and completely. • identifies all important elements of the problem and shows a complete understanding of the relationships among them. • provides clear and complete explanations and/or interpretations when required.
1	A score of one indicates a **partial understanding** of the problem-solving concepts embodied in the task. The response contains one or more of the following errors. The response • shows an appropriate strategy to solve the problem. However, the execution of the strategy contains errors and/or is incomplete. • identifies some of the important elements of the problem and shows a general understanding of the relationships among them. • provides incomplete, partial, or unclear explanations and/or interpretations when required.
0	A score of zero indicates **limited or no understanding** of the problem-solving concepts embodied in the task.

Extended-Response Rubric

CONTENT RUBRIC	
3	A score of three indicates a **thorough understanding** of the mathematical concepts embodied in the task. The response • shows algorithms, computations, and other content related work executed correctly and completely.
2	A score of two indicates a **partial understanding** of the mathematical concepts embodied in the task. The response • shows an attempt to execute algorithms, computations, and other content related work correctly and completely; computation errors may be present.
1	A score of one indicates a **limited understanding** of the mathematical concepts embodied in the task. The response • contains major errors, or only a partial process. • contains algorithms, computations, and other content related work which may only be partially correct.
0	A score of zero indicates **no understanding** of the mathematical concepts embodied in the task.

PROBLEM-SOLVING RUBRIC	
3	A score of three indicates a **thorough understanding** of the problem-solving concepts embodied in the task. The response • shows an appropriate strategy to solve the problem, and the strategy is executed correctly and completely. • identifies all important elements of the problem and shows a complete understanding of the relationships among them. • provides clear and complete explanations and/or interpretations when required.
2	A score of two indicates a **partial understanding** of the problem-solving concepts embodied in the task. The response contains one or more of the following errors. The response • shows an appropriate strategy to solve the problem. However, the execution of the strategy lacks an essential element. • identifies some of the important elements of the problem and shows a general understanding of the relationships among them. • provides incomplete or unclear explanations and/or interpretations when required.
1	A score of one indicates a **limited understanding** of the problem-solving concepts embodied in the task. The response contains one or more of the following errors. The response • shows an appropriate strategy to solve the problem. However, the execution of the strategy is applied incorrectly and/or is incomplete. • shows a limited understanding of the relationships among the elements of the problem. • provides incomplete, unclear, or omitted explanations and/or interpretations when required.
0	A score of zero indicates no understanding of the problem-solving concepts embodied in the task.

Name Date

Problem Solving

This **Four-Step Plan** can help you find a method for solving any word problem.

1 UNDERSTAND

- Read the problem carefully.
- What question do you need to answer?
- What information do you need to solve the problem?
- What information do you NOT need to solve the problem?

2 PLAN

- Decide on *one or more* strategies to use.
  - o Use Benchmarks
  - o Draw a Diagram
  - o Make a Table
  - o Make a Model
  - o Choose the Best Method of Computation
  - o Solve a Simpler Problem
  - o Determine Reasonable Answers
  - o Make an Organized List
  - o Work Backward
  - o Act it Out
  - o Look for a Pattern

3 SOLVE

- Carry out your plan.
- Perform the operations needed to find the solution.
- Revise your plan as needed.

4 CHECK

- Reread the problem.
- Does your answer make sense?
- Is your answer reasonable?
- Revise your plan as needed.

Mastering the ISTEP+, Grade 6 IN1

Name Date

Problem Solving (continued)

Follow the Four-Step Plan below to help you answer Problem 1.

1 Ronnie wants to hang a $12\frac{3}{4}$-inch wide painting of her dog in the center of a $36\frac{1}{2}$-inch wide wall.

How far from the edge of the wall should Ronnie hang the painting?

Answer $11\frac{7}{8}$ **inches from the edge of the wall**

UNDERSTAND Read the problem.

What information is given in the problem?
The painting is $12\frac{3}{4}$ inches wide. The wall is $36\frac{1}{2}$ inches wide, and the painting will be centered on the wall.

What question will you answer?
How far from the edge of the wall should Ronnie hang the painting?

Name Date

Problem Solving (continued)

PLAN The *draw a diagram* strategy can help you visualize how the facts in the problem can help you solve the problem. The *choose the best method of computation* strategy can help you determine which operation to use for each step of a multi-step problem.

What kind of diagram can you draw to help you with this problem?
a diagram of the wall with the painting hanging on it

SOLVE Draw and label your diagram.

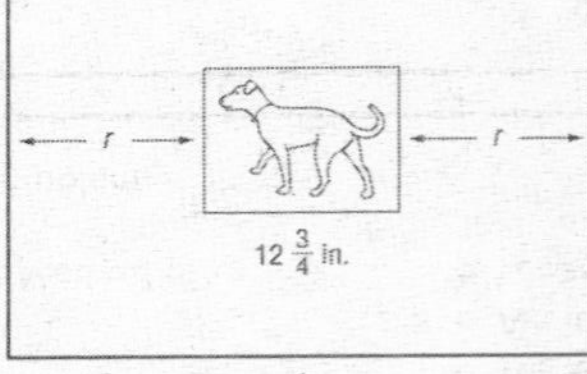

What operation can you use to determine the difference between the width of the painting and the width of the wall?
subtraction

Find the difference. Show all your work.

$36\frac{1}{2} = \quad 36\frac{2}{4} = \quad 35\frac{6}{4}$

$-12\frac{3}{4} = \quad -12\frac{3}{4} = \quad -12\frac{3}{4}$

$23\frac{3}{4}$

Name Date

Problem Solving (continued)

What operation can you use to determine the distance the painting will be hung from the edge of the wall?

division

Show all your work.

$23\frac{3}{4} \div 2 = 23\frac{3}{4} \times \frac{1}{2} = \frac{95}{4} \times \frac{1}{2} = \frac{95}{8} = 11\frac{7}{8}$

How many inches from the edge of the wall should the painting be hung?

Answer $11\frac{7}{8}$ **inches**

CHECK Reread the problem.

How do you know your answer is reasonable?

The width of the picture plus twice the distance from the edge should equal the width of the wall.

$12\frac{3}{4} + 11\frac{7}{8} + 11\frac{7}{8} = 12\frac{6}{8} + 11\frac{7}{8} + 11\frac{7}{8} = 34\frac{20}{8} = 36\frac{4}{8} = 36\frac{1}{2}$

6.1.6 (DOK4)

Name Date

Problem Solving (continued)

Follow the Four-Step Plan below to help you answer Problem 2.

2 A department store where Kerry likes to shop discounts certain items an additional 5% off their marked prices every Monday until they are sold. This week the store is discounting the guitar shown below. The price shown is its original price.

$100

How much will this guitar cost after it is marked down for 4 Mondays?

Answer 81.45 **dollars**

Kerry plans to buy the guitar when it costs less than $85. During which week will Kerry buy the guitar?

Answer 4 **weeks**

UNDERSTAND

What information is given in the problem?

The guitar originally cost $100. Every Monday the price is reduced by 5%.

What questions will you answer?

How much will this guitar cost after it is marked down for 4 Mondays?

During which week will the price first be less than $85?

Name ______ Date ______

Problem Solving (continued)

PLAN Use the *choose the best method of computation* strategy to help you determine which operation to calculate the discounted price each week.

What operation will you use to determine each week's discounted amount?

multiplication

What is 5% written as a decimal?

0.05

How will you find the amount of discount the first week?

Multiply $100 times 0.05.

Once you have the discount, how will you find the discounted price?

Subtract the discount from the price.

Complete the following formulas for finding the price of the guitar each week.

original price – (original price × **0.05**) = sale price week 1

sale price week 1 – (sale price week 1 × **0.05**) = sale price week 2

sale price week 2 – (**sale price week 2** × **0.05**) = sale price week 3

sale price week 3 – (**sale price week 3** × **0.05**) = sale price week 4

The *make a table strategy* can help you organize the data associated with the price of the guitar each week for four weeks.

What will you need to include in the table you make?

the weeks, original price, discount, new price each week

Name ______ Date ______

Problem Solving (continued)

SOLVE Complete the table. Show all your calculations for determining the amount of discount each week.

Week	Cost of Guitar	Discount	New Price
1	$100	$5	$95
2	$95	$4.75	$90.25
3	$90.25	$4.51	$85.74
4	$85.74	$4.29	$81.45

$100 – ($100 × 0.05) =
100 – 5 = $95
$95 – ($95 × 0.05) =
95 – 4.75 = $90.25
90.25 – ($90.25 × 0.05) =
90.25 – 4.51 = 85.74
85.74 – ($85.74 × 0.05) =
85.74 – 4.29 = 81.45

How much will this guitar cost after it is marked down for 4 Mondays?

Answer **81.45** **dollars**

Kerry plans to buy the guitar when it costs less than $85. During which week will Kerry buy the guitar?

The week 4 discount makes the price less than $85. I know this because $85.74 > $85 > $81.45.

CHECK Reread the problem. Be sure you answered the questions that were asked. Check your calculations for any errors you might have made.

6.1.9 (DOK4)

Name Date

Problem Solving (continued)

YOUR TURN **Use what you have learned about the Four-Step Plan to answer Problem 3.**

UNDERSTAND Read the problem.

PLAN You can use the *choose the best method of computation* strategy.

SOLVE Show all your work. Be sure to place the decimal point in the correct place in your calculations.

3 Zoe is saving money to buy a concert ticket that costs $35.

Zoe receives $4 every week for doing her chores at home. Zoe spends $1.50 every week and saves the rest.

How many weeks will it take Zoe to have enough money to purchase the concert ticket?

Show All Work

$4 – $1.50 = $2.50 saved each week
35 ÷ 2.5 = 14 weeks are needed

Answer 14 **weeks**

Zoe can earn extra money by dog-walking for her neighbor. Her neighbor will pay her $2.25 for every half hour she walks the dog.

What is the minimum amount of time, in hours, that Zoe will have to walk the dog for her neighbor to be able to buy a second concert ticket for her sister?

Show All Work

$2.25 for every half hour, so $4.50 for every hour.
35 ÷ 4.50 = 7. 7 or 8 hours

Answer 8 **hours**

CHECK Reread the problem. Be sure you use the correct units when you answer the questions. Check your calculations for any errors you might have made.

6.1.6 (DOK3)

Name Date

Problem Solving (continued)

YOUR TURN **Use what you have learned about the Four-Step Plan to answer Problem 4.**

UNDERSTAND Read the problem.

PLAN You can use the *draw a diagram* strategy or *choose the best method of computation* strategy.

SOLVE Show all your work. Draw a diagram whenever it helps you understand the problem better.

4 Jerome sent the following text message to his mom's cell phone at 8 A.M.

INBOX
To: Mom
Windchill temp last night: –16°.
Windchill temp now: –28°.
Windchill temp has warmed up 12°!
Received: 8:00 A.M

Determine if Jerome's statement about the windchill temperature increasing is correct. Justify your answer.

Show All Work

Jerome's statement is incorrect.

–12, –16, –28
–30 –27 –24 –21 –18 –15 –12 –9 –6 –3 0 3 6 9 12

–28 is farther from 0 than –16 is. This means that –28 is less than –16 and –28° is colder than –16°. It is not warming up. The windchill temperature is colder by –12°.

At 8:00 A.M., the windchill temperature was 10° colder than the actual temperature. What was the actual temperature at 8:00 A.M.?

Show All Work

–28° + 10° = –18°

Answer –18 **degrees**

CHECK Reread the problem. How can you check your answer?

Answers may vary. Accept all reasonable answers.

6.1.5 (DOK3)

Name Date

Problem Solving (continued)

YOUR TURN

Use what you have learned about the Four-Step Plan to answer Problem 5.

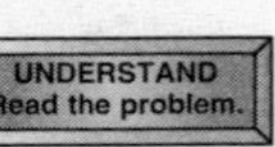

5 Alicia has some plastic blocks in the shape of the figure shown below. Each of the three cylindrical posts has a diameter of 1 inch and a height of 3 inches. The base of each block is a rectangular solid with the dimensions shown on the diagram.

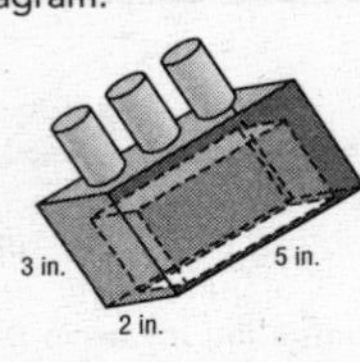

PLAN
You can use the *choose an operation* and *solve a simpler problem* strategies.

The blocks are solid plastic except for a 1-inch by 2-inch by 4-inch rectangular prism that has been removed from the interior of the base. Find the number of cubic inches of plastic needed to make each block. Use 3.14 for π.

SOLVE
Show all your work. What formulas will you need from your reference sheet?

Show All Work

Volume of a rectangular prism: $V = l \times w \times h$
Volume of base with smaller rectangular prism removed: $V = (5 \times 2 \times 3) - (1 \times 2 \times 4) = 30 - 8 = 22$ cubic inches
Volume of a cylinder: $V = \pi r^2 h$
Volume of one post: $V = \pi(0.5)^2(3) = (3.14)(0.25)(3) = 2.355$ cubic inches
Volume of three posts: $V = 3(2.355) = 7.065$ cubic inches
Total volume of one block: $22 + 7.065 = 29.065$ cubic inches

Answer 29.065 **cubic inches**

CHECK Reread the problem.

How can you check that your answer is reasonable?

Answers may vary. Accept all reasonable answers.

6.3.5 (DOK4)

Name Date

Problem Solving (continued)

UNDERSTAND PLAN 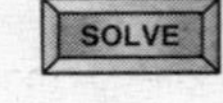 SOLVE CHECK

6 Brandie served a pizza divided into 5 equal slices.
What percent of the pizza is not eaten if 3 slices remain?

Show All Work

$3 \div 5 = 0.60$ or 60%

Answer 60%

Shade 20% of the pizza.

Show All Work

$20\% \times 5 = 0.20 \times 5 = 1$
Check that students have shaded one section of the circle above.

6.1.3 (DOK3)

7 Betsy made 6 out of 30 free throws. Assuming Betsy's success rate continues, how many free throws can she expect to make in 50 attempts?

Show All Work

$\frac{6}{30} = \frac{n}{50}$
$6 \times 50 = 30n$
$300 = 30n$
$n = 10$

Answer 10 **free throws**

6.1.8 (DOK2)

Name ____________ Date ____________

Problem Solving (continued)

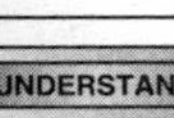     

UNDERSTAND | PLAN | SOLVE | CHECK

8 April has to determine the cost of perennials to plant along the perimeter of her rectangular garden. Her garden measures 9 feet by 13 feet. Each perennial costs $0.45 not including tax. April plans to plant them 1 foot apart.

April thinks that $25 will be enough money to cover the cost of the plants including a 7% sales tax.

Is April correct? Justify your answer using words, numbers, and/or symbols.

Show All Work

Perimeter of garden: $2(9) + 2(13) = 18 + 26 = 44$ feet
Cost of plants: $44 \times \$0.45 = \$19.80$
Cost of plants including tax: $\$19.80 \times 1.07 = \$21.19$

April's thoughts are correct. $25 is enough money to cover the cost of the plants including tax. The total cost when tax is included is $21.19.

6.1.9 (DOK3)

9 Rolf pedaled his bike at a constant speed for 5 hours, going 70 miles. What is the ratio of distance to time as a fraction in reduced form?

Show All Work

$r = \frac{d}{t} = \frac{70}{5} = \frac{14}{1} = 14$ **miles per hour**

Answer 14 **miles per hour**

At this same rate, how many miles did Rolf pedal in 2 hours?

Show All Work

$14 \times 2 = 28$

Answer 28 **miles**

6.1.7 (DOK3)

Copyright © Glencoe/McGraw-Hill, a division of The McGraw-Hill Companies, Inc.

Name ____________ Date ____________

Problem Solving (continued)

 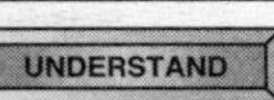  

UNDERSTAND | PLAN | SOLVE | CHECK

10 Use the coordinate grid shown below to answer the questions.

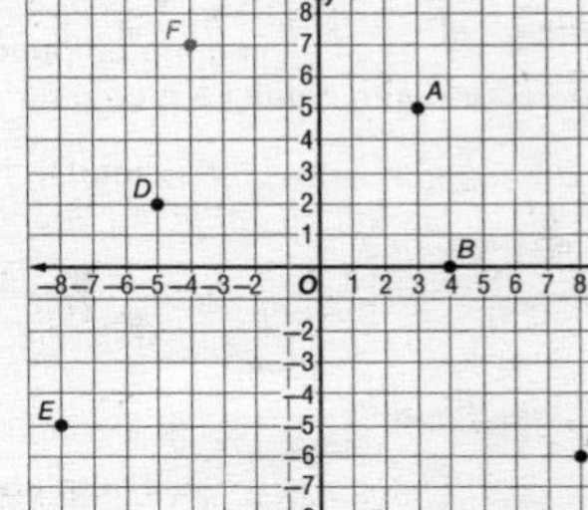

Write the ordered pair for each of the points plotted on the coordinated grid.

A(3 , 5) B(4 , 0) C(8 , −6) D(−5 , 2) E(−8 , −5)

Plot point *F* located 4 units to the left of the origin and 7 units above the origin.

If the *x*-coordinate of point *G* is positive and the *y*-coordinate is negative, in which quadrant is point *G* located? Explain how you know.

The signs of the coordinates indicate the direction from the origin. Point *G* is to the right of and below the origin. Point *G* is located in Quadrant IV.

6.2.4 (DOK4)

Name Date

Problem Solving (continued)

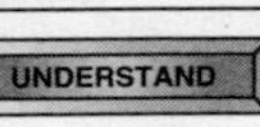   

UNDERSTAND PLAN SOLVE CHECK

11 One day while at work, Byron checks his E-mail account hourly. The first hour (hour 0) that he checks, he has 2 new E-mails. Each hour after that, his account always has another 3 new E-mails.

Write an equation that can be used to connect the hour (x) and the number of E-mails (y) in his account.

Answer $3x + 2 = y$

Draw a graph of the situation.

Show All Work

x	y
0	2
1	5
2	8
3	11
4	14
5	17

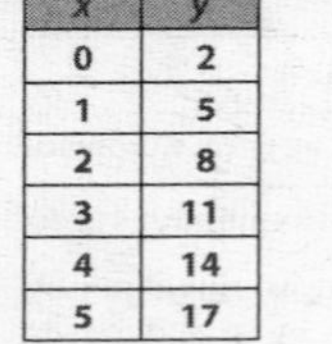

After 6 hours, how many E-mails will Byron have in his email account?

Show All Work

$3(6) + 2 = y; y = 20$

Answer 20 **emails**

6.2.5 (DOK4)

Name Date

Problem Solving (continued)

UNDERSTAND PLAN SOLVE CHECK

12 Mike and Marianne read this sign to help them decide on a hike to take.

Loop Trail	$\frac{7}{8}$-mile walk round trip
Rocky Trail	$\frac{3}{4}$-mile walk one way
Paved Trail	$\frac{3}{5}$-hour walk
Family Trail	$\frac{5}{6}$-hour walk

Mike and Marianne decide to walk the Family Trail first. They walk $\frac{1}{3}$ hour, stop for $\frac{1}{8}$ hour to photograph a squirrel, and then walked another $\frac{1}{4}$ hour to finish the trail. How long did they take on the Family Trail?

Show All Work

$\frac{1}{3} + \frac{1}{8} + \frac{1}{4} = \frac{8}{24} + \frac{3}{24} + \frac{6}{24} = \frac{17}{24}$

Answer $\frac{17}{24}$ **hour**

How much less was their time on the Family Trail compared to the time the sign suggested they might spend on the trail?

Show All Work

$\frac{5}{6} - \frac{17}{24} = \frac{20}{24} - \frac{17}{24} = \frac{3}{24} = \frac{1}{8}$

Answer $\frac{1}{8}$ **hour**

6.1.6 (DOK3)

Copyright © Glencoe/McGraw-Hill, a division of The McGraw-Hill Companies, Inc.

Name Date

Problem Solving (continued)

UNDERSTAND PLAN SOLVE CHECK

13 Each student going to the museum must have a ticket to enter. The museum charges $150 for each group of 25 students.

Write an equation that can be used to determine the cost (c) of one ticket.

Equation $25c = 150$

For an additional price, students at the museum can view a special 30-minute movie about dinosaurs. The cost per student is equal to half the cost of their ticket to enter the museum.

The theater holds only 15 people. How many times does the movie need to be shown to a full theater of students for the museum to earn the same amount as the cost of tickets to the museum for 3 groups of 25 students?

Show All Work

$25c = 150$
$c = \$6$ per ticket

$0.5c = \$3$ per movie ticket

$15 \times \$3 = \$45$ for 1 full theater showing to students
$\$150 \times 3 = \$450$ for 3 groups of 25 students to enter the museum
$\$450 \div \$45 = 10$

Answer 10 **movie showings**

6.2.1 (DOK4)

Copyright © Glencoe/McGraw-Hill, a division of The McGraw-Hill Companies, Inc.

Name Date

Prerequisite Skills Check

Fill in the bubble next to the correct answer. Be sure to fill in the bubble completely.

1 Each shelf of Mr. Lazo's bookcase can hold 39 math books. The bookcase has a total of 13 shelves. What is the greatest number of math books Mr. Lazo's bookcase can hold?

- Ⓐ 26
- Ⓑ 52
- Ⓒ 487
- ● 507

5.1.5 (DOK1)

2 Anita and Miguel are each painting a mural. Anita has painted $\frac{5}{12}$ of her mural and Miguel has painted $\frac{1}{3}$ of his mural. Which of the following shows the correct relationship between $\frac{5}{12}$ and $\frac{1}{3}$?

- Ⓐ $\frac{5}{12} < \frac{1}{3}$
- Ⓑ $\frac{5}{12} = \frac{1}{3}$
- Ⓒ $\frac{5}{12} < \frac{6}{12}$
- ● $\frac{5}{12} > \frac{1}{3}$

5.1.2 (DOK2)

3 Fuel oil is the source of heat for 0.09% of the homes in Indiana. What is the word form of 0.09?

- Ⓐ nine
- Ⓑ nine tenths
- ● nine hundredths
- Ⓓ nine thousandths

5.1.1 (DOK1)

4 Students are conducting an experiment with four bags of marbles. They draw a marble without looking, record the color, then replace the marble in its bag. The table shows data about the experiment so far.

Bag	Total number of marbles drawn	Number of red marbles drawn
Bag 1	12	3
Bag 2	16	6
Bag 3	20	7
Bag 4	25	6

The students will draw one more marble from each bag. From which bag is it most likely that they will draw a red marble?

- Ⓐ bag 1
- ● bag 2
- Ⓒ bag 3
- Ⓓ bag 4

5.1.9 (DOK3)

5 Which figure has exactly 4 vertices and 6 edges?

- Ⓐ square pyramid
- ● triangular pyramid
- Ⓒ cube
- Ⓓ cylinder

5.3.3 (DOK1)

Go on

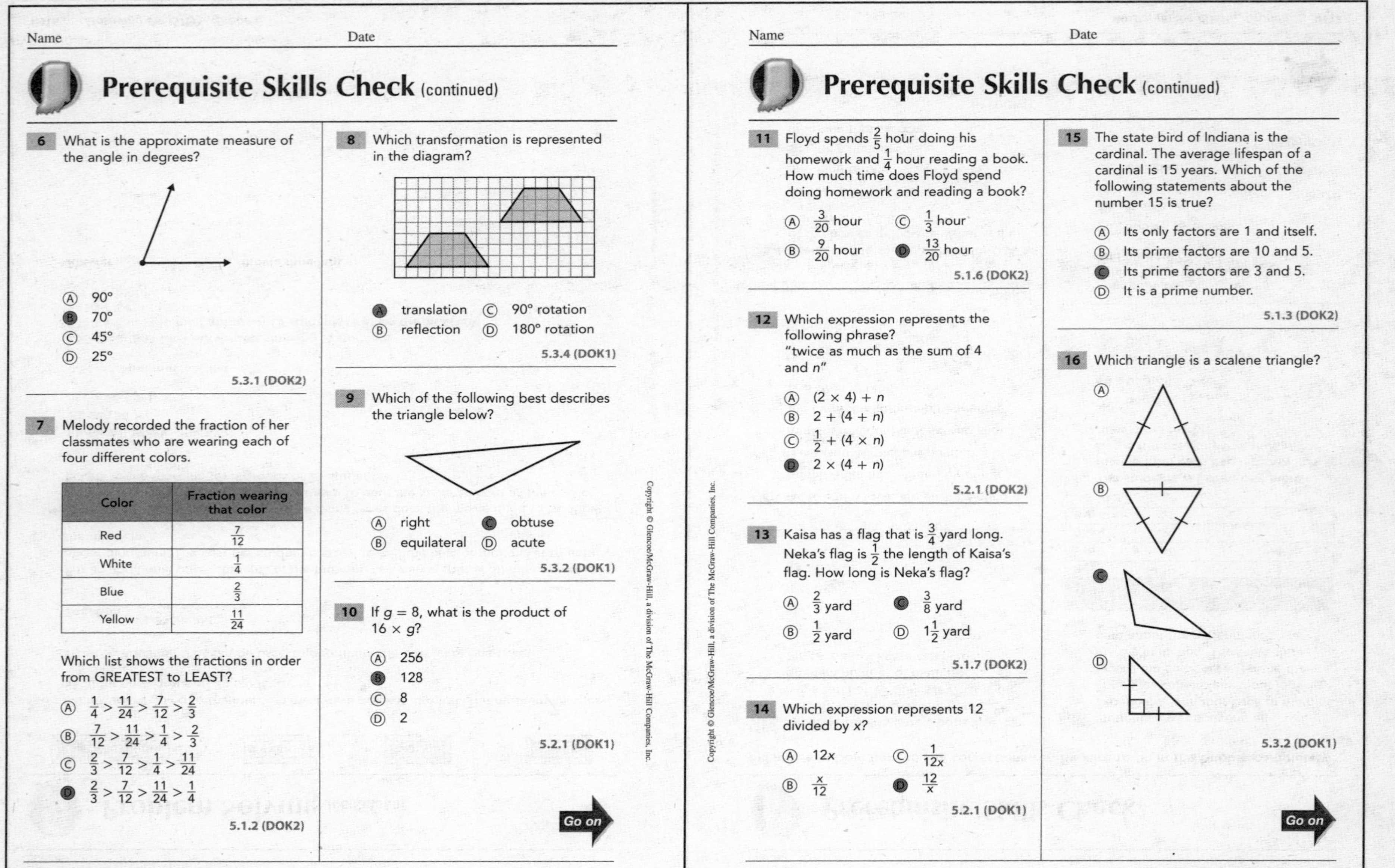

Name Date

Prerequisite Skills Check (continued)

6 What is the approximate measure of the angle in degrees?

Ⓐ 90°
● 70°
Ⓒ 45°
Ⓓ 25°

5.3.1 (DOK2)

7 Melody recorded the fraction of her classmates who are wearing each of four different colors.

Color	Fraction wearing that color
Red	$\frac{7}{12}$
White	$\frac{1}{4}$
Blue	$\frac{2}{3}$
Yellow	$\frac{11}{24}$

Which list shows the fractions in order from GREATEST to LEAST?

Ⓐ $\frac{1}{4} > \frac{11}{24} > \frac{7}{12} > \frac{2}{3}$
Ⓑ $\frac{7}{12} > \frac{11}{24} > \frac{1}{4} > \frac{2}{3}$
Ⓒ $\frac{2}{3} > \frac{7}{12} > \frac{1}{4} > \frac{11}{24}$
● $\frac{2}{3} > \frac{7}{12} > \frac{11}{24} > \frac{1}{4}$

5.1.2 (DOK2)

8 Which transformation is represented in the diagram?

● translation Ⓒ 90° rotation
Ⓑ reflection Ⓓ 180° rotation

5.3.4 (DOK1)

9 Which of the following best describes the triangle below?

Ⓐ right ● obtuse
Ⓑ equilateral Ⓓ acute

5.3.2 (DOK1)

10 If $g = 8$, what is the product of $16 \times g$?

Ⓐ 256
● 128
Ⓒ 8
Ⓓ 2

5.2.1 (DOK1)

Go on

Name Date

Prerequisite Skills Check (continued)

11 Floyd spends $\frac{2}{5}$ hour doing his homework and $\frac{1}{4}$ hour reading a book. How much time does Floyd spend doing homework and reading a book?

Ⓐ $\frac{3}{20}$ hour Ⓒ $\frac{1}{3}$ hour
Ⓑ $\frac{9}{20}$ hour ● $\frac{13}{20}$ hour

5.1.6 (DOK2)

12 Which expression represents the following phrase?
"twice as much as the sum of 4 and n"

Ⓐ $(2 \times 4) + n$
Ⓑ $2 + (4 + n)$
Ⓒ $\frac{1}{2} + (4 \times n)$
● $2 \times (4 + n)$

5.2.1 (DOK2)

13 Kaisa has a flag that is $\frac{3}{4}$ yard long. Neka's flag is $\frac{1}{2}$ the length of Kaisa's flag. How long is Neka's flag?

Ⓐ $\frac{2}{3}$ yard ● $\frac{3}{8}$ yard
Ⓑ $\frac{1}{2}$ yard Ⓓ $1\frac{1}{2}$ yard

5.1.7 (DOK2)

14 Which expression represents 12 divided by x?

Ⓐ $12x$ Ⓒ $\frac{1}{12x}$
Ⓑ $\frac{x}{12}$ ● $\frac{12}{x}$

5.2.1 (DOK1)

15 The state bird of Indiana is the cardinal. The average lifespan of a cardinal is 15 years. Which of the following statements about the number 15 is true?

Ⓐ Its only factors are 1 and itself.
Ⓑ Its prime factors are 10 and 5.
● Its prime factors are 3 and 5.
Ⓓ It is a prime number.

5.1.3 (DOK2)

16 Which triangle is a scalene triangle?

Ⓐ
Ⓑ
●
Ⓓ

5.3.2 (DOK1)

Go on

Name Date

Prerequisite Skills Check (continued)

17 Which ordered pair is located on line *h*?

- Ⓐ (4, 3) (filled)
- Ⓑ (3, 4)
- Ⓒ (3, 0)
- Ⓓ (3, 2)

5.2.2 (DOK1)

18 Which transformation is represented in the diagram?

- Ⓐ reflection (filled)
- Ⓑ translation
- Ⓒ 90° rotation
- Ⓓ 180° rotation

5.3.4 (DOK1)

19 What is the product of 4 × 746?

- Ⓐ 2,864
- Ⓑ 2,884
- Ⓒ 2,964
- Ⓓ 2,984 (filled)

5.1.5 (DOK1)

Use the parallelogram below for Questions 20 and 21.

10 in. 8 in. 14 in.

20 What is the area of the parallelogram?

Area of a parallelogram
$= b \times h =$ base × height

- Ⓐ 56 square inches
- Ⓑ 80 square inches
- Ⓒ 112 square inches (filled)
- Ⓓ 140 square inches

5.3.5 (DOK2)

21 What is the perimeter of the parallelogram?

Perimeter of a parallelogram
= (2 × side A) + (2 × side B)

- Ⓐ 24 inches
- Ⓑ 32 inches
- Ⓒ 44 inches
- Ⓓ 48 inches (filled)

5.3.5 (DOK2)

Go on

Name Date

Prerequisite Skills Check (continued)

22 The number of endangered species at The Indianapolis Zoo is a composite number. Which of the following could be that number?

- Ⓐ 11
- Ⓑ 14 (filled)
- Ⓒ 17
- Ⓓ 19

5.1.3 (DOK1)

23 Odessa has a board that is $5\frac{1}{2}$ inches long. She uses $1\frac{1}{3}$ inches of the board for a bookshelf. How many inches of the board does Odessa have left?

- Ⓐ 4
- Ⓑ $4\frac{1}{6}$ (filled)
- Ⓒ $4\frac{5}{6}$
- Ⓓ $6\frac{5}{6}$

5.1.6 (DOK2)

24 Look at the graph below. How many more students attended the talent show on Friday than Sunday?

Talent Show Attendance

Day	Adults	Students
Friday	80	60
Saturday	80	70
Sunday	50	40

Number of People; Day

- Ⓐ 20 (filled)
- Ⓑ 30
- Ⓒ 40
- Ⓓ 100

5.1.8 (DOK2)

25 The diagram below shows a factor tree for the number 48.

48 → 2, 24; 24 → 2, 12; 12 → 2, 6; 6 → 2, 3

According to the diagram, which numbers are the only prime factors of 48?

- Ⓐ 2 and 6
- Ⓑ 2 and 3 (filled)
- Ⓒ 2 and 12
- Ⓓ 2 and 24

5.1.3 (DOK1)

26 Seventy-three thousandths of the total population of Indiana is between the ages of 10 and 14. What is the standard form of seventy-three thousandths?

- Ⓐ 0.073 (filled)
- Ⓑ 0.73
- Ⓒ 7.3
- Ⓓ 73,000

5.1.4 (DOK1)

Go on

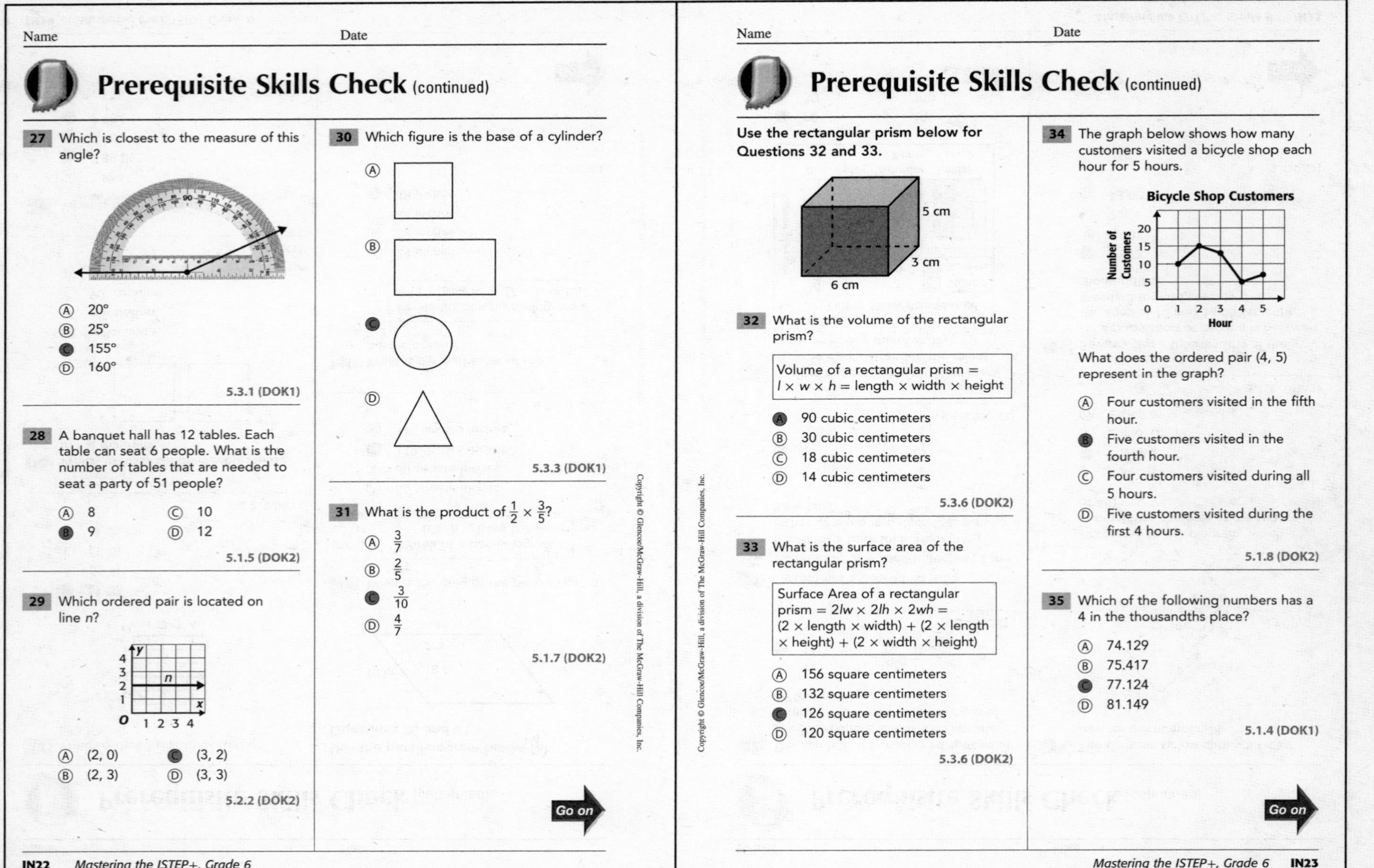

Name Date

Prerequisite Skills Check (continued)

27 Which is closest to the measure of this angle?

- (A) 20°
- (B) 25°
- (C) 155°
- (D) 160°

5.3.1 (DOK1)

28 A banquet hall has 12 tables. Each table can seat 6 people. What is the number of tables that are needed to seat a party of 51 people?

- (A) 8
- (B) 9
- (C) 10
- (D) 12

5.1.5 (DOK2)

29 Which ordered pair is located on line n?

- (A) (2, 0)
- (B) (2, 3)
- (C) (3, 2)
- (D) (3, 3)

5.2.2 (DOK2)

30 Which figure is the base of a cylinder?

- (A)
- (B)
- (C)
- (D)

5.3.3 (DOK1)

31 What is the product of $\frac{1}{2} \times \frac{3}{5}$?

- (A) $\frac{3}{7}$
- (B) $\frac{2}{5}$
- (C) $\frac{3}{10}$
- (D) $\frac{4}{7}$

5.1.7 (DOK2)

Go on

Name Date

Prerequisite Skills Check (continued)

Use the rectangular prism below for Questions 32 and 33.

32 What is the volume of the rectangular prism?

Volume of a rectangular prism = $l \times w \times h$ = length × width × height

- (A) 90 cubic centimeters
- (B) 30 cubic centimeters
- (C) 18 cubic centimeters
- (D) 14 cubic centimeters

5.3.6 (DOK2)

33 What is the surface area of the rectangular prism?

Surface Area of a rectangular prism = $2lw \times 2lh \times 2wh$ = (2 × length × width) + (2 × length × height) + (2 × width × height)

- (A) 156 square centimeters
- (B) 132 square centimeters
- (C) 126 square centimeters
- (D) 120 square centimeters

5.3.6 (DOK2)

34 The graph below shows how many customers visited a bicycle shop each hour for 5 hours.

What does the ordered pair (4, 5) represent in the graph?

- (A) Four customers visited in the fifth hour.
- (B) Five customers visited in the fourth hour.
- (C) Four customers visited during all 5 hours.
- (D) Five customers visited during the first 4 hours.

5.1.8 (DOK2)

35 Which of the following numbers has a 4 in the thousandths place?

- (A) 74.129
- (B) 75.417
- (C) 77.124
- (D) 81.149

5.1.4 (DOK1)

Go on

Name Date

Prerequisite Skills Check (continued)

36 Julia bought 3.4 pounds of chicken and 5.75 pounds of beef. How many pounds of meat did Julia buy in all?

Ⓐ 2.35 pounds
Ⓑ 6.09 pounds
Ⓒ 8.15 pounds
● 9.15 pounds

5.1.6 (DOK1)

37 Harold asked 20 students to name his or her favorite season. The results are shown in the table.

Favorite Season	
Season	Number of Students
Winter	4
Spring	7
Summer	8
Fall	1

If Harold asks 40 students, what is a reasonable prediction of the number of students that will say spring?

Ⓐ 7
Ⓑ 8
● 14
Ⓓ 18

5.1.9 (DOK3)

38 Jack measured his height in meters and found out that he is 1.47 meters tall. What is 1.47 in expanded form?

Ⓐ $1 + 0.04 + 0.7$
Ⓑ $1 + 4 + 7$
● $1 + 0.4 + 0.07$
Ⓓ $1 + 0.4 + 0.7$

5.1.4 (DOK1)

39 Which point on the number line represents the location of 4.5?

K L M N
2 3 4 5

Ⓐ K
Ⓑ L
● M
Ⓓ N

5.1.1 (DOK1)

40 Students ran a 1-mile race. The fastest times are shown in the table below.

Students' Names	Time (minutes)
Pedro	7.519
Amanda	7.099
Lai	7.527
Eddie	7.512

Which list shows the times in order from GREATEST to LEAST?

Ⓐ $7.512 > 7.099 > 7.527 > 7.519$
● $7.527 > 7.519 > 7.512 > 7.099$
Ⓒ $7.519 > 7.099 > 7.527 > 7.512$
Ⓓ $7.099 > 7.512 > 7.519 > 7.527$

5.1.2 (DOK2)

STOP

Copyright © Glencoe/McGraw-Hill, a division of The McGraw-Hill Companies, Inc.

Name Date

Diagnostic Test

Fill in the bubble next to the correct answer. Be sure to fill in the bubble completely.

1 What is the measure of angle 1 in the figure below?

75° 1

Ⓐ 15°
Ⓑ 75°
● 105°
Ⓓ 115°

[Lesson 9-3] 6.3.1 (DOK1)

2 Which list of numbers is ordered from least to greatest?

Ⓕ $-\frac{1}{4}, 1\frac{1}{4}, 0.2, 1.2$
Ⓖ $0.2, 1.2, -\frac{1}{4}, 1\frac{1}{4}$
● $-\frac{1}{4}, 0.2, 1.2, 1\frac{1}{4}$
Ⓙ $0.2, -\frac{1}{4}, 1.2, 1\frac{1}{4}$

[Lesson 4-6] 6.1.1 (DOK2)

3 On Saturday morning, the temperature was 3°F below zero. By 2:00 P.M., the temperature had risen 16°. What was the temperature at 2:00 P.M.?

● 13°
Ⓑ 16°
Ⓒ 18°
Ⓓ 19°

[Lesson 11-2] 6.1.5 (DOK1)

4 The Yangs' dinner bill came to $63.00. If they left a 20% tip, how much money did the Yangs spend on dinner?

Ⓕ $12.60
Ⓖ $50.40
Ⓗ $65.00
● $75.60

[Lesson IN2] 6.1.9 (DOK2)

5 Kiarra worked for 5 hours and made $32. Which equation could she use to find how much money she made per hour, *h*?

Ⓐ $h + \$32 = 5$
● $\$32 \div 5 = h$
Ⓒ $\$32 - 5 = h$
Ⓓ $h + 5 = \$32$

[Lesson 1-8] 6.2.1 (DOK1)

Go on

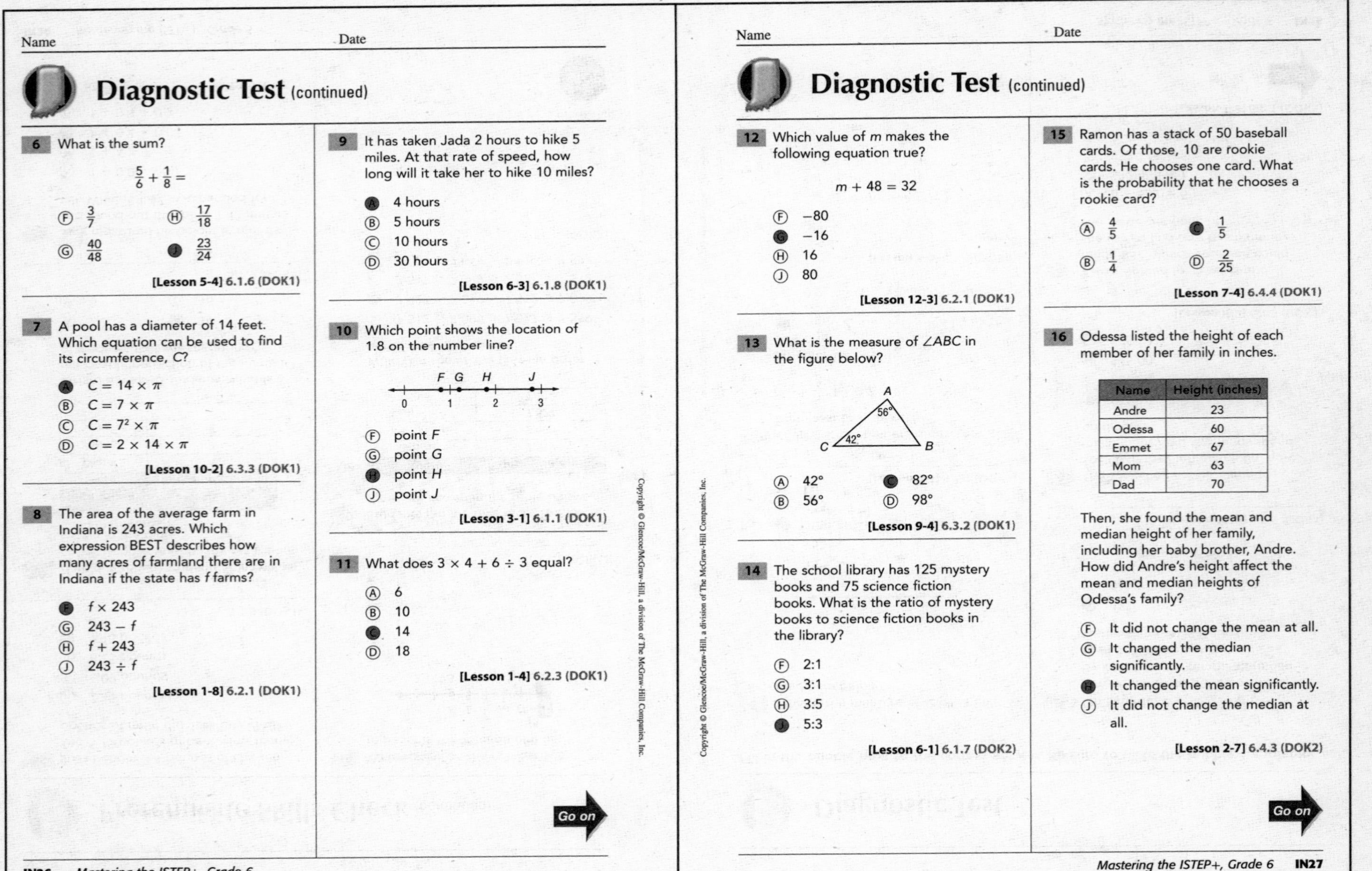

Name ____________ Date ____________

Diagnostic Test (continued)

6 What is the sum?

$$\frac{5}{6} + \frac{1}{8} =$$

Ⓕ $\frac{3}{7}$
Ⓖ $\frac{40}{48}$
Ⓗ $\frac{17}{18}$
● $\frac{23}{24}$

[Lesson 5-4] 6.1.6 (DOK1)

7 A pool has a diameter of 14 feet. Which equation can be used to find its circumference, *C*?

● $C = 14 \times \pi$
Ⓑ $C = 7 \times \pi$
Ⓒ $C = 7^2 \times \pi$
Ⓓ $C = 2 \times 14 \times \pi$

[Lesson 10-2] 6.3.3 (DOK1)

8 The area of the average farm in Indiana is 243 acres. Which expression BEST describes how many acres of farmland there are in Indiana if the state has *f* farms?

● $f \times 243$
Ⓖ $243 - f$
Ⓗ $f + 243$
Ⓙ $243 \div f$

[Lesson 1-8] 6.2.1 (DOK1)

9 It has taken Jada 2 hours to hike 5 miles. At that rate of speed, how long will it take her to hike 10 miles?

● 4 hours
Ⓑ 5 hours
Ⓒ 10 hours
Ⓓ 30 hours

[Lesson 6-3] 6.1.8 (DOK1)

10 Which point shows the location of 1.8 on the number line?

Ⓕ point *F*
Ⓖ point *G*
● point *H*
Ⓙ point *J*

[Lesson 3-1] 6.1.1 (DOK1)

11 What does $3 \times 4 + 6 \div 3$ equal?

Ⓐ 6
Ⓑ 10
● 14
Ⓓ 18

[Lesson 1-4] 6.2.3 (DOK1)

Go on

Name ____________ Date ____________

Diagnostic Test (continued)

12 Which value of *m* makes the following equation true?

$$m + 48 = 32$$

Ⓕ −80
● −16
Ⓗ 16
Ⓙ 80

[Lesson 12-3] 6.2.1 (DOK1)

13 What is the measure of $\angle ABC$ in the figure below?

Ⓐ 42°
Ⓑ 56°
● 82°
Ⓓ 98°

[Lesson 9-4] 6.3.2 (DOK1)

14 The school library has 125 mystery books and 75 science fiction books. What is the ratio of mystery books to science fiction books in the library?

Ⓕ 2:1
Ⓖ 3:1
Ⓗ 3:5
● 5:3

[Lesson 6-1] 6.1.7 (DOK2)

15 Ramon has a stack of 50 baseball cards. Of those, 10 are rookie cards. He chooses one card. What is the probability that he chooses a rookie card?

Ⓐ $\frac{4}{5}$
Ⓑ $\frac{1}{4}$
● $\frac{1}{5}$
Ⓓ $\frac{2}{25}$

[Lesson 7-4] 6.4.4 (DOK1)

16 Odessa listed the height of each member of her family in inches.

Name	Height (inches)
Andre	23
Odessa	60
Emmet	67
Mom	63
Dad	70

Then, she found the mean and median height of her family, including her baby brother, Andre. How did Andre's height affect the mean and median heights of Odessa's family?

Ⓕ It did not change the mean at all.
Ⓖ It changed the median significantly.
● It changed the mean significantly.
Ⓙ It did not change the median at all.

[Lesson 2-7] 6.4.3 (DOK2)

Go on

Copyright © Glencoe/McGraw-Hill, a division of The McGraw-Hill Companies, Inc.

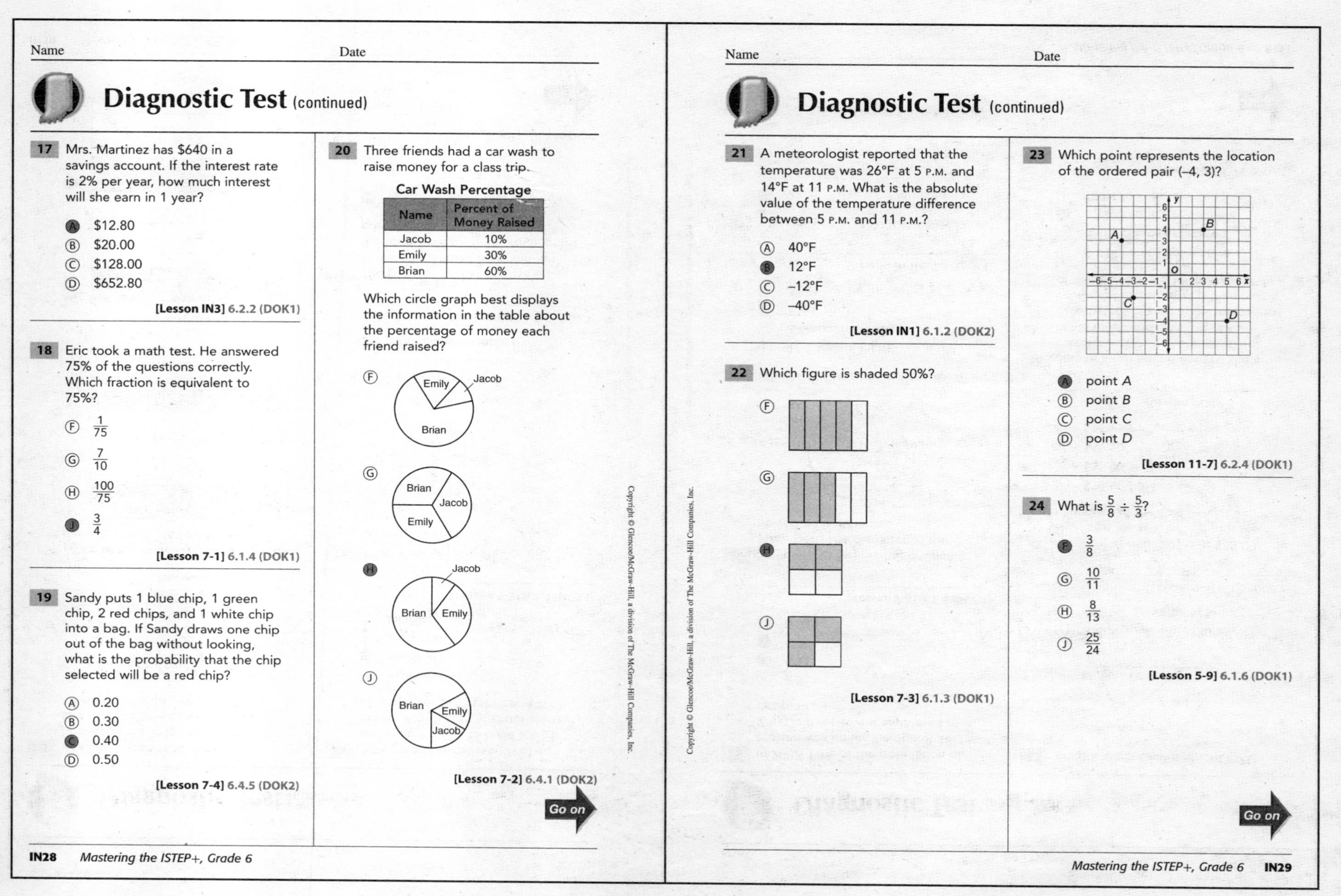

Name Date

Diagnostic Test (continued)

17 Mrs. Martinez has $640 in a savings account. If the interest rate is 2% per year, how much interest will she earn in 1 year?

- Ⓐ $12.80
- Ⓑ $20.00
- Ⓒ $128.00
- Ⓓ $652.80

[Lesson IN3] 6.2.2 (DOK1)

18 Eric took a math test. He answered 75% of the questions correctly. Which fraction is equivalent to 75%?

- Ⓕ $\frac{1}{75}$
- Ⓖ $\frac{7}{10}$
- Ⓗ $\frac{100}{75}$
- Ⓙ $\frac{3}{4}$

[Lesson 7-1] 6.1.4 (DOK1)

19 Sandy puts 1 blue chip, 1 green chip, 2 red chips, and 1 white chip into a bag. If Sandy draws one chip out of the bag without looking, what is the probability that the chip selected will be a red chip?

- Ⓐ 0.20
- Ⓑ 0.30
- Ⓒ 0.40
- Ⓓ 0.50

[Lesson 7-4] 6.4.5 (DOK2)

20 Three friends had a car wash to raise money for a class trip.

Car Wash Percentage

Name	Percent of Money Raised
Jacob	10%
Emily	30%
Brian	60%

Which circle graph best displays the information in the table about the percentage of money each friend raised?

Ⓕ Ⓖ Ⓗ Ⓙ

[Lesson 7-2] 6.4.1 (DOK2)

Go on

Copyright © Glencoe/McGraw-Hill, a division of The McGraw-Hill Companies, Inc.

Name Date

Diagnostic Test (continued)

21 A meteorologist reported that the temperature was 26°F at 5 P.M. and 14°F at 11 P.M. What is the absolute value of the temperature difference between 5 P.M. and 11 P.M.?

- Ⓐ 40°F
- Ⓑ 12°F
- Ⓒ −12°F
- Ⓓ −40°F

[Lesson IN1] 6.1.2 (DOK2)

22 Which figure is shaded 50%?

Ⓕ Ⓖ Ⓗ Ⓙ

[Lesson 7-3] 6.1.3 (DOK1)

23 Which point represents the location of the ordered pair (−4, 3)?

- Ⓐ point A
- Ⓑ point B
- Ⓒ point C
- Ⓓ point D

[Lesson 11-7] 6.2.4 (DOK1)

24 What is $\frac{5}{8} \div \frac{5}{3}$?

- Ⓕ $\frac{3}{8}$
- Ⓖ $\frac{10}{11}$
- Ⓗ $\frac{8}{13}$
- Ⓙ $\frac{25}{24}$

[Lesson 5-9] 6.1.6 (DOK1)

Go on

Name Date

Diagnostic Test (continued)

25 Lisa filled a fish tank with water. She made the following graph to show the volume of water in the tank each minute that she filled it.

Volume of Water (gallons) vs. Time (minutes)

Which of the following data tables shows the data represented in the graph?

Ⓐ

Time (minutes)	Volume of water (gallons)
0	0
1	1
2	2
3	3

Ⓑ

Time (minutes)	Volume of water (gallons)
2	4
3	8
4	12
5	16

Ⓒ

Time (minutes)	Volume of water (gallons)
4	1
8	2
12	3
16	4

Ⓓ

Time (minutes)	Volume of water (gallons)
1	4
2	8
3	12
4	16

[Lesson 4-9] 6.2.5 (DOK2)

26 Toby measures the length of a board he is using to build a bird house. Which is an appropriate unit of length for this measurement?

Ⓕ millimeter
Ⓖ centimeter
Ⓗ meter
Ⓙ kilometer

[Lesson 8-3] 6.3.4 (DOK1)

27 What is the surface area of the cylinder?

3 in.
10 in.

Ⓐ 56.52 square inches
Ⓑ 188.44 square inches
Ⓒ 216.66 square inches
Ⓓ 244.92 square inches

[Lesson IN5] 6.3.5 (DOK2)

28 The probability that Marissa's favorite basketball team will win the tournament is 0.45. What is this probability expressed as a ratio?

Ⓕ $\frac{9}{20}$ Ⓗ $\frac{45}{55}$

Ⓖ $\frac{1}{2}$ Ⓙ $\frac{100}{45}$

[Lesson 7-4] 6.4.5 (DOK1)

Go on

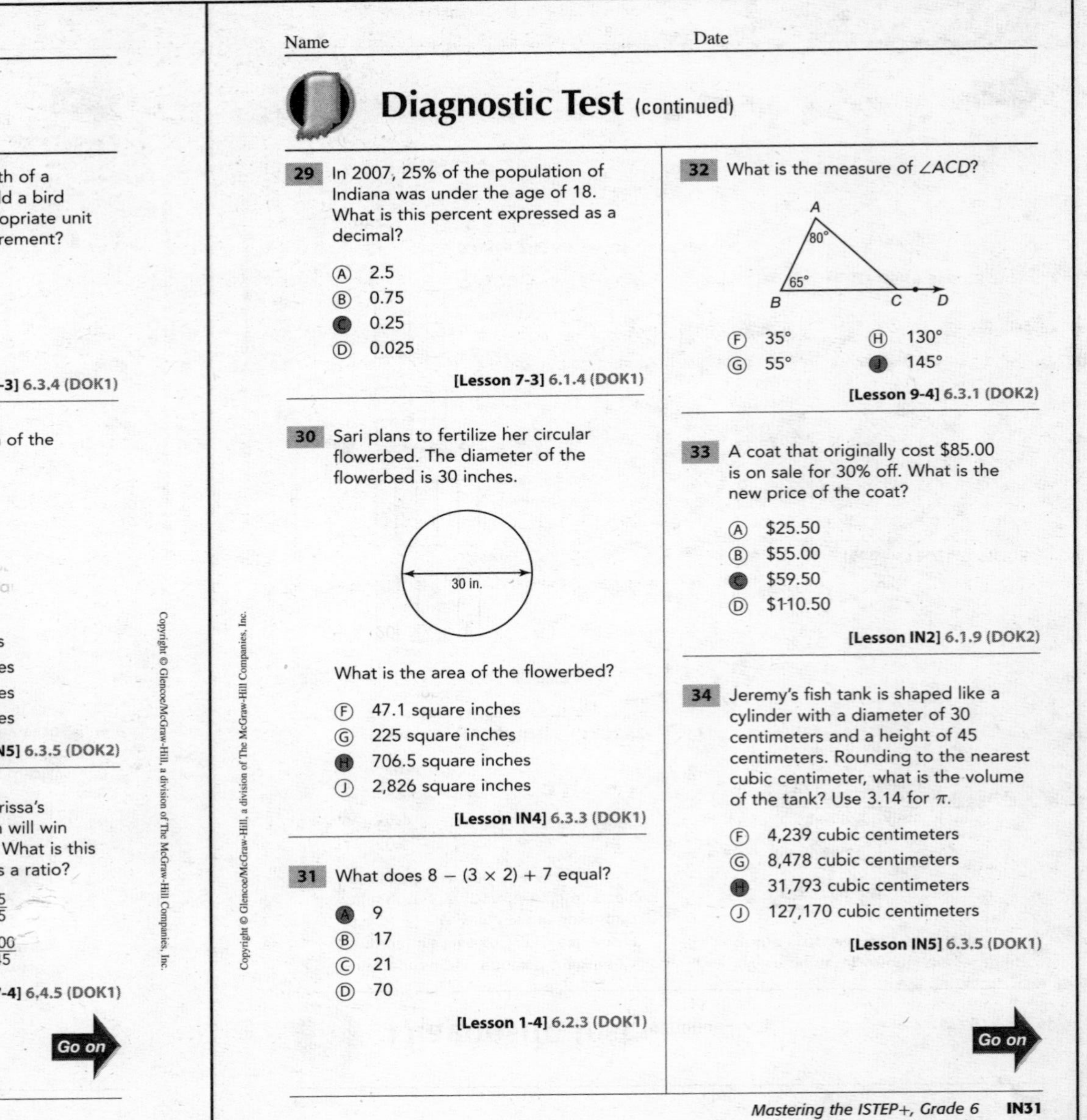

Name Date

Diagnostic Test (continued)

29 In 2007, 25% of the population of Indiana was under the age of 18. What is this percent expressed as a decimal?

Ⓐ 2.5
Ⓑ 0.75
Ⓒ 0.25
Ⓓ 0.025

[Lesson 7-3] 6.1.4 (DOK1)

30 Sari plans to fertilize her circular flowerbed. The diameter of the flowerbed is 30 inches.

30 in.

What is the area of the flowerbed?

Ⓕ 47.1 square inches
Ⓖ 225 square inches
Ⓗ 706.5 square inches
Ⓙ 2,826 square inches

[Lesson IN4] 6.3.3 (DOK1)

31 What does 8 − (3 × 2) + 7 equal?

Ⓐ 9
Ⓑ 17
Ⓒ 21
Ⓓ 70

[Lesson 1-4] 6.2.3 (DOK1)

32 What is the measure of ∠ACD?

A, 80°, 65°, B, C, D

Ⓕ 35° Ⓗ 130°
Ⓖ 55° Ⓙ 145°

[Lesson 9-4] 6.3.1 (DOK2)

33 A coat that originally cost $85.00 is on sale for 30% off. What is the new price of the coat?

Ⓐ $25.50
Ⓑ $55.00
Ⓒ $59.50
Ⓓ $110.50

[Lesson IN2] 6.1.9 (DOK2)

34 Jeremy's fish tank is shaped like a cylinder with a diameter of 30 centimeters and a height of 45 centimeters. Rounding to the nearest cubic centimeter, what is the volume of the tank? Use 3.14 for π.

Ⓕ 4,239 cubic centimeters
Ⓖ 8,478 cubic centimeters
Ⓗ 31,793 cubic centimeters
Ⓙ 127,170 cubic centimeters

[Lesson IN5] 6.3.5 (DOK1)

Go on

Name Date

Diagnostic Test (continued)

35 Whooping cranes are endangered birds. Each fall, scientists help the whooping cranes migrate from Wisconsin through Indiana and other states to Florida. The following table shows the number of whooping cranes that migrated each year from 2001 until 2009.

Year	Number of Whooping Cranes
2001	9
2002	22
2003	37
2004	50
2005	65
2006	88
2007	78
2008	87
2009	81

Which of the following is the BEST way to display the data?

- Ⓐ bar graph
- Ⓑ circle graph
- Ⓒ line graph
- Ⓓ stem-and-leaf plot

[Lesson 2-8] 6.4.2 (DOK2)

36 Which is the correct value for *m*?

$$\frac{2}{15} = \frac{m}{67.5}$$

- Ⓕ 9
- Ⓖ 54.5
- Ⓗ 90
- Ⓙ 120

[Lesson 6-7] 6.1.8 (DOK1)

37 Luis wants to know which color is most popular among students at his school. He asks a random sample of 30 students to choose their favorite colors from red, blue, or green. Which of the following is the BEST way for him to display the results?

- Ⓐ bar graph
- Ⓑ line graph
- Ⓒ stem-and-leaf plot
- Ⓓ circle graph

[Lesson 2-8] 6.4.2 (DOK1)

38 Madison is training for a race. The table below shows the distance that she has run each day for the last four days.

Date	Miles Ran
March 2	1.5
March 3	2
March 4	2
March 5	2.5

Which statement about the data in the table is true?

- Ⓕ The mode is less than the median.
- Ⓖ The median is greater than the mean.
- Ⓗ The mean is the same as the median.
- Ⓙ The mode is greater than the mean.

[Lesson 2-7] 6.4.3 (DOK2)

Go on

Copyright © Glencoe/McGraw-Hill, a division of The McGraw-Hill Companies, Inc.

Name Date

Diagnostic Test (continued)

39 The table shows how many of each type of animal a pet shop has.

Animal	Animals Available
Dog	9
Cat	8
Bird	5
Hamster	6
Snake	2

If pet sales are chosen randomly, what is the probability that the next animal the pet shop sells will be a hamster?

- Ⓐ 6%
- Ⓑ 20%
- Ⓒ 50%
- Ⓓ 60%

[Lesson 7-4] 6.4.4 (DOK2)

40 Mr. Ruiz is measuring the lengths of four pieces of lumber. Which list shows the lengths in order from shortest to longest?

- Ⓕ 3.5 ft, 3.75 ft, 3.3 ft, 3.25 ft
- Ⓖ 3.5 ft, 3.25 ft, 3.3 ft, 3.75 ft
- Ⓗ 3.25 ft, 3.3 ft, 3.5 ft, 3.75 ft
- Ⓙ 3.75 ft, 3.25 ft, 3.3 ft, 3.5 ft

[Lesson 3-2] 6.1.1 (DOK1)

41 What is the absolute value of –14?

- Ⓐ –14
- Ⓑ –5
- Ⓒ 5
- Ⓓ 14

[Lesson IN1] 6.1.2 (DOK1)

42 There are 18,345 seats in Conseco Fieldhouse in Indianapolis. If 60% of the seats are occupied, how many people are seated in the fieldhouse?

- Ⓕ 7,338
- Ⓖ 11,007
- Ⓗ 18,405
- Ⓙ 29,352

[Lesson 7-1] 6.1.3 (DOK2)

43 What is 18 ÷ –3?

- Ⓐ –6
- Ⓑ –5
- Ⓒ 6
- Ⓓ 15

[Lesson 11-6] 6.1.5 (DOK1)

44 Kyle has a recipe for muffins. The recipe calls for 3 cups of flour to make 12 muffins. What is the ratio in simplest form of cups of flour to muffins?

- Ⓕ 3 to 12
- Ⓖ 1 to 3
- Ⓗ 1 to 4
- Ⓙ 4 to 1

[Lesson 6-1] 6.1.7 (DOK1)

Go on

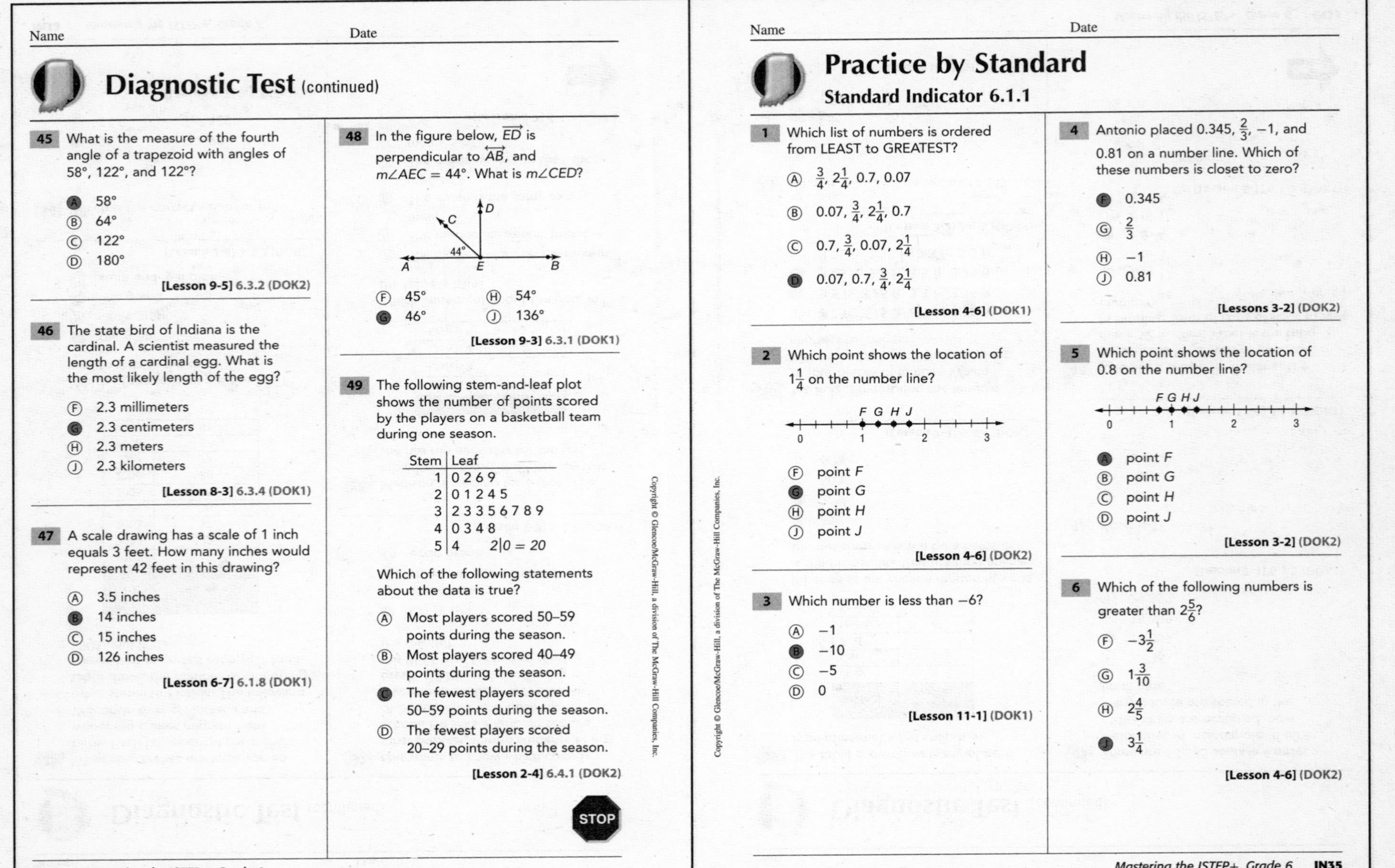

Name Date

Diagnostic Test (continued)

45 What is the measure of the fourth angle of a trapezoid with angles of 58°, 122°, and 122°?

- **(A) 58°**
- (B) 64°
- (C) 122°
- (D) 180°

[Lesson 9-5] 6.3.2 (DOK2)

46 The state bird of Indiana is the cardinal. A scientist measured the length of a cardinal egg. What is the most likely length of the egg?

- (F) 2.3 millimeters
- **(G) 2.3 centimeters**
- (H) 2.3 meters
- (J) 2.3 kilometers

[Lesson 8-3] 6.3.4 (DOK1)

47 A scale drawing has a scale of 1 inch equals 3 feet. How many inches would represent 42 feet in this drawing?

- (A) 3.5 inches
- **(B) 14 inches**
- (C) 15 inches
- (D) 126 inches

[Lesson 6-7] 6.1.8 (DOK1)

48 In the figure below, $\overrightarrow{ED}$ is perpendicular to $\overleftrightarrow{AB}$, and $m\angle AEC = 44°$. What is $m\angle CED$?

- (F) 45°
- **(G) 46°**
- (H) 54°
- (J) 136°

[Lesson 9-3] 6.3.1 (DOK1)

49 The following stem-and-leaf plot shows the number of points scored by the players on a basketball team during one season.

Stem	Leaf
1	0 2 6 9
2	0 1 2 4 5
3	2 3 3 5 6 7 8 9
4	0 3 4 8
5	4

$2|0 = 20$

Which of the following statements about the data is true?

- (A) Most players scored 50–59 points during the season.
- (B) Most players scored 40–49 points during the season.
- **(C) The fewest players scored 50–59 points during the season.**
- (D) The fewest players scored 20–29 points during the season.

[Lesson 2-4] 6.4.1 (DOK2)

STOP

Name Date

Practice by Standard

Standard Indicator 6.1.1

1 Which list of numbers is ordered from LEAST to GREATEST?

- (A) $\frac{3}{4}$, $2\frac{1}{4}$, 0.7, 0.07
- (B) 0.07, $\frac{3}{4}$, $2\frac{1}{4}$, 0.7
- (C) 0.7, $\frac{3}{4}$, 0.07, $2\frac{1}{4}$
- **(D) 0.07, 0.7, $\frac{3}{4}$, $2\frac{1}{4}$**

[Lesson 4-6] (DOK1)

2 Which point shows the location of $1\frac{1}{4}$ on the number line?

- (F) point *F*
- **(G) point *G***
- (H) point *H*
- (J) point *J*

[Lesson 4-6] (DOK2)

3 Which number is less than −6?

- (A) −1
- **(B) −10**
- (C) −5
- (D) 0

[Lesson 11-1] (DOK1)

4 Antonio placed 0.345, $\frac{2}{3}$, −1, and 0.81 on a number line. Which of these numbers is closet to zero?

- **(F) 0.345**
- (G) $\frac{2}{3}$
- (H) −1
- (J) 0.81

[Lessons 3-2] (DOK2)

5 Which point shows the location of 0.8 on the number line?

- **(A) point *F***
- (B) point *G*
- (C) point *H*
- (D) point *J*

[Lesson 3-2] (DOK2)

6 Which of the following numbers is greater than $2\frac{5}{6}$?

- (F) $-3\frac{1}{2}$
- (G) $1\frac{3}{10}$
- (H) $2\frac{4}{5}$
- **(J) $3\frac{1}{4}$**

[Lesson 4-6] (DOK2)

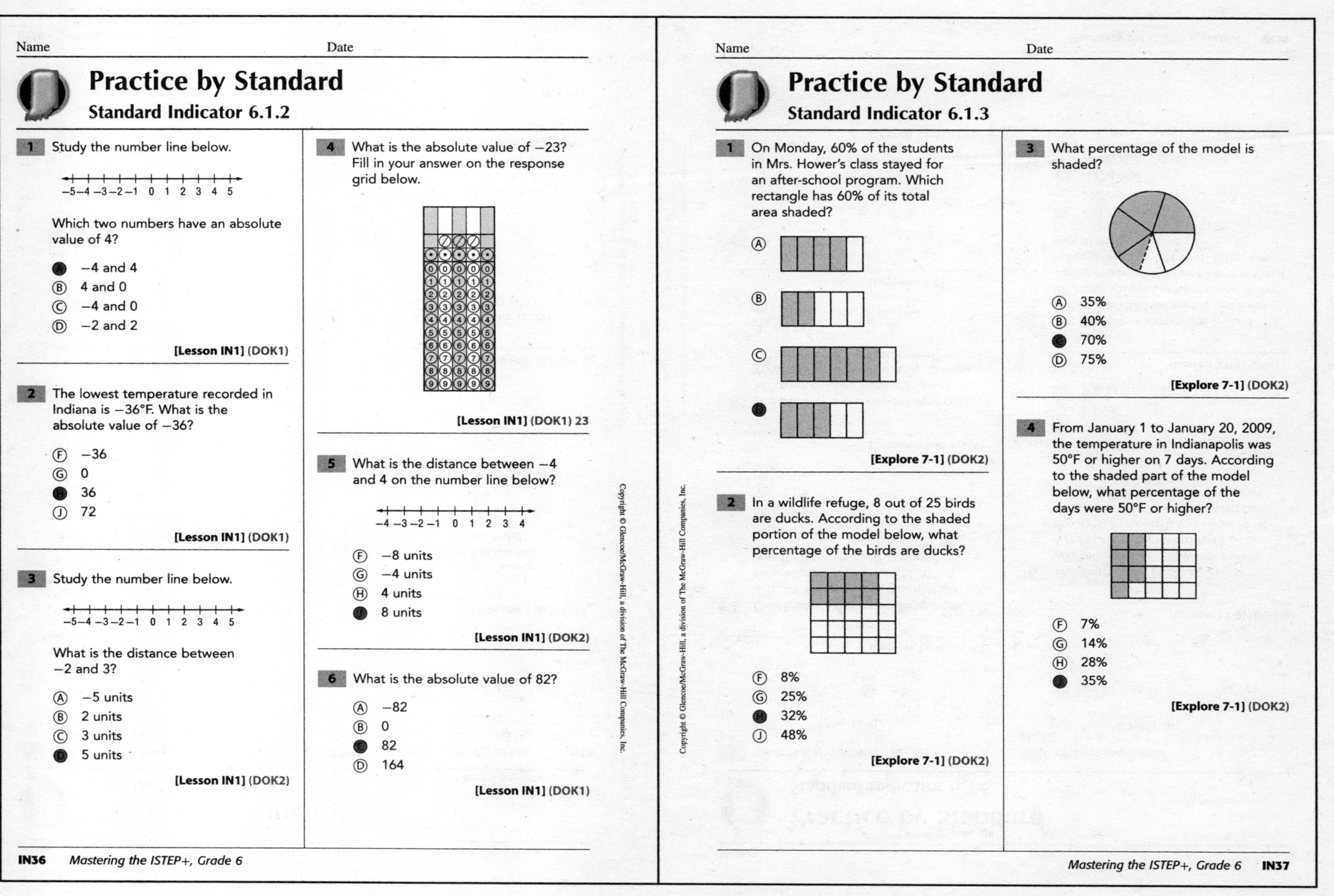

Name Date

Practice by Standard

Standard Indicator 6.1.2

1 Study the number line below.

–5 –4 –3 –2 –1 0 1 2 3 4 5

Which two numbers have an absolute value of 4?

● –4 and 4
Ⓑ 4 and 0
Ⓒ –4 and 0
Ⓓ –2 and 2

[Lesson IN1] (DOK1)

2 The lowest temperature recorded in Indiana is –36°F. What is the absolute value of –36?

Ⓕ –36
Ⓖ 0
● 36
Ⓙ 72

[Lesson IN1] (DOK1)

3 Study the number line below.

–5 –4 –3 –2 –1 0 1 2 3 4 5

What is the distance between –2 and 3?

Ⓐ –5 units
Ⓑ 2 units
Ⓒ 3 units
● 5 units

[Lesson IN1] (DOK2)

4 What is the absolute value of –23? Fill in your answer on the response grid below.

[Lesson IN1] (DOK1) 23

5 What is the distance between –4 and 4 on the number line below?

–4 –3 –2 –1 0 1 2 3 4

Ⓕ –8 units
Ⓖ –4 units
Ⓗ 4 units
● 8 units

[Lesson IN1] (DOK2)

6 What is the absolute value of 82?

Ⓐ –82
Ⓑ 0
● 82
Ⓓ 164

[Lesson IN1] (DOK1)

Name Date

Practice by Standard

Standard Indicator 6.1.3

1 On Monday, 60% of the students in Mrs. Hower's class stayed for an after-school program. Which rectangle has 60% of its total area shaded?

Ⓐ
Ⓑ
Ⓒ
●

[Explore 7-1] (DOK2)

2 In a wildlife refuge, 8 out of 25 birds are ducks. According to the shaded portion of the model below, what percentage of the birds are ducks?

Ⓕ 8%
Ⓖ 25%
● 32%
Ⓙ 48%

[Explore 7-1] (DOK2)

3 What percentage of the model is shaded?

Ⓐ 35%
Ⓑ 40%
● 70%
Ⓓ 75%

[Explore 7-1] (DOK2)

4 From January 1 to January 20, 2009, the temperature in Indianapolis was 50°F or higher on 7 days. According to the shaded part of the model below, what percentage of the days were 50°F or higher?

Ⓕ 7%
Ⓖ 14%
Ⓗ 28%
● 35%

[Explore 7-1] (DOK2)

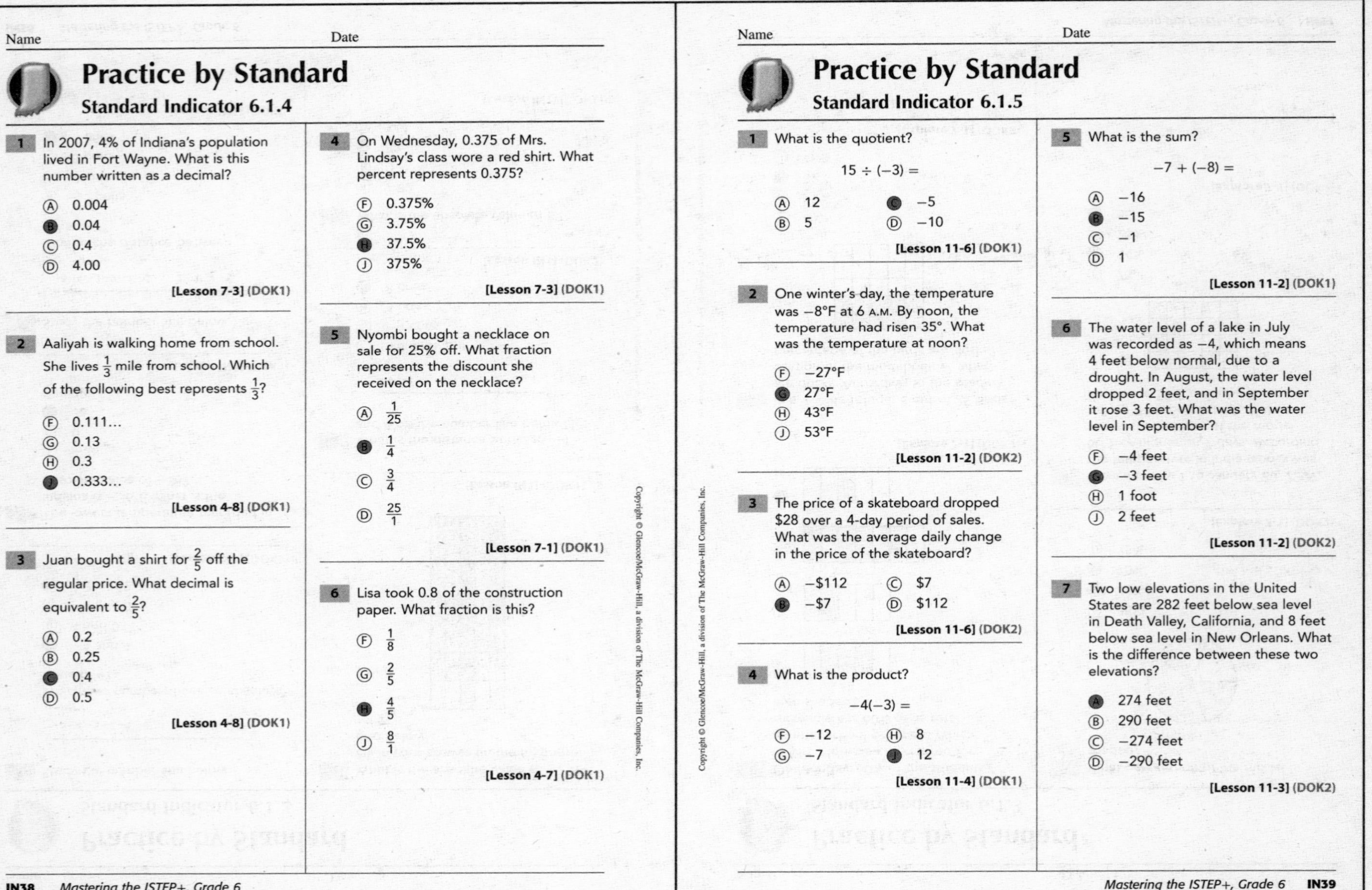

Name Date

Practice by Standard

Standard Indicator 6.1.4

1 In 2007, 4% of Indiana's population lived in Fort Wayne. What is this number written as a decimal?

Ⓐ 0.004
● 0.04
Ⓒ 0.4
Ⓓ 4.00

[Lesson 7-3] (DOK1)

2 Aaliyah is walking home from school. She lives $\frac{1}{3}$ mile from school. Which of the following best represents $\frac{1}{3}$?

Ⓕ 0.111...
Ⓖ 0.13
Ⓗ 0.3
● 0.333...

[Lesson 4-8] (DOK1)

3 Juan bought a shirt for $\frac{2}{5}$ off the regular price. What decimal is equivalent to $\frac{2}{5}$?

Ⓐ 0.2
Ⓑ 0.25
● 0.4
Ⓓ 0.5

[Lesson 4-8] (DOK1)

4 On Wednesday, 0.375 of Mrs. Lindsay's class wore a red shirt. What percent represents 0.375?

Ⓕ 0.375%
Ⓖ 3.75%
● 37.5%
Ⓙ 375%

[Lesson 7-3] (DOK1)

5 Nyombi bought a necklace on sale for 25% off. What fraction represents the discount she received on the necklace?

Ⓐ $\frac{1}{25}$
● $\frac{1}{4}$
Ⓒ $\frac{3}{4}$
Ⓓ $\frac{25}{1}$

[Lesson 7-1] (DOK1)

6 Lisa took 0.8 of the construction paper. What fraction is this?

Ⓕ $\frac{1}{8}$
Ⓖ $\frac{2}{5}$
● $\frac{4}{5}$
Ⓙ $\frac{8}{1}$

[Lesson 4-7] (DOK1)

Copyright © Glencoe/McGraw-Hill, a division of The McGraw-Hill Companies, Inc.

Name Date

Practice by Standard

Standard Indicator 6.1.5

1 What is the quotient?

$15 \div (-3) =$

Ⓐ 12
Ⓑ 5
● −5
Ⓓ −10

[Lesson 11-6] (DOK1)

2 One winter's day, the temperature was −8°F at 6 A.M. By noon, the temperature had risen 35°. What was the temperature at noon?

Ⓕ −27°F
● 27°F
Ⓗ 43°F
Ⓙ 53°F

[Lesson 11-2] (DOK2)

3 The price of a skateboard dropped $28 over a 4-day period of sales. What was the average daily change in the price of the skateboard?

Ⓐ −$112
● −$7
Ⓒ $7
Ⓓ $112

[Lesson 11-6] (DOK2)

4 What is the product?

$-4(-3) =$

Ⓕ −12
Ⓖ −7
Ⓗ 8
● 12

[Lesson 11-4] (DOK1)

5 What is the sum?

$-7 + (-8) =$

Ⓐ −16
● −15
Ⓒ −1
Ⓓ 1

[Lesson 11-2] (DOK1)

6 The water level of a lake in July was recorded as −4, which means 4 feet below normal, due to a drought. In August, the water level dropped 2 feet, and in September it rose 3 feet. What was the water level in September?

Ⓕ −4 feet
● −3 feet
Ⓗ 1 foot
Ⓙ 2 feet

[Lesson 11-2] (DOK2)

7 Two low elevations in the United States are 282 feet below sea level in Death Valley, California, and 8 feet below sea level in New Orleans. What is the difference between these two elevations?

● 274 feet
Ⓑ 290 feet
Ⓒ −274 feet
Ⓓ −290 feet

[Lesson 11-3] (DOK2)

Copyright © Glencoe/McGraw-Hill, a division of The McGraw-Hill Companies, Inc.

Name Date

Practice by Standard

Standard Indicator 6.1.6

1 Noah had $2\frac{3}{4}$ feet of wood and used $\frac{2}{3}$ of it to build a frame. How much wood did he use to build the frame?

- ● $1\frac{5}{6}$ feet
- Ⓑ $2\frac{1}{12}$ feet
- Ⓒ $3\frac{5}{12}$ feet
- Ⓓ $4\frac{1}{8}$ feet

[Lesson 5-8] (DOK2)

2 Jenna stops at a convenience store. She wants to buy a drink for $1.29, a bag of nuts for $0.99, a loaf of bread for $1.89, and a pen for $1.29. The tax was $0.44. She discovers she only has $5. How much more money does she need to buy all of the items?

- Ⓕ $0.35
- Ⓖ $0.44
- Ⓗ $0.46
- ● $0.90

[Lesson 3-5] (DOK2)

3 A library charges $0.15 per day for an overdue book. Jayden's book is 14 days overdue. How much does he owe?

- Ⓐ $0.75
- Ⓑ $2.00
- ● $2.10
- Ⓓ $3.75

[Lesson 3-7] (DOK2)

4 Abdul and Josh spent $16.50 to play pool. If it cost them $5.50 per half hour to play, how long did they play?

- Ⓕ 0.5 hour
- Ⓖ 1 hour
- Ⓗ 1.2 hours
- ● 1.5 hours

[Lesson 3-9] (DOK2)

5 On Monday morning, $\frac{1}{3}$ of the students in Kelsey's class walked to school, $\frac{1}{4}$ of the students were driven to school, and the rest of the class rode the bus. What fraction of her classmates rode the bus?

- Ⓐ $\frac{2}{7}$
- ● $\frac{5}{12}$
- Ⓑ $\frac{3}{7}$
- Ⓓ $\frac{7}{12}$

[Lesson 5-4] (DOK2)

Copyright © Glencoe/McGraw-Hill, a division of The McGraw-Hill Companies, Inc.

Name Date

Practice by Standard

Standard Indicator 6.1.7

1 A convenience store sold 18 cartons of plain milk and 6 cartons of chocolate milk. What is the ratio of plain milk cartons to chocolate milk cartons sold?

- Ⓐ 6:1
- Ⓑ 9:2
- ● 3:1
- Ⓓ 2:1

[Lesson 6-1] (DOK1)

2 Kaiko is making dinner for her family. Including Kaiko, 5 family members do not like broccoli and 4 others do. Which ratio shows the number of family members who do not like broccoli compared to the total number of family members?

- Ⓕ $\frac{4}{5}$
- ● $\frac{5}{9}$
- Ⓖ $\frac{9}{5}$
- Ⓙ $\frac{4}{9}$

[Lesson 6-1] (DOK1)

3 On a math test, Kevin had 26 correct answers and 4 incorrect answers. What is the ratio of correct answers to total number of questions in simplest form?

- ● 13 to 15
- Ⓑ 15 to 13
- Ⓒ 2 to 13
- Ⓓ 2 to 15

[Lesson 6-1] (DOK1)

4 The Eagles scored 34 points and the Falcons scored 28 points in a football game. Which ratio shows the number of points scored by the Eagles to the total number of points scored by both teams?

- ● 17 to 31
- Ⓖ 14 to 31
- Ⓗ 31 to 17
- Ⓙ 7 to 25

[Lesson 6-1] (DOK1)

5 Of the 26 students in a book club, 12 will read a science fiction book and 14 will read a nonfiction book. Which ratio shows the number of students who will read a science fiction book to the total number of students in the club?

- ● $\frac{6}{13}$
- Ⓒ $\frac{31}{40}$
- Ⓑ $\frac{13}{6}$
- Ⓓ $\frac{7}{3}$

[Lesson 6-1] (DOK1)

6 A bagel shop baked 65 plain bagels and 20 wheat bagels. What is the ratio of plain bagels to wheat bagels that the shop baked?

- Ⓕ 4:13
- Ⓖ 6:2
- ● 13:4
- Ⓙ 10:2

[Lesson 6-1] (DOK1)

Name Date

Practice by Standard

Standard Indicator 6.1.8

1 There are 8 children for every 3 adults at the skating rink. If there are 24 children at the skating rink, how many adults are there?

Ⓐ 3
Ⓑ 8
● 9
Ⓓ 24

[Lesson 6-3] (DOK2)

2 Tyrell entered a bubblegum blowing contest. He can blow 9 bubbles in 90 seconds. If he continues to blow bubbles at this rate, how many bubbles can he blow in 3 minutes?

Ⓕ 9
● 18
Ⓗ 27
Ⓙ 90

[Lesson 6-3] (DOK3)

3 Floor plans for a library are sized so that 1 inch in the floor plan equals 75 feet in the actual library. How many feet in the actual library are represented by 4 inches in the floor plan?

Ⓐ 79
Ⓑ 150
● 300
Ⓓ 400

[Lesson 6-3] (DOK3)

4 Mr. Buchanan drove his boat on Brookville Lake at a speed of 12 miles per hour. At this rate, how long will it take him to go 30 miles?

Ⓕ 2 hours
● 2.5 hours
Ⓗ 3 hours
Ⓙ 4 hours

[Lesson 6-3] (DOK2)

5 Alyssa packed a total of 30 boxes in 3 hours. At this rate, how many boxes can Alyssa pack in 5 hours?

Ⓐ 10
Ⓑ 30
● 50
Ⓓ 80

[Lesson 6-3] (DOK2)

6 A scale model of a new office building uses a scale of 1 inch to 12 feet. How many feet are represented by 8 inches on this model?

Ⓕ 6
Ⓖ 84
Ⓗ 92
● 96

[Lesson 6-3] (DOK2)

Copyright © Glencoe/McGraw-Hill, a division of The McGraw-Hill Companies, Inc.

Name Date

Practice by Standard

Standard Indicator 6.1.9

1 Mr. Evans sold 15% of his lawn equipment on the first day of his yard sale. If he had 20 pieces of lawn equipment, how many pieces did he sell?

● 3
Ⓑ 6
Ⓒ 9
Ⓓ 15

[Lesson 6-7] (DOK2)

2 Louisa bought a new jacket on sale for 40% off the original price. If the jacket originally cost $120, what was the sale price?

Ⓕ $48
● $72
Ⓗ $102
Ⓙ $116

[Lesson IN2] (DOK1)

3 Miguel and his friends bought lunch at a café. The total price of the lunch was $24.50. They left a 20% tip. What was the tip?

Ⓐ $0.49
Ⓑ $2.00
Ⓒ $2.45
● $4.90

[Lesson IN2] (DOK1)

4 Logan borrowed $800 to buy a computer. He paid 8% interest for one year. How much was the loan, including interest?

● $864
Ⓖ $880
Ⓗ $900
Ⓙ $1,440

[Lesson IN3] (DOK2)

5 Mrs. Perez took her daughters to the salon to have their hair cut. The bill was $80. Mrs. Perez gave the hairdresser a 15% tip. How much did she pay in all?

Ⓐ $95
● $92
Ⓒ $15
Ⓓ $12

[Lesson IN2] (DOK1)

6 Andre bought a helmet on sale for 30% off the original price. If the original price of the helmet was $85, what was the sale price?

Ⓕ $25.50
● $59.50
Ⓗ $82.45
Ⓙ $79.05

[Lesson IN2] (DOK1)

Copyright © Glencoe/McGraw-Hill, a division of The McGraw-Hill Companies, Inc.

Name Date

Practice by Standard

Standard Indicator 6.2.1

1 Raheem wants to spend no more than $28 on 4 tickets to a ball game. Which inequality can be use to find the most he can spend per ticket t?

- Ⓐ (filled) $4t \leq 28$
- Ⓑ $4t \geq 28$
- Ⓒ $t + 4 > 28$
- Ⓓ $t - 4 < 28$

[Lesson IN7] (DOK3)

2 Kianna is selling bracelets b at the swap meet. She used the inequality $12b \geq 30$ to find the least amount of profit she wants to make on the bracelets. What is the least amount she should charge for a bracelet?

- Ⓕ (filled) $2.50
- Ⓖ $3
- Ⓗ $3.50
- Ⓙ $18

[Lesson IN7] (DOK2)

3 Sean used the equation $12t = 84$ to find the cost of a discount ticket t to Indiana's state fair. How much does one discount ticket cost?

- Ⓐ $4
- Ⓑ (filled) $7
- Ⓒ $8
- Ⓓ $12

[Lesson 12-4] (DOK2)

4 Aja wants to read 20 pages per day to finish a 240 page novel. Which equation can she use to find how many days d it will take to finish the novel?

- Ⓕ $d + 20 = 240$
- Ⓖ $d - 20 = 240$
- Ⓗ $d \div 20 = 240$
- Ⓙ (filled) $20d = 240$

[Lesson 1-8] (DOK3)

5 Juliet used the equation $w + 46 = 82$ to find the number of wins w for the Indiana Pacers in the 2008–2009 season. How many wins did the Pacers have?

- Ⓐ (filled) 36
- Ⓑ 46
- Ⓒ 118
- Ⓓ 128

[Lesson 12-3] (DOK2)

6 Hasan's mother gave him some money to buy a loaf of bread. After paying $3.15 for the bread, Hasan had $6.35 left. Which equation can he use to find the original amount of money m his mother gave him?

- Ⓕ $m + 3.15 = 6.35$
- Ⓖ (filled) $m - 3.15 = 6.35$
- Ⓗ $3.15m = 6.35$
- Ⓙ $m + 6.35 = 3.15$

[Lesson 1-8] (DOK3)

Copyright © Glencoe/McGraw-Hill, a division of The McGraw-Hill Companies, Inc.

Name Date

Practice by Standard

Standard Indicator 6.2.2

1 What is the distance Ryan would travel if he drove at a rate of 55 miles per hour for 4 hours?

$d = rt$
d = distance, r = rate, t = time

- Ⓐ 13.75 miles
- Ⓑ 59 miles
- Ⓒ 210 miles
- Ⓓ (filled) 220 miles

[Explore 1-9] (DOK2)

2 How much interest would Meagan earn on $500 principal if she saves it for 2 years at a rate of 4.5%. How much interest would she earn?

$I = prt$
I = interest, p = principal, r = rate, t = time

- Ⓕ $22.50
- Ⓖ $40.00
- Ⓗ (filled) $45.00
- Ⓙ $90.00

[Lesson IN3] (DOK2)

3 Nate used the formula for the area of a rectangle to find the length of the rectangle if the area is 175 square feet and the width is 14 feet. What is the length of the rectangle?

- Ⓐ 6.25 feet
- Ⓑ (filled) 12.5 feet
- Ⓒ 25 feet
- Ⓓ 29.75 feet

[Lesson 1-9] (DOK2)

4 Maria used the formula $d = mg$ to find the distance d she can drive on 18 gallons g of gas if she gets 32 miles per gallon m on the highway. How far can she drive?

- Ⓕ 278 miles
- Ⓖ 287 miles
- Ⓗ 566 miles
- Ⓙ (filled) 576 miles

[Explore 1-9] (DOK2)

5 How fast did Sam drive if he drove 60 miles from Muncie to Indianapolis in 1.25 hours?

$d = rt$
d = distance, r = rate, t = time

- Ⓐ 25 mph
- Ⓑ 40 mph
- Ⓒ (filled) 48 mph
- Ⓓ 75 mph

[Explore 1-9] (DOK2)

6 Sydney used the formula $I = prt$ to find the rate r at the bank if she had a principal of $200 in the bank for 3 years, and earned $36 of interest. What was the rate?

- Ⓕ (filled) 6%
- Ⓖ 12%
- Ⓗ 18%
- Ⓙ 54%

[Lesson IN3] (DOK2)

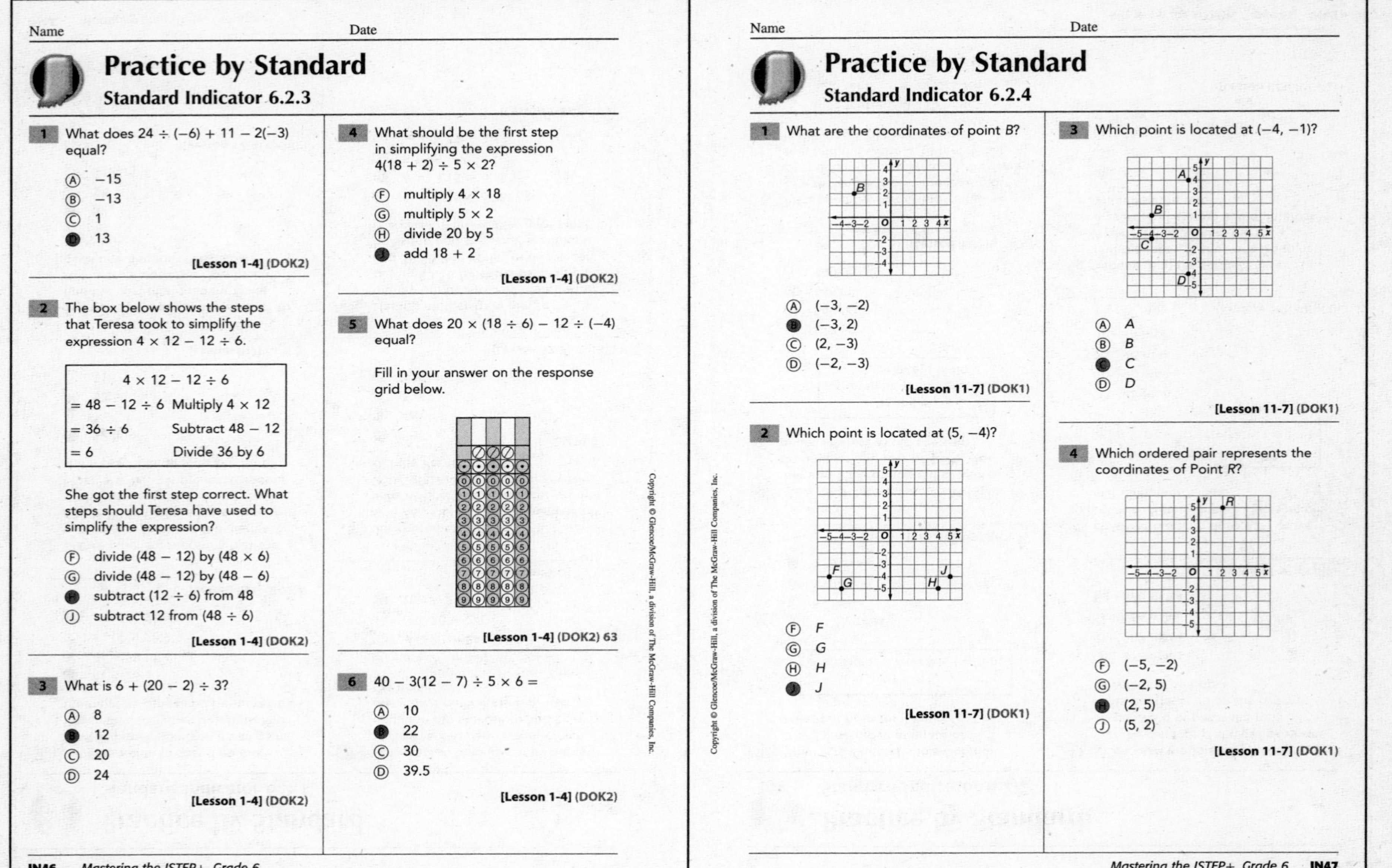

Name Date

Practice by Standard

Standard Indicator 6.2.3

1 What does 24 ÷ (−6) + 11 − 2(−3) equal?

Ⓐ −15
Ⓑ −13
Ⓒ 1
● 13

[Lesson 1-4] (DOK2)

2 The box below shows the steps that Teresa took to simplify the expression 4 × 12 − 12 ÷ 6.

4 × 12 − 12 ÷ 6	
= 48 − 12 ÷ 6	Multiply 4 × 12
= 36 ÷ 6	Subtract 48 − 12
= 6	Divide 36 by 6

She got the first step correct. What steps should Teresa have used to simplify the expression?

Ⓕ divide (48 − 12) by (48 × 6)
Ⓖ divide (48 − 12) by (48 − 6)
● subtract (12 ÷ 6) from 48
Ⓙ subtract 12 from (48 ÷ 6)

[Lesson 1-4] (DOK2)

3 What is 6 + (20 − 2) ÷ 3?

Ⓐ 8
● 12
Ⓒ 20
Ⓓ 24

[Lesson 1-4] (DOK2)

4 What should be the first step in simplifying the expression 4(18 + 2) ÷ 5 × 2?

Ⓕ multiply 4 × 18
Ⓖ multiply 5 × 2
Ⓗ divide 20 by 5
● add 18 + 2

[Lesson 1-4] (DOK2)

5 What does 20 × (18 ÷ 6) − 12 ÷ (−4) equal?

Fill in your answer on the response grid below.

[Lesson 1-4] (DOK2) 63

6 40 − 3(12 − 7) ÷ 5 × 6 =

Ⓐ 10
● 22
Ⓒ 30
Ⓓ 39.5

[Lesson 1-4] (DOK2)

Name Date

Practice by Standard

Standard Indicator 6.2.4

1 What are the coordinates of point *B*?

Ⓐ (−3, −2)
● (−3, 2)
Ⓒ (2, −3)
Ⓓ (−2, −3)

[Lesson 11-7] (DOK1)

2 Which point is located at (5, −4)?

Ⓕ *F*
Ⓖ *G*
Ⓗ *H*
● *J*

[Lesson 11-7] (DOK1)

3 Which point is located at (−4, −1)?

Ⓐ *A*
Ⓑ *B*
● *C*
Ⓓ *D*

[Lesson 11-7] (DOK1)

4 Which ordered pair represents the coordinates of Point *R*?

Ⓕ (−5, −2)
Ⓖ (−2, 5)
● (2, 5)
Ⓙ (5, 2)

[Lesson 11-7] (DOK1)

Name Date

Practice by Standard

Standard Indicator 6.2.5

1 Balloons at the Party Store cost $1.50 each, plus a one-time cost of $3 to have the balloons filled with helium. Which function can be used to find *c*, the cost of filled balloons for *b* balloons?

- Ⓐ $c = 3b + 1.50$
- Ⓑ $c = 1.50(b + 3)$
- Ⓒ $c = 3(b + 1.50)$
- ● $c = 1.50b + 3$

[Lesson 1-6] (DOK3)

2 The graph below shows that the cost of an adult meal *y* at a restaurant, is a function of the cost of a child's meal *x*.

Adult's Meal Cost

Child's Meal Cost

Which equation below represents the function shown in the graph?

- Ⓕ $y = x - 1$
- Ⓖ $y = x + 1$
- Ⓗ $y = 2x - 1$
- ● $y = 2x + 1$

[Lesson 4-9] (DOK3)

3 In the table below, the number of books Gino owns *y* is a function of the number of books Angie owns *x*.

Angie's Books x	Gino's Books y
5	7
6	9
7	11
8	13

Which equation below represents the relationship between Gino and Angie's books as shown in the table?

- Ⓐ $y = x + 2$
- Ⓑ $y = x + 3$
- ● $y = 2x - 3$
- Ⓓ $y = 3x - 8$

[Lesson 1-6] (DOK3)

4 The daily cost to attend a dance class is shown in the graph. Which equation represents the graph?

- Ⓕ $y = 2x + 2$
- Ⓖ $y = 2x - 1$
- ● $y = x + 3$
- Ⓙ $y = 3x$

[Lesson 4-9] (DOK3)

Copyright © Glencoe/McGraw-Hill, a division of The McGraw-Hill Companies, Inc.

Copyright © Glencoe/McGraw-Hill, a division of The McGraw-Hill Companies, Inc.

Name Date

Practice by Standard

Standard Indicator 6.3.1

1 Which is a true statement about angles 1 and 2 as shown below?

- Ⓐ ∠1 is supplementary to ∠2.
- ● ∠1 is complementary to ∠2.
- Ⓒ Both angles are obtuse.
- Ⓓ ∠2 is obtuse.

[Lesson 9-3] (DOK2)

2 *ABCD* is a rectangle. What is the measure of ∠*CAB* in degrees?

Fill in your answer on the response grid below.

[Lesson 9-3] (DOK3) 33

3 In the figure below, $m\angle BAC = 55°$, and $m\angle ABC = 42°$. What is the measure of ∠*BCD*?

- Ⓕ 277°
- Ⓖ 107°
- ● 97°
- Ⓙ 83°

[Lesson 9-3] (DOK3)

4 What is the measure of angle *A* in the figure below?

- Ⓐ 35°
- ● 125°
- Ⓒ 135°
- Ⓓ 205°

[Lesson 9-3] (DOK2)

5 *EFGH* is a square. What is the measure of ∠*GFH*?

- ● 45°
- Ⓖ 55°
- Ⓗ 65°
- Ⓙ 75°

[Lesson 9-3] (DOK3)

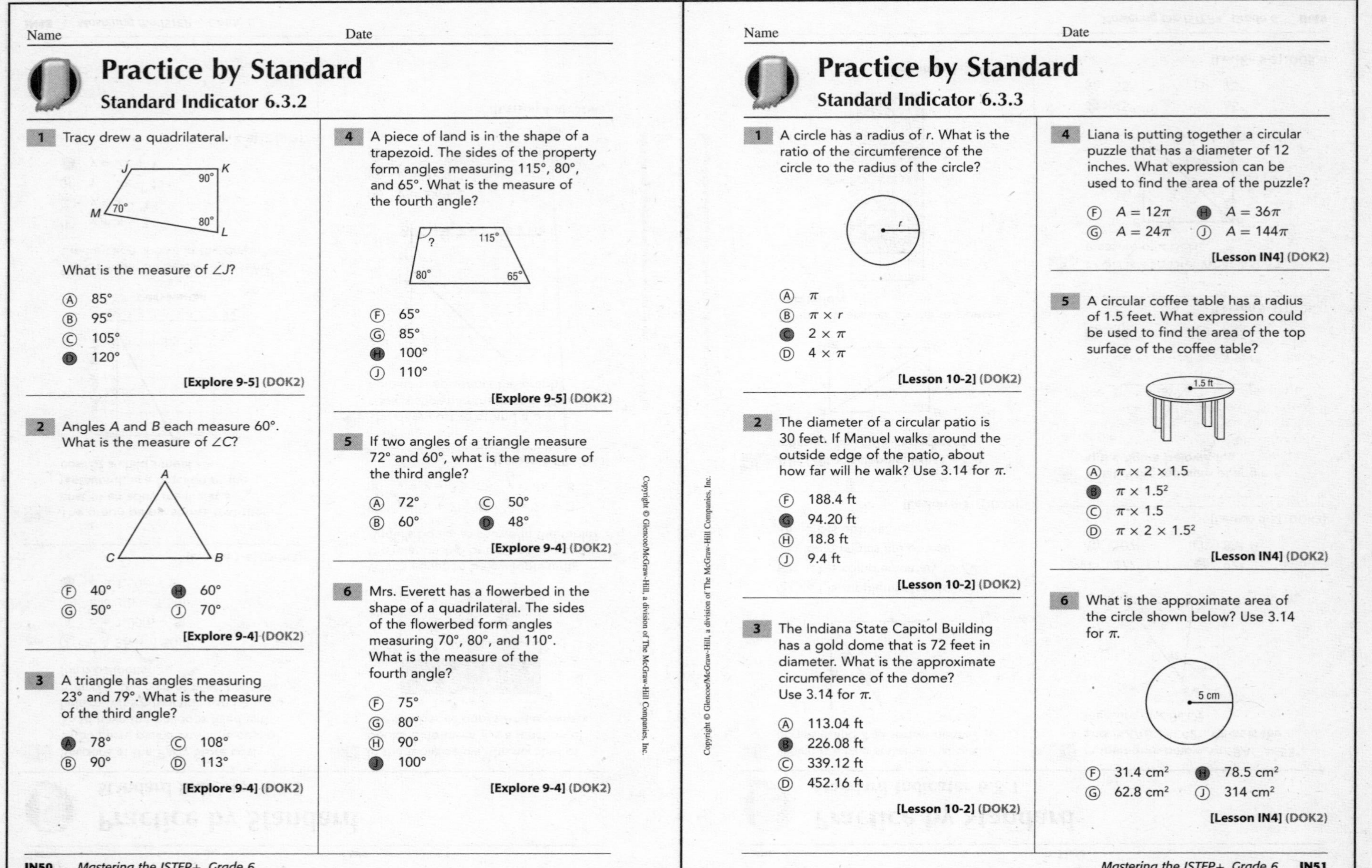

Name Date

Practice by Standard

Standard Indicator 6.3.2

1 Tracy drew a quadrilateral.

What is the measure of ∠*J*?

Ⓐ 85°
Ⓑ 95°
Ⓒ 105°
Ⓓ 120°

[Explore 9-5] (DOK2)

2 Angles *A* and *B* each measure 60°. What is the measure of ∠*C*?

Ⓕ 40°
Ⓖ 50°
Ⓗ 60°
Ⓙ 70°

[Explore 9-4] (DOK2)

3 A triangle has angles measuring 23° and 79°. What is the measure of the third angle?

Ⓐ 78°
Ⓑ 90°
Ⓒ 108°
Ⓓ 113°

[Explore 9-4] (DOK2)

4 A piece of land is in the shape of a trapezoid. The sides of the property form angles measuring 115°, 80°, and 65°. What is the measure of the fourth angle?

Ⓕ 65°
Ⓖ 85°
Ⓗ 100°
Ⓙ 110°

[Explore 9-5] (DOK2)

5 If two angles of a triangle measure 72° and 60°, what is the measure of the third angle?

Ⓐ 72°
Ⓑ 60°
Ⓒ 50°
Ⓓ 48°

[Explore 9-4] (DOK2)

6 Mrs. Everett has a flowerbed in the shape of a quadrilateral. The sides of the flowerbed form angles measuring 70°, 80°, and 110°. What is the measure of the fourth angle?

Ⓕ 75°
Ⓖ 80°
Ⓗ 90°
Ⓙ 100°

[Explore 9-4] (DOK2)

Name Date

Practice by Standard

Standard Indicator 6.3.3

1 A circle has a radius of *r*. What is the ratio of the circumference of the circle to the radius of the circle?

Ⓐ π
Ⓑ $\pi \times r$
Ⓒ $2 \times \pi$
Ⓓ $4 \times \pi$

[Lesson 10-2] (DOK2)

2 The diameter of a circular patio is 30 feet. If Manuel walks around the outside edge of the patio, about how far will he walk? Use 3.14 for π.

Ⓕ 188.4 ft
Ⓖ 94.20 ft
Ⓗ 18.8 ft
Ⓙ 9.4 ft

[Lesson 10-2] (DOK2)

3 The Indiana State Capitol Building has a gold dome that is 72 feet in diameter. What is the approximate circumference of the dome? Use 3.14 for π.

Ⓐ 113.04 ft
Ⓑ 226.08 ft
Ⓒ 339.12 ft
Ⓓ 452.16 ft

[Lesson 10-2] (DOK2)

4 Liana is putting together a circular puzzle that has a diameter of 12 inches. What expression can be used to find the area of the puzzle?

Ⓕ $A = 12\pi$
Ⓖ $A = 24\pi$
Ⓗ $A = 36\pi$
Ⓙ $A = 144\pi$

[Lesson IN4] (DOK2)

5 A circular coffee table has a radius of 1.5 feet. What expression could be used to find the area of the top surface of the coffee table?

Ⓐ $\pi \times 2 \times 1.5$
Ⓑ $\pi \times 1.5^2$
Ⓒ $\pi \times 1.5$
Ⓓ $\pi \times 2 \times 1.5^2$

[Lesson IN4] (DOK2)

6 What is the approximate area of the circle shown below? Use 3.14 for π.

Ⓕ 31.4 cm²
Ⓖ 62.8 cm²
Ⓗ 78.5 cm²
Ⓙ 314 cm²

[Lesson IN4] (DOK2)

Copyright © Glencoe/McGraw-Hill, a division of The McGraw-Hill Companies, Inc.

Name Date

Practice by Standard

Standard Indicator 6.3.4

1 Jordan wants to determine how much sports drink will fit into a large thermos. Which unit is the MOST appropriate to use?

Ⓐ gallons
Ⓑ pounds
● fluid ounces
Ⓓ quarts

[Extend 8-8] (DOK2)

2 The Indianapolis Annual Marathon requires that participants complete a mile every 15 minutes or drop out of the event. Which is the BEST tool for determining how quickly a participant finishes a mile?

Ⓕ egg timer
● stopwatch
Ⓗ pedometer
Ⓙ minute timer

[Extend 8-8] (DOK2)

3 For a science project, Savannah is measuring the mass of hardbound and paperbound books. Which tool should Savannah use?

● large pan balance
Ⓑ electronic scale in ounces
Ⓒ graduated cylinder
Ⓓ metric ruler

[Extend 8-8] (DOK2)

4 April is feeding baby birds with a medicine dropper. Which is the MOST appropriate unit to measure the capacity of a medicine dropper?

Ⓕ liters
● milliliters
Ⓗ grams
Ⓙ milligrams

[Extend 8-8] (DOK2)

5 Neil needs to measure the dimensions of a vegetable garden so that he can determine how much fencing to buy. Which is the BEST tool for measuring the dimensions of the garden in customary units?

Ⓐ meter stick
● yard stick
Ⓒ inch ruler
Ⓓ centimeter ruler

[Extend 8-8] (DOK2)

6 Ariel is looking at a label that gives the weight of a box of crackers. Which unit is most likely on the label?

Ⓕ kilometers
Ⓖ meters
Ⓗ kilograms
● grams

[Extend 8-8] (DOK2)

Copyright © Glencoe/McGraw-Hill, a division of The McGraw-Hill Companies, Inc.

Name Date

Practice by Standard

Standard Indicator 6.3.5

1 What is the surface area of the cylinder, in square inches, to the nearest whole number?

8 in.
4 in.

Fill in your answer on the response grid below.

[Lesson IN5] (DOK3) 201

2 What is the volume of the tin? Use 3.14 for π.

22 cm
7 cm

Ⓐ 1,243.4 cm³
● 2,659.6 cm³
Ⓒ 4,006.6 cm³
Ⓓ 10,638.3 cm³

[Lesson IN5] (DOK2)

3 What is the approximate surface area of the paint bottle below?

3 cm
1 cm
5 cm
5 cm
5 cm

● 160 cm²
Ⓖ 169 cm²
Ⓗ 174 cm²
Ⓙ 225 cm²

[Lesson IN6] (DOK3)

4 A candle in the shape of a cylinder is placed in a rectangular box for gift wrapping. The candle has a diameter of 3 inches and a height of 10 inches. The rectangular box has a height of 10.5 inches, and length and width of 4 inches. What is the approximate volume of space around the candle inside the box?

3 in.
10 in.
10.5 in.
4 in.
4 in.

Ⓐ 60 in³
Ⓑ 92 in³
● 97 in³
Ⓓ 129 in³

[Lesson IN6] (DOK3)

Name Date

Practice by Standard

Standard Indicator 6.4.1

1 The stem-and-leaf plot displays the game scores for the Colts in 2008. Which best describes the data?

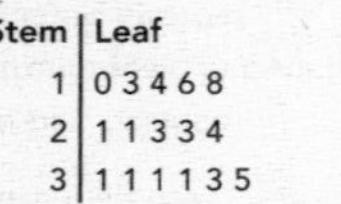

Stem	Leaf
1	0 3 4 6 8
2	1 1 3 3 4
3	1 1 1 1 3 5

2 | 3 = 23

Ⓐ Half of the scores are less than 20 points.
● The Colts scored 31 points most often.
Ⓒ Half of the scores are over 30 points.
Ⓓ The scores range by 35 points.

[Lesson 2-4] (DOK3)

2 The circle graph shows the type of music played at a radio station. Which best describes the data?

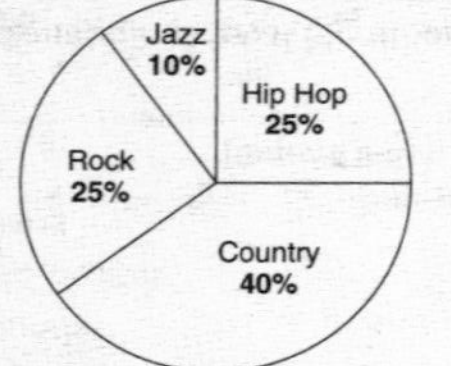

Ⓕ Hip hop is the station favorite.
Ⓖ Country plays twice as often as rock and hip hop combined.
Ⓗ Hip hop plays more often than rock.
● Either country or jazz plays half the time.

[Lesson 7-2] (DOK3)

3 Katie talks on her cell phone every day. The table shows a breakdown of the phone calls she receives.

Received Calls	Percentage
Friends	65%
Family	32%
Work	3%

Which circle graph best displays the information in the table?

Ⓐ Friends, Family, Work
Ⓑ Friends, Work, Family
● Family, Friends, Work
Ⓓ Friends, Work, Family

[Lesson 7-2] (DOK2)

Name Date

Practice by Standard

Standard Indicator 6.4.2

1 Gaby is investigating how the average price of gasoline changed in Indiana for the past 4 months. Which of the following statements explains the type of graph that would best display the data?

Ⓐ A circle graph because it would show the percentage of different prices for 4 months.
● A line graph because it would show the change in prices over 4 months.
Ⓒ A stem-and-leaf plot because it would show the mean price for 4 months.
Ⓓ A bar graph because it would compare the different prices over 4 months.

[Lesson 2-8] (DOK3)

2 Trey is using a circle graph to display the results of a survey on favorite places to visit in Indiana. Which is NOT a good reason for choosing a circle graph?

Ⓕ It makes it easy to compare the different categories.
Ⓖ It allows him to quickly see the most popular places.
Ⓗ It gives a general picture of parts (places) to the whole (Indiana).
● It allows him to determine the range of choices.

[Lesson 2-8] (DOK3)

3 Sara collected data on the number of campsites available in different state parks. Which type of display should she use to compare the number of sites at the parks?

Ⓐ A circle graph because it shows percentages.
Ⓑ A stem-and-leaf plot because it shows the mean and median.
● A bar graph because it compares categories of data.
Ⓓ A line graph because it shows changes in numbers.

[Lesson 2-8] (DOK3)

4 James wants to display data on completed passes in Colts games over the past 5 years. He wants to use the data to determine ranges, averages, and most frequent number of completed passes. Which data display should he use?

● stem-and-leaf plot
Ⓖ line graph
Ⓗ bar graph
Ⓙ circle graph

[Lesson 2-8] (DOK3)

Name Date

Practice by Standard

Standard Indicator 6.4.3

1 The table shows the number of boxes of greeting cards Mandy sold to gift stores last week.

Day	Number Sold
Monday	10
Tuesday	8
Wednesday	8
Thursday	14
Friday	8
Saturday	15

Which comparison is true?

Ⓐ median > mean
Ⓑ mean > median (filled)
Ⓒ mode = median
Ⓓ mean < mode

[Lesson 2-7] (DOK3)

2 The high temperatures in Muncie from May 1, 2009 to May 10, 2009 are shown below.

67°, 63°, 67°, 70°, 71°,
61°, 73°, 69°, 62°, 64°

If another day of 90° is added to the temperatures, which measure would be most affected?

Ⓕ mean only (filled)
Ⓖ median only
Ⓗ mode only
Ⓙ mean and median

[Lesson 2-7] (DOK3)

3 Trees were randomly sampled to find which were infected with a fungus. The results are shown in the table.

Sample Plot	Number of Infected Trees
1	3
2	18
3	6
4	3
5	10

Which measure is most appropriate for describing the data?

Ⓐ Median because it is the value in the middle.
Ⓑ Mean and median because they are about the same.
Ⓒ Median because extreme data of 18 mostly affects the mean. (filled)
Ⓓ Mean because extreme data of 18 mostly affects the median.

[Lesson 2-7] (DOK3)

4 A pizza shop sold 51, 55, 60, 64, and 45 pizzas on five consecutive nights. Which measure would be most affected if 55 pizzas were sold on the sixth night?

Ⓕ mean only
Ⓖ median only
Ⓗ mode only (filled)
Ⓙ mean and median

[Lesson 2-7] (DOK3)

Copyright © Glencoe/McGraw-Hill, a division of The McGraw-Hill Companies, Inc.

Name Date

Practice by Standard

Standard Indicator 6.4.4

1 A box has 2 red paperclips, 1 blue paperclip, 1 yellow paperclip, and 1 white paperclip. If Martin draws at random, what is the probability that he will select a red paperclip?

Ⓐ 0.2
Ⓑ 0.25
Ⓒ 0.4 (filled)
Ⓓ 0.8

[Lesson 7-4] (DOK2)

2 Maia has a number cube numbered 1–6. What is the probability that she will roll a number less than 2?

Ⓕ $16\frac{2}{3}\%$ (filled)
Ⓖ 25%
Ⓗ 30%
Ⓙ $33\frac{1}{3}\%$

[Lesson 7-4] (DOK2)

3 Lonny spins a fair spinner with the numbers 2, 5, 8, 3, 1, and 7. What is the probability that the spinner will land on an even number?

Ⓐ $\frac{1}{6}$
Ⓑ $\frac{2}{3}$
Ⓒ $\frac{5}{6}$
Ⓓ $\frac{1}{3}$ (filled)

[Lesson 7-4] (DOK2)

4 A bag of letter tiles has the following letters.

N	R	R	N	S	T	R	A

What is the probability of drawing a tile with the letter R?

Ⓕ 0.125
Ⓖ 0.25
Ⓗ 0.375 (filled)
Ⓙ 0.38

[Lesson 7-4] (DOK2)

5 Madison filled a box with 10 red toys, 15 blue toys, and 20 yellow toys. Children will select a toy from the box without looking. What is the probability that the first child will select a blue toy?

Ⓐ $\frac{2}{3}$
Ⓑ $\frac{1}{3}$ (filled)
Ⓒ $\frac{1}{20}$
Ⓓ $\frac{1}{15}$

[Lesson 7-4] (DOK2)

6 A spinner has 10 equal sections numbered 1 through 10. What is the probability of NOT spinning a number greater than 3?

Ⓕ 20%
Ⓖ 30% (filled)
Ⓗ 70%
Ⓙ 80%

[Lesson 7-4] (DOK2)

Name Date

Practice by Standard

Standard Indicator 6.4.5

1 Ricardo experimented with spinning a spinner with four equal sections of colors. The results of his experiment are shown in the table below.

Color	Number of Spins
Blue	11
Red	14
Gold	10
Green	15

What is the relative frequency of spinning red written as a decimal and a ratio?

Ⓐ 0.14 and 7:50
● 0.28 and 7:25
Ⓒ 0.28 and 1:25
Ⓓ 0.3888... and 7:18

[Lesson 7-4] (DOK2)

2 Nadia has been practicing shooting baskets for the upcoming basketball game. The probability that she will make the next basket is 0.625. What is this probability written as a percent and a ratio?

Ⓕ 6.25% and 5:8
● 62.5% and 5:8
Ⓗ 62.5% and 62:5
Ⓙ 625% and 62:5

[Lesson 7-4] (DOK2)

3 The probability that a teammate on a baseball team will hit a homerun is 7:20. What is this probability written as a decimal and a percentage?

Ⓐ 0.28 and 28%
● 0.35 and 35%
Ⓒ 0.65 and 65%
Ⓓ 0.72 and 72%

[Lesson 7-4] (DOK2)

4 The table below shows the results of drawing marbles out of a bag.

Color	Number of Draws
Blue	13
Red	20
Yellow	7

What is the relative frequency of drawing a yellow marble written as a decimal?

● 0.175 Ⓗ 0.325
Ⓖ 0.2121... Ⓙ 0.5

[Lesson 7-4] (DOK2)

5 The probability of electing a girl for Student Council is 60%. What is the probability written as a ratio?

Ⓐ 6:1
Ⓑ 5:3
● 3:5
Ⓓ 1:6

[Lesson 7-4] (DOK2)

Copyright © Glencoe/McGraw-Hill, a division of The McGraw-Hill Companies, Inc.

Name Date

Practice Test

Applied Skills

Write your answers in the space provided. Be sure to show all your work.

1 Mary fills a dishpan with water. She pours water from a cylindrical can into the rectangular prism dishpan.

The can is 20 centimeters high and has a diameter of 6 centimeters.

The dishpan is 40 centimeters long, 30 centimeters deep, and 15 centimeters high.

Mary thinks that she can fill the dishpan by pouring water from her full can 25 times.

Determine if Mary's idea is correct. If not, how many times must she pour the full can of water into the dishpan to fill it?

Justify your answer using words, numbers, and/or symbols.

Show All Work

Volume of dishpan: $40 \times 30 \times 15 = 18{,}000$ cm^3

Volume of can: $\pi \times r^2 \times h$, or 565.2 cm^3

$\frac{18,000}{565.2} = 31.85$ times

Mary is incorrect. She will need to pour the can into the dishpan more than 31 times to fill the dishpan.

[Lesson IN5] 6.3.5 (DOK3)

Go on

Copyright © Glencoe/McGraw-Hill, a division of The McGraw-Hill Companies, Inc.

Name ____________ Date ____________

Practice Test

Applied Skills (continued)

2 Quinton went to a car show with his father and his uncle. They bought 3 tickets for $12.50 each, 3 T-shirts for $15.00 each, and 3 drinks for $2.00 each.

Write an equation that can be used to find the total amount of money Quinton, his father, and his uncle spent at the car show. Then solve the equation.

Equation **(3 × 12.50) + (3 × 15.00) + (3 × 2.00) = 88.50 The total spent was $88.50.**

If the total amount of money spent was split evenly among all 3 people, how much money did each person spend?

Show All Work

88.50 ÷ 3 = 29.50

Answer **Each person spent $29.50.**

[Lesson 3-6] 6.1.6 (DOK2)

3 Mya knows that the area of her desktop is 660 square inches and its length is 30 inches. Write an equation to find the width of her desktop. Then solve the equation.

Equation **660 in² = 30 in. × *w*; the width is 22 inches.**

Mya has 7 pieces of glitter paper. Each piece is 9 inches by 12 inches. Does she have enough paper to cover her desktop with the glitter paper?

Show All Work

9 × 12 = 108
108 × 7 = 756

Answer **Yes, she has 756 square inches of glitter paper, which is more than enough to cover the 660 square inches of her desktop.**

[Lesson 12-5] 6.2.1 (DOK2)

Go on

Copyright © Glencoe/McGraw-Hill, a division of The McGraw-Hill Companies, Inc.

Name ____________ Date ____________

Practice Test

Applied Skills (continued)

4 A mail sorter takes 5 minutes to sort 120 pieces of mail. At that rate, about how many minutes will it take the mail sorter to sort 1,000 pieces of mail?

Justify your answer using words, numbers, and/or symbols.

Show All Work

$$\frac{5 \text{ minutes}}{120 \text{ pieces of mail}} = \frac{x \text{ minutes}}{1{,}000 \text{ pieces of mail}}$$
$$\frac{5}{120} = \frac{x}{1{,}000}$$
$$120x = 5000$$
$$\frac{120x}{120} = \frac{5000}{120}$$
$$x = 41.7 \text{ or about } 42$$

Answer **about 42** minutes

At the same rate, how many pieces of mail can one mail sorter sort in 3.5 hours?

Show All Work

$$3.5 \text{ hours} = 210 \text{ minutes}$$
$$\frac{5 \text{ minutes}}{120 \text{ pieces of mail}} = \frac{210 \text{ minutes}}{x \text{ pieces of mail}}$$
$$\frac{5}{120} = \frac{210}{x}$$
$$5x = 25{,}200$$
$$\frac{5x}{5} = \frac{25{,}200}{5}$$
$$x = 5{,}040$$

Answer **5,040** pieces of mail

[Lesson 6-3] 6.1.8 (DOK2)

Go on

Name Date

Practice Test
Applied Skills (continued)

5 Rory is making trail mix. He uses the following ingredients: raisins, sunflower seeds, chocolate chips, pretzels, and peanuts.

If Rory adds $\frac{1}{4}$ cup of each ingredient to his mix, how many cups of trail mix will he make?

Show All Work

$\frac{1}{4} \times 5 = \frac{5}{4}$

$\frac{5}{4} = 1\frac{1}{4}$

Answer $1\frac{1}{4}$ **cups**

If Rory adds another $\frac{1}{4}$ cup of each ingredient to his mix, how many cups of trail mix will he have?

Show All Work

$1\frac{1}{4} + 1\frac{1}{4} = 2\frac{2}{4}$ or $2\frac{1}{2}$

Answer $2\frac{1}{2}$ **cups**

[Lesson 5-3] 6.1.6 (DOK1)

6 Simplify the following expression. Explain each step you take.

$4(12 - 4) \div 2 - 10$

Answer **6; first I solve what's inside the parentheses, (12 − 4) = 8, then I multiply that solution by 4; which equals 32, then I divide 32 by 2 which equals 16, then finally subtract 10.**

Write another expression with more than 2 operations with the same value as the expression above.

Answer $3 \times 6 + (12 - 10) - 14 = 6$

[Lesson 1-4] 6.2.3 (DOK1)

Go on

Copyright © Glencoe/McGraw-Hill, a division of The McGraw-Hill Companies, Inc.

Name Date

Practice Test
Applied Skills (continued)

7 Austin receives $500 as a gift. He wants to save it for one year and earn interest on his savings. He may choose to invest it at a bank that pays 4% interest per year, without any additional fees. Or he may choose to invest it at a bank that pays 4.5% interest but charges a one-time service fee of $5.

Compare Austin's investment choices. Which choice will result in earning him the most money, including the cost of any extra fees?

Show All Work

$I = prt$

$I = 500 \times 0.04 \times 1$

$I = 20$; first bank would earn him $20 in interest

$I = prt$

$I = 500 \times 0.045 \times 1 - 5$

$I = 17.5$; second bank would earn him $17.50 in interest

Answer **The bank with 4% interest and no fees will earn him more money.**

How would the situation change if the bank with 4% interest added a one-time fee of $2?

Show All Work

$20 − $2 = $18; $18 > $17.50

This bank will still allow Austin to earn more money than the bank with 4.5% interest and a one-time fee of $5.

[Lesson IN3] 6.2.2 (DOK3)

Go on

Copyright © Glencoe/McGraw-Hill, a division of The McGraw-Hill Companies, Inc.

Name Date

Practice Test

Applied Skills (continued)

8 Ushma plans to build a small shed to store her lawn mower and tools.

What dimensions would be appropriate for Ushma's shed, without the roof?

Answer **Answers will vary. Sample answer: 8 feet long, 8 feet wide, 10 feet tall**

What tools might she use to measure the lumber to build her shed?

Answer **tape measure, yard stick, ruler**

How much lumber will Ushma need to buy to build the walls and floor of the shed?

Show All Work

Sample Answer:

1 side = 8 × 10 = 80 square feet

80 × 4 = 320 square feet for the sides

floor = 8 × 8 = 64 square feet

320 + 64 = 384 square feet total

Answer **Sample answer: 384 square feet.**

How much storage space will Ushma have in her shed? What will the volume of the shed be?

Show All Work

Sample Answer:

8 × 8 × 10 = 640

Answer **Sample answer: 640 cubic feet**

[Extend 8-8] 6.3.4 (DOK3)

STOP

Name Date

Practice Test

Session 1

Fill in the bubble next to the correct answer.

1 Which point shows the location of $\frac{3}{4}$ on the number line?

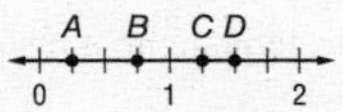

Ⓐ point *A*
● point *B*
Ⓒ point *C*
Ⓓ point *D*

[Lesson 4-6] 6.1.1 (DOK1)

2 What value of *b* makes the following equation true?

$b \div 4 = 24$

Ⓕ 144
● 96
Ⓗ 48
Ⓙ 24

[Lesson 1-8] 6.2.1 (DOK1)

3 What does $\frac{5}{8} + \frac{5}{12}$ equal?

Ⓐ $\frac{15}{24}$
Ⓑ $\frac{20}{24}$
● $1\frac{1}{24}$
Ⓓ $1\frac{5}{24}$

[Lesson 5-4] 6.1.6 (DOK1)

4 Ada and her friends ate dinner at a restaurant. The bill came to $85.00. If they gave their server a 15% tip, how much did they spend in all for dinner?

● $97.75
Ⓖ $102.25
Ⓗ $103.75
Ⓙ 105.25

[Lesson IN2] 6.1.9 (DOK1)

5 A bicycle shop made the following graph to show the different kinds of bicycles sold last year.

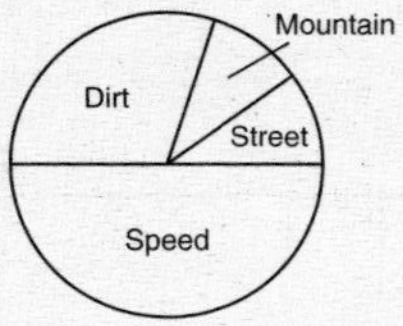

According to the circle graph, approximately what percent of the bicycles sold were speed bikes?

Ⓐ 4%
Ⓑ 25%
● 50%
Ⓓ 100%

[Lesson 7-1] 6.1.3 (DOK1)

Go on

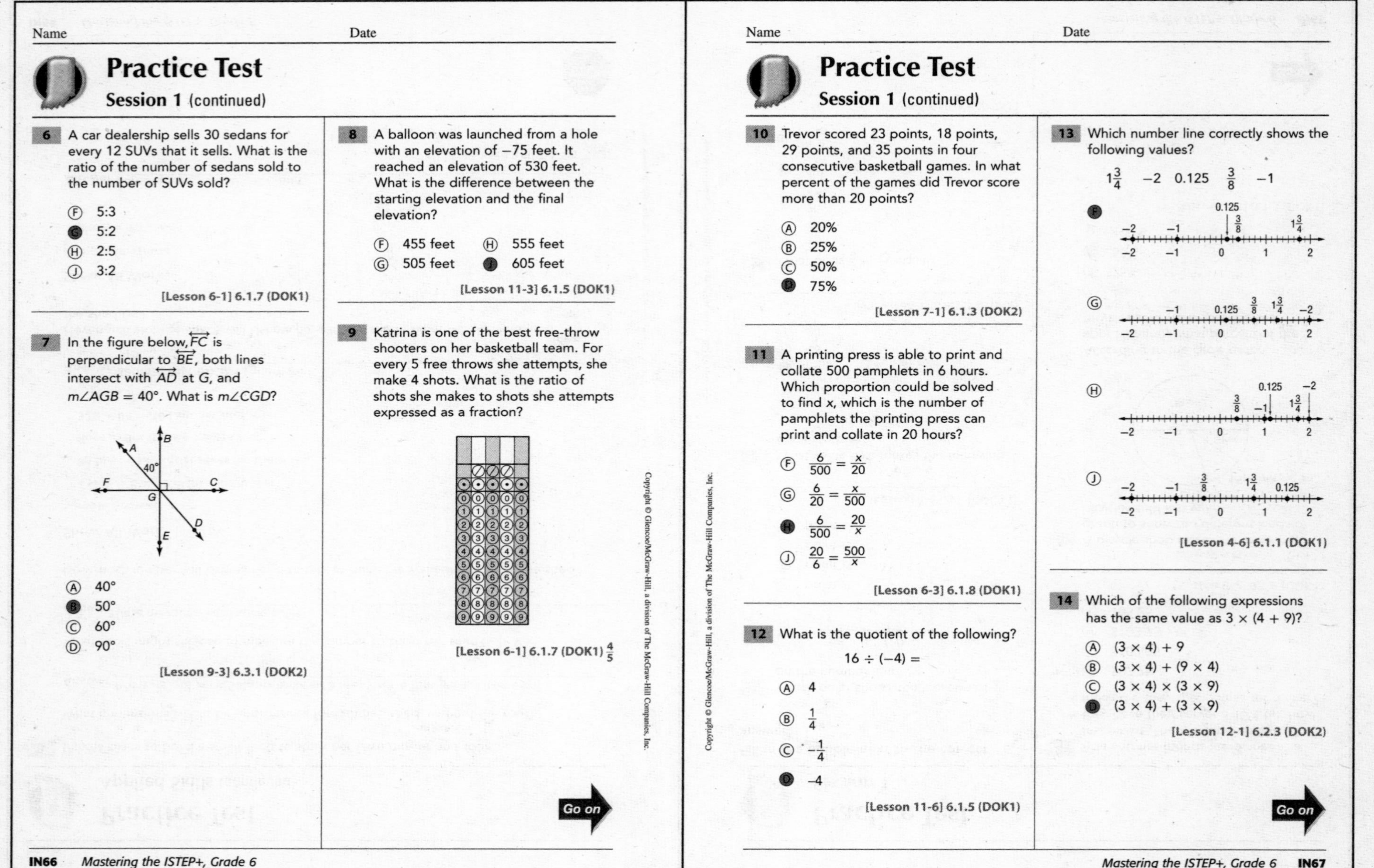

Name Date

Practice Test

Session 1 (continued)

6 A car dealership sells 30 sedans for every 12 SUVs that it sells. What is the ratio of the number of sedans sold to the number of SUVs sold?

Ⓕ 5:3
Ⓖ 5:2
Ⓗ 2:5
Ⓙ 3:2

[Lesson 6-1] 6.1.7 (DOK1)

7 In the figure below, $\overleftrightarrow{FC}$ is perpendicular to $\overleftrightarrow{BE}$, both lines intersect with $\overleftrightarrow{AD}$ at G, and $m\angle AGB = 40°$. What is $m\angle CGD$?

Ⓐ 40°
Ⓑ 50°
Ⓒ 60°
Ⓓ 90°

[Lesson 9-3] 6.3.1 (DOK2)

8 A balloon was launched from a hole with an elevation of −75 feet. It reached an elevation of 530 feet. What is the difference between the starting elevation and the final elevation?

Ⓕ 455 feet Ⓗ 555 feet
Ⓖ 505 feet Ⓙ 605 feet

[Lesson 11-3] 6.1.5 (DOK1)

9 Katrina is one of the best free-throw shooters on her basketball team. For every 5 free throws she attempts, she make 4 shots. What is the ratio of shots she makes to shots she attempts expressed as a fraction?

[Lesson 6-1] 6.1.7 (DOK1) $\frac{4}{5}$

Go on

Name Date

Practice Test

Session 1 (continued)

10 Trevor scored 23 points, 18 points, 29 points, and 35 points in four consecutive basketball games. In what percent of the games did Trevor score more than 20 points?

Ⓐ 20%
Ⓑ 25%
Ⓒ 50%
Ⓓ 75%

[Lesson 7-1] 6.1.3 (DOK2)

11 A printing press is able to print and collate 500 pamphlets in 6 hours. Which proportion could be solved to find x, which is the number of pamphlets the printing press can print and collate in 20 hours?

Ⓕ $\frac{6}{500} = \frac{x}{20}$
Ⓖ $\frac{6}{20} = \frac{x}{500}$
Ⓗ $\frac{6}{500} = \frac{20}{x}$
Ⓙ $\frac{20}{6} = \frac{500}{x}$

[Lesson 6-3] 6.1.8 (DOK1)

12 What is the quotient of the following?

$16 \div (-4) =$

Ⓐ 4
Ⓑ $\frac{1}{4}$
Ⓒ $-\frac{1}{4}$
Ⓓ −4

[Lesson 11-6] 6.1.5 (DOK1)

13 Which number line correctly shows the following values?

$1\frac{3}{4}$ −2 0.125 $\frac{3}{8}$ −1

Ⓕ
Ⓖ
Ⓗ
Ⓙ

[Lesson 4-6] 6.1.1 (DOK1)

14 Which of the following expressions has the same value as $3 \times (4 + 9)$?

Ⓐ $(3 \times 4) + 9$
Ⓑ $(3 \times 4) + (9 \times 4)$
Ⓒ $(3 \times 4) \times (3 \times 9)$
Ⓓ $(3 \times 4) + (3 \times 9)$

[Lesson 12-1] 6.2.3 (DOK2)

Go on

Copyright © Glencoe/McGraw-Hill, a division of The McGraw-Hill Companies, Inc.

Name Date

Practice Test

Session 1 (continued)

15 A circus trampoline has a diameter of 8 meters. What is the circumference of the trampoline? Use 3.14 for π.

8 m

Ⓕ 12.56 meters
● 25.12 meters
Ⓗ 50.24 meters
Ⓙ 100.48 meters

[Lesson 10-2] 6.3.3 (DOK1)

16 Find the measure of $\angle X$ in the triangle below.

Z 35° x X 45° Y

Ⓐ 80°
Ⓑ 90°
● 100°
Ⓓ 110°

[Explore 9-4] 6.3.2 (DOK1)

17 Lupe's bank account pays 3.5% simple interest per year. If there is $940.00 in Lupe's account today, how much money will there be in Lupe's account 1 year from today?

Ⓕ $943.29
Ⓖ $970.29
● $972.90
Ⓙ $1,269.00

[Lesson IN3] 6.2.2 (DOK1)

18 The Indiana Department of Transportation is rebuilding U.S. Route 31 between South Bend and Plymouth, Indiana. What is the most likely length of this road?

Ⓐ 20 millimeters
Ⓑ 20 centimeters
Ⓒ 20 yards
● 20 miles

[Extend 10-7] 6.3.4 (DOK1)

19 Every year, Sue's town hosts a soccer tournament. About 75% of the players are from her town. Which decimal represents 75%?

Ⓕ 75.0
● 0.75
Ⓗ 0.57
Ⓙ 0.075

[Lesson 4-8] 6.1.4 (DOK1)

Go on

Name Date

Practice Test

Session 1 (continued)

20 A children's hospital is having an artist paint a picture of a sun on the wall of the hospital's main lobby. The sun has a radius of 5 feet. What is the circumference, in feet, of the painted sun? Use 3.14 for π. Fill in your answer on the response grid below.

[Lesson 10-2] 6.3.3 (DOK1) 31.4

21 Jeremy has a piece of lumber that measures 12 feet in length. He cuts off a $1\frac{1}{2}$-foot-long piece and a $2\frac{1}{4}$-foot-long piece. What is the length of the piece of lumber now?

Ⓐ $3\frac{1}{4}$ ft
Ⓑ $3\frac{3}{4}$ ft
Ⓒ $6\frac{3}{4}$ ft
● $8\frac{1}{4}$ ft

[Lesson 5-4] 6.1.6 (DOK2)

22 Angela has a bag with 200 jelly beans. 12% of the jelly beans are green. How many jelly beans are green?

Ⓕ 12
Ⓖ 17
Ⓗ 20
● 24

[Lesson 7-1] 6.1.3 (DOK2)

23 On January 20, 1985, the low temperature in Fort Wayne was −11°F. On the same day, the low temperature in Delphi was −8°F. What is the absolute value of the difference between these two temperatures?

Ⓐ −19
Ⓑ −3
● 3
Ⓓ 19

[Lesson IN1] 6.1.2 (DOK1)

24 Sasha is measuring the lengths of four pieces of yarn. Which list shows the yarn lengths in order from longest to shortest?

● 4.75, 4.5, 4.3, 4.25
Ⓖ 4.75, 4.5, 4.25, 4.3
Ⓗ 4.25, 4.3, 4.5, 4.75
Ⓙ 4.75, 4.25, 4.5, 4.3

[Lesson 3-2] 6.1.1 (DOK1)

25 Kwame has 14 books. He got 5 books from his brother yesterday afternoon. Which equation shows how to find how many books Kwame had yesterday morning?

Ⓐ $5 \times b = 14$
● $5 + b = 14$
Ⓒ $\frac{5}{b} = 14$
Ⓓ $5 - b = 14$

[Explore 1-9] 6.2.2 (DOK2)

Go on

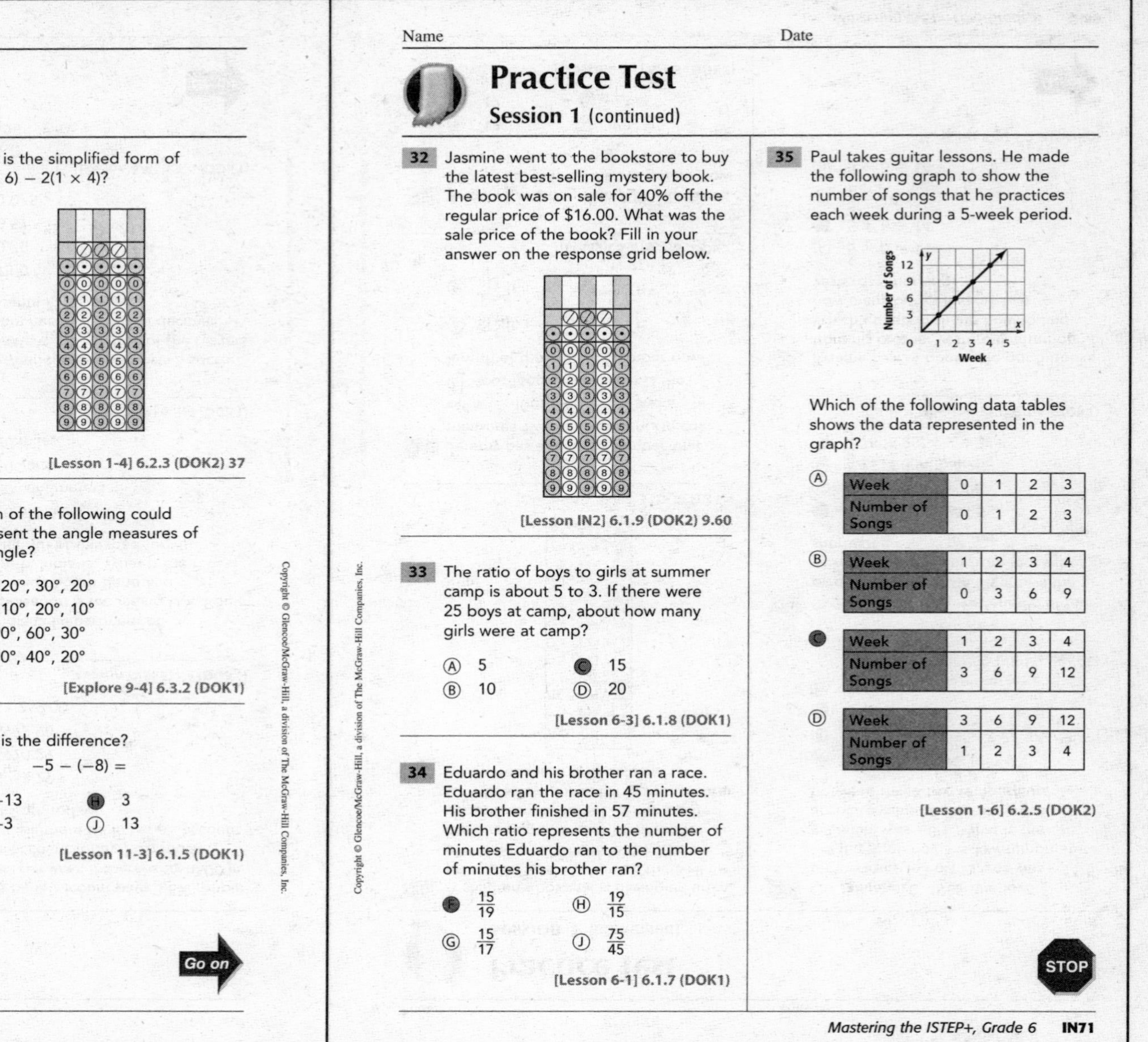

Name Date

Practice Test

Session 1 (continued)

26 Which point represents the location of the ordered pair (4, −5)?

Ⓕ point *A*
● point *B*
Ⓗ point *C*
Ⓙ point *D*

[Lesson 11-7] 6.2.4 (DOK1)

27 What is the surface area of a cylinder with a diameter of 18 inches and a height of 12 inches?

Ⓐ 932.58 square inches
Ⓑ 1017.36 square inches
● 1186.92 square inches
Ⓓ 3391.2 square inches

[Lesson IN5] 6.3.5 (DOK1)

28 In 2007, $\frac{1}{4}$ of the population of Indiana was under the age of 18. How can you represent this fraction as a percent?

Ⓕ 1%
Ⓖ 5%
● 25%
Ⓙ 50%

[Lesson 7-1] 6.1.4 (DOK1)

29 What is the simplified form of $5(3 + 6) - 2(1 \times 4)$?

[Lesson 1-4] 6.2.3 (DOK2) 37

30 Which of the following could represent the angle measures of a triangle?

Ⓐ 120°, 30°, 20°
Ⓑ 110°, 20°, 10°
● 90°, 60°, 30°
Ⓓ 70°, 40°, 20°

[Explore 9-4] 6.3.2 (DOK1)

31 What is the difference?

$$-5 - (-8) =$$

Ⓕ −13 ● 3
Ⓖ −3 Ⓙ 13

[Lesson 11-3] 6.1.5 (DOK1)

Go on

Name Date

Practice Test

Session 1 (continued)

32 Jasmine went to the bookstore to buy the latest best-selling mystery book. The book was on sale for 40% off the regular price of $16.00. What was the sale price of the book? Fill in your answer on the response grid below.

[Lesson IN2] 6.1.9 (DOK2) 9.60

33 The ratio of boys to girls at summer camp is about 5 to 3. If there were 25 boys at camp, about how many girls were at camp?

Ⓐ 5 ● 15
Ⓑ 10 Ⓓ 20

[Lesson 6-3] 6.1.8 (DOK1)

34 Eduardo and his brother ran a race. Eduardo ran the race in 45 minutes. His brother finished in 57 minutes. Which ratio represents the number of minutes Eduardo ran to the number of minutes his brother ran?

● $\frac{15}{19}$ Ⓗ $\frac{19}{15}$
Ⓖ $\frac{15}{17}$ Ⓙ $\frac{75}{45}$

[Lesson 6-1] 6.1.7 (DOK1)

35 Paul takes guitar lessons. He made the following graph to show the number of songs that he practices each week during a 5-week period.

Which of the following data tables shows the data represented in the graph?

Ⓐ

Week	0	1	2	3
Number of Songs	0	1	2	3

Ⓑ

Week	1	2	3	4
Number of Songs	0	3	6	9

●

Week	1	2	3	4
Number of Songs	3	6	9	12

Ⓓ

Week	3	6	9	12
Number of Songs	1	2	3	4

[Lesson 1-6] 6.2.5 (DOK2)

STOP

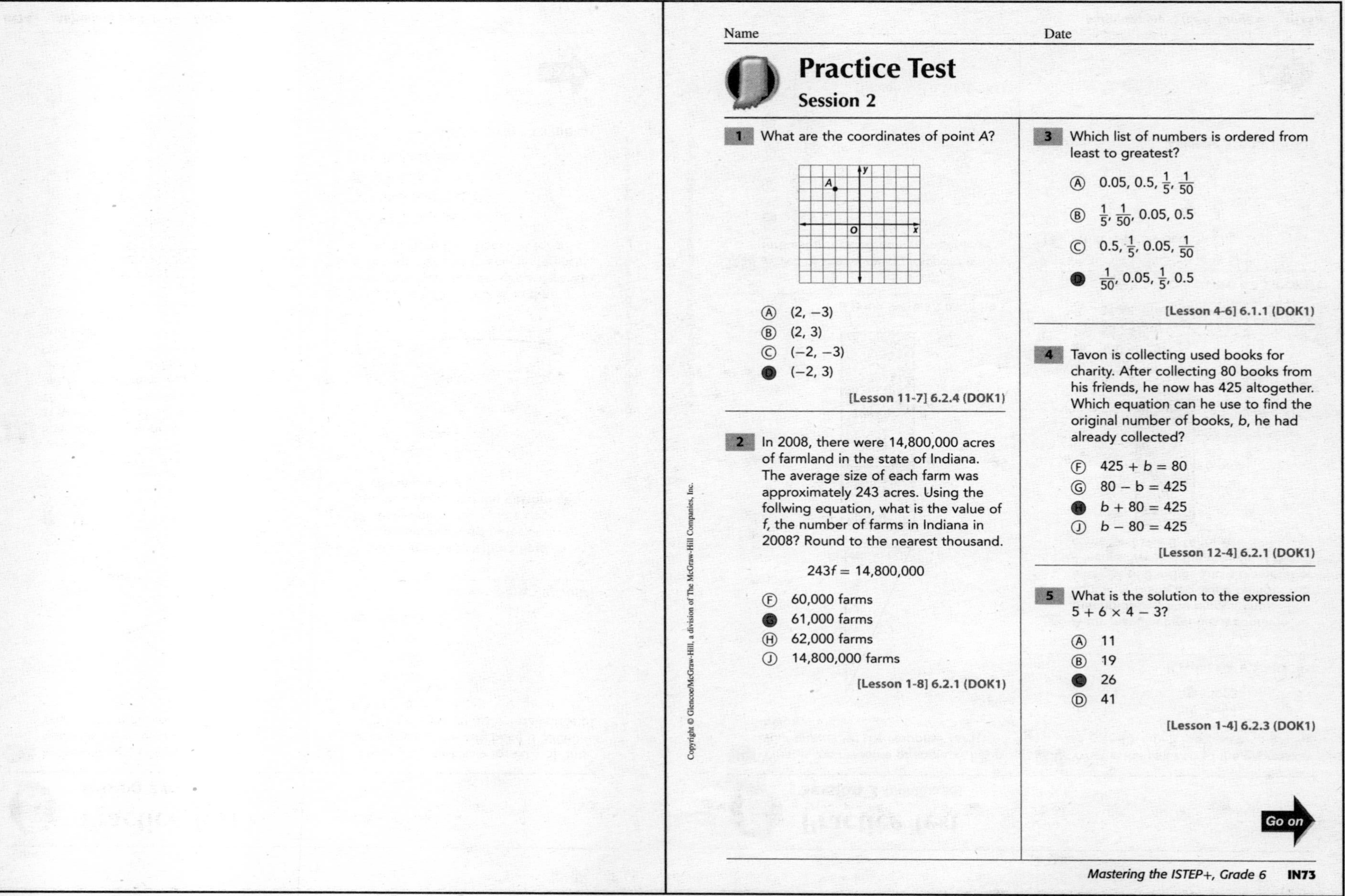

Name Date

Practice Test
Session 2

1 What are the coordinates of point A?

Ⓐ (2, −3)
Ⓑ (2, 3)
Ⓒ (−2, −3)
Ⓓ (−2, 3)

[Lesson 11-7] 6.2.4 (DOK1)

2 In 2008, there were 14,800,000 acres of farmland in the state of Indiana. The average size of each farm was approximately 243 acres. Using the follwing equation, what is the value of f, the number of farms in Indiana in 2008? Round to the nearest thousand.

$$243f = 14{,}800{,}000$$

Ⓕ 60,000 farms
Ⓖ 61,000 farms
Ⓗ 62,000 farms
Ⓙ 14,800,000 farms

[Lesson 1-8] 6.2.1 (DOK1)

3 Which list of numbers is ordered from least to greatest?

Ⓐ $0.05, 0.5, \frac{1}{5}, \frac{1}{50}$
Ⓑ $\frac{1}{5}, \frac{1}{50}, 0.05, 0.5$
Ⓒ $0.5, \frac{1}{5}, 0.05, \frac{1}{50}$
Ⓓ $\frac{1}{50}, 0.05, \frac{1}{5}, 0.5$

[Lesson 4-6] 6.1.1 (DOK1)

4 Tavon is collecting used books for charity. After collecting 80 books from his friends, he now has 425 altogether. Which equation can he use to find the original number of books, b, he had already collected?

Ⓕ $425 + b = 80$
Ⓖ $80 - b = 425$
Ⓗ $b + 80 = 425$
Ⓙ $b - 80 = 425$

[Lesson 12-4] 6.2.1 (DOK1)

5 What is the solution to the expression $5 + 6 \times 4 - 3$?

Ⓐ 11
Ⓑ 19
Ⓒ 26
Ⓓ 41

[Lesson 1-4] 6.2.3 (DOK1)

Go on

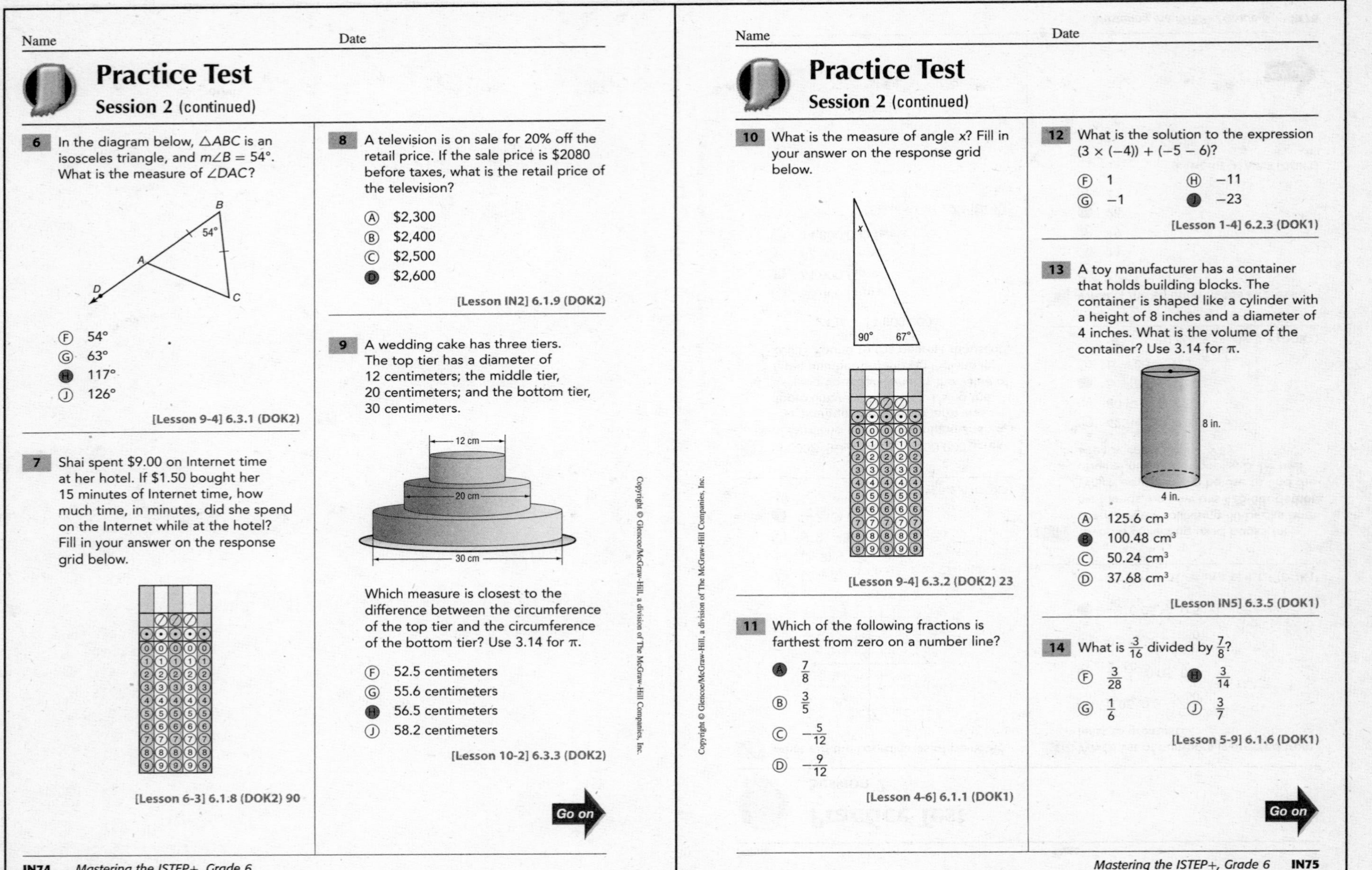

Name Date

Practice Test
Session 2 (continued)

6 In the diagram below, $\triangle ABC$ is an isosceles triangle, and $m\angle B = 54°$. What is the measure of $\angle DAC$?

Ⓕ 54°
Ⓖ 63°
● 117°
Ⓙ 126°

[Lesson 9-4] 6.3.1 (DOK2)

7 Shai spent $9.00 on Internet time at her hotel. If $1.50 bought her 15 minutes of Internet time, how much time, in minutes, did she spend on the Internet while at the hotel? Fill in your answer on the response grid below.

[Lesson 6-3] 6.1.8 (DOK2) 90

8 A television is on sale for 20% off the retail price. If the sale price is $2080 before taxes, what is the retail price of the television?

Ⓐ $2,300
Ⓑ $2,400
Ⓒ $2,500
● $2,600

[Lesson IN2] 6.1.9 (DOK2)

9 A wedding cake has three tiers. The top tier has a diameter of 12 centimeters; the middle tier, 20 centimeters; and the bottom tier, 30 centimeters.

Which measure is closest to the difference between the circumference of the top tier and the circumference of the bottom tier? Use 3.14 for π.

Ⓕ 52.5 centimeters
Ⓖ 55.6 centimeters
● 56.5 centimeters
Ⓙ 58.2 centimeters

[Lesson 10-2] 6.3.3 (DOK2)

Go on

Name Date

Practice Test
Session 2 (continued)

10 What is the measure of angle x? Fill in your answer on the response grid below.

[Lesson 9-4] 6.3.2 (DOK2) 23

11 Which of the following fractions is farthest from zero on a number line?

● $\frac{7}{8}$
Ⓑ $\frac{3}{5}$
Ⓒ $-\frac{5}{12}$
Ⓓ $-\frac{9}{12}$

[Lesson 4-6] 6.1.1 (DOK1)

12 What is the solution to the expression $(3 \times (-4)) + (-5 - 6)$?

Ⓕ 1
Ⓖ −1
Ⓗ −11
● −23

[Lesson 1-4] 6.2.3 (DOK1)

13 A toy manufacturer has a container that holds building blocks. The container is shaped like a cylinder with a height of 8 inches and a diameter of 4 inches. What is the volume of the container? Use 3.14 for π.

Ⓐ 125.6 cm³
● 100.48 cm³
Ⓒ 50.24 cm³
Ⓓ 37.68 cm³

[Lesson IN5] 6.3.5 (DOK1)

14 What is $\frac{3}{16}$ divided by $\frac{7}{8}$?

Ⓕ $\frac{3}{28}$
Ⓖ $\frac{1}{6}$
● $\frac{3}{14}$
Ⓙ $\frac{3}{7}$

[Lesson 5-9] 6.1.6 (DOK1)

Go on

Copyright © Glencoe/McGraw-Hill, a division of The McGraw-Hill Companies, Inc.

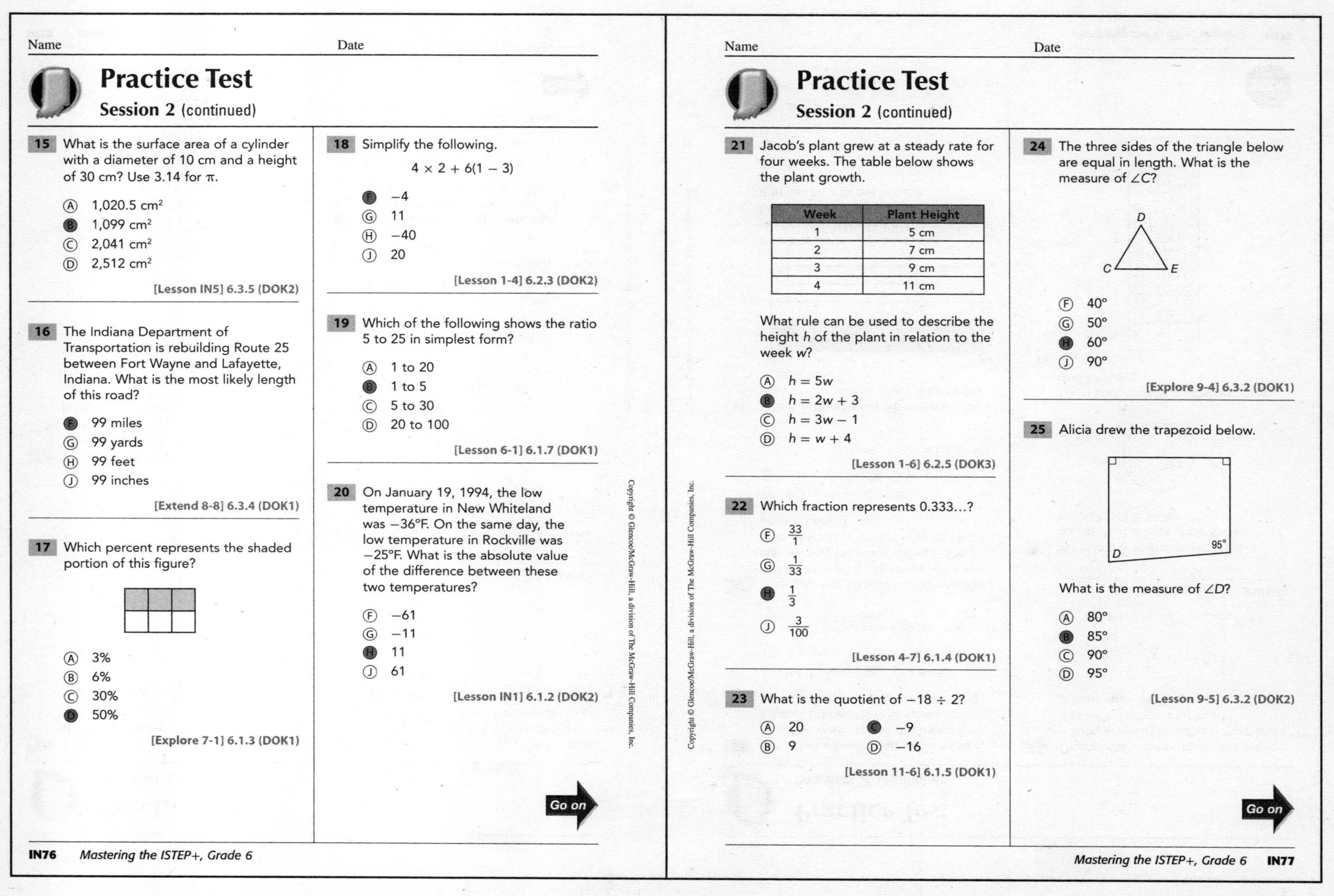

Name Date

Practice Test

Session 2 (continued)

15 What is the surface area of a cylinder with a diameter of 10 cm and a height of 30 cm? Use 3.14 for π.

Ⓐ 1,020.5 cm^2
● 1,099 cm^2
Ⓒ 2,041 cm^2
Ⓓ 2,512 cm^2

[Lesson IN5] 6.3.5 (DOK2)

16 The Indiana Department of Transportation is rebuilding Route 25 between Fort Wayne and Lafayette, Indiana. What is the most likely length of this road?

● 99 miles
Ⓖ 99 yards
Ⓗ 99 feet
Ⓙ 99 inches

[Extend 8-8] 6.3.4 (DOK1)

17 Which percent represents the shaded portion of this figure?

Ⓐ 3%
Ⓑ 6%
Ⓒ 30%
● 50%

[Explore 7-1] 6.1.3 (DOK1)

18 Simplify the following.

$$4 \times 2 + 6(1 - 3)$$

● −4
Ⓖ 11
Ⓗ −40
Ⓙ 20

[Lesson 1-4] 6.2.3 (DOK2)

19 Which of the following shows the ratio 5 to 25 in simplest form?

Ⓐ 1 to 20
● 1 to 5
Ⓒ 5 to 30
Ⓓ 20 to 100

[Lesson 6-1] 6.1.7 (DOK1)

20 On January 19, 1994, the low temperature in New Whiteland was −36°F. On the same day, the low temperature in Rockville was −25°F. What is the absolute value of the difference between these two temperatures?

Ⓕ −61
Ⓖ −11
● 11
Ⓙ 61

[Lesson IN1] 6.1.2 (DOK2)

Go on

Name Date

Practice Test

Session 2 (continued)

21 Jacob's plant grew at a steady rate for four weeks. The table below shows the plant growth.

Week	Plant Height
1	5 cm
2	7 cm
3	9 cm
4	11 cm

What rule can be used to describe the height h of the plant in relation to the week w?

Ⓐ $h = 5w$
● $h = 2w + 3$
Ⓒ $h = 3w - 1$
Ⓓ $h = w + 4$

[Lesson 1-6] 6.2.5 (DOK3)

22 Which fraction represents 0.333…?

Ⓕ $\frac{33}{1}$
Ⓖ $\frac{1}{33}$
● $\frac{1}{3}$
Ⓙ $\frac{3}{100}$

[Lesson 4-7] 6.1.4 (DOK1)

23 What is the quotient of −18 ÷ 2?

Ⓐ 20
Ⓑ 9
● −9
Ⓓ −16

[Lesson 11-6] 6.1.5 (DOK1)

24 The three sides of the triangle below are equal in length. What is the measure of ∠C?

Ⓕ 40°
Ⓖ 50°
● 60°
Ⓙ 90°

[Explore 9-4] 6.3.2 (DOK1)

25 Alicia drew the trapezoid below.

What is the measure of ∠D?

Ⓐ 80°
● 85°
Ⓒ 90°
Ⓓ 95°

[Lesson 9-5] 6.3.2 (DOK2)

Go on

Name Date

Practice Test

Session 2 (continued)

26 Which point represents the location of the ordered pair (−5, −2)?

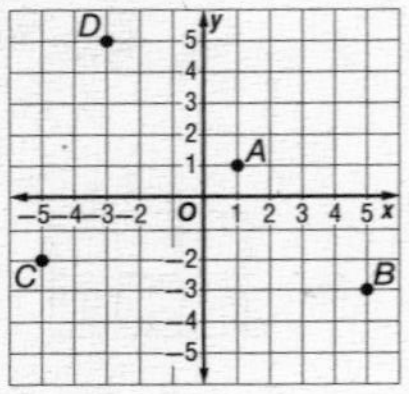

Ⓕ A
Ⓖ B
Ⓗ C
Ⓙ D

[Lesson 11-7] 6.2.4 (DOK1)

27 What is the area of the circle below to the nearest tenth of a centimeter? Use 3.14 for π. Fill in your answer on the response grid below.

15 cm

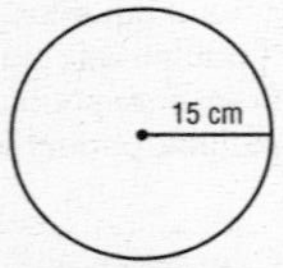

[Lesson IN4] 6.3.3 (DOK2) 706.5

28 Anna's bank account pays 2.8% simple interest per year. If Anna has $800.00 in her account today, how much money will there be in Anna's account 1 year from today?

Ⓐ $777.60
Ⓑ $822.40
Ⓒ $1,024.00
Ⓓ $2,240.00

[Lesson IN3] 6.2.2 (DOK1)

29 Which equation is represented by the following graph?

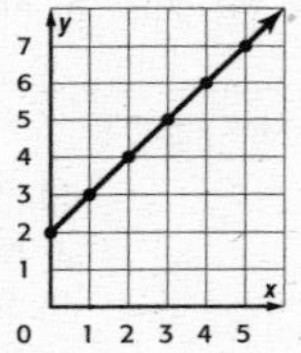

Ⓕ $x = y + 2$
Ⓖ $y = x + 2$
Ⓗ $x = y$
Ⓙ $y = 2$

[Lesson 4-9] 6.2.5 (DOK2)

30 On Friday, 40% of Mr. Garcia's math class went to a math competition. What decimal represents 40%?

Ⓐ 40.00
Ⓑ 4.00
Ⓒ 0.40
Ⓓ 0.04

[Lesson 7-3] 6.1.4 (DOK1)

Go on

Name Date

Practice Test

Session 2 (continued)

31 Jamal has a board that is 2.4 meters long. He wants to cut the board into 6 equal pieces. How long will each piece be?

Ⓕ 14.4 meters
Ⓖ 4 meters
Ⓗ 0.4 meter
Ⓙ 0.04 meter

[Lesson 3-8] 6.1.6 (DOK2)

32 Julia counted 30 sport utility vehicles and 90 cars on a city street while she was waiting for a bus. What is the ratio of sport utility vehicles to cars, in simplest form?

Ⓐ 2:1
Ⓑ 1:3
Ⓒ 3:1
Ⓓ 3:9

[Lesson 6-1] 6.1.7 (DOK1)

33 Rick is putting away his sweaters for the summer. He can pack 6 sweaters in each box.

Boxes	Number of Sweaters
1	6
2	12
3	18

Which equation describes the relationship between *b*, the number of boxes, and *s*, the number of sweaters that can fit into the boxes?

Ⓕ $b = 6 + s$
Ⓖ $b = s \div 6$
Ⓗ $b = 6 - s$
Ⓙ $b = 6 \div s$

[Lesson 1-6] 6.2.5 (DOK2)

34 On Saturday, the temperature was −10°F. A week later, the temperature was 24°F. By how much did the temperature rise?

Ⓐ 34°
Ⓑ 14°
Ⓒ −14°
Ⓓ −34°

[Lesson 11-3] 6.1.5 (DOK2)

35 What is the approximate area, in square feet, of the circle shown below? Use 3.14 for π.

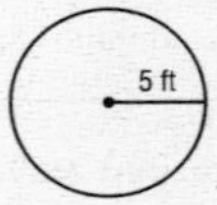

5 ft

Fill in your answer on the response grid below.

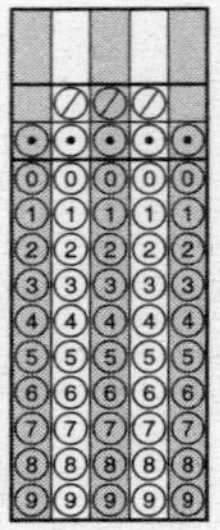

[Lesson IN4] 6.3.3 (DOK1) 78.5

STOP

Glencoe McGraw-Hill
Math Connects
Course 1
Study Guide and Intervention
and Practice Workbook

Mc
Graw
Hill
Glencoe

CONTENTS

NAME ______________________ DATE ____________ PERIOD ____

1-1 Study Guide and Intervention

A Plan for Problem Solving

Lesson 1–1

When solving problems, it is helpful to have an organized plan to solve the problem. The following four steps can be used to solve any math problem.

1 Understand – Read and get a general understanding of the problem.

2 Plan – Make a plan to solve the problem and estimate the solution.

3 Solve – Use your plan to solve the problem.

4 Check – Check the reasonableness of your solution.

Example 1 SPORTS **The table shows the number of field goals made by Henry High School's top three basketball team members during last year's season. How many more field goals did Brad make than Denny?**

Name	3-Point Field Goals
Brad	216
Chris	201
Denny	195

Understand You know the number of field goals made. You need to find how many more field goals Brad made than Denny.

Plan Use only the needed information, the goals made by Brad and Denny. To find the difference, subtract 195 from 216.

Solve $216 - 195 = 21$; Brad made 21 more field goals than Denny.

Check Check the answer by adding. Since $195 + 21 = 216$, the answer is correct.

Exercises

1. During which step do you check your work to make sure your answer is correct? **Check**

2. Explain what you do during the first step of the problem-solving plan. **read and get a general understanding of the problem**

SPORTS **For Exercises 3 and 4, use the field goal table above and the four-step plan.**

3. How many more field goals did Chris make than Denny? **6 more field goals**

4. How many field goals did the three boys make all together? **612 three-point field goals**

Copyright © Glencoe/McGraw-Hill, a division of The McGraw-Hill Companies, Inc.

NAME ______ DATE ______ PERIOD ____

1-1 Practice

A Plan for Problem Solving

PATTERNS Complete each pattern.

1. 17, 21, 25, 29, ____, ____, ____, **33, 37, 41**
2. 32, 29, 26, 23, ____, ____, ____, **20, 17, 14**
3. 1, 2, 4, 7, ____, ____, ____, **11, 16, 22**
4. 64, 32, 16, 8, ____, ____, ____, **4, 2, 1**

5. **ANALYZE GRAPHS** Refer to the graph. How many acres smaller is Lake Meredith National Recreation Area than Big Thicket National Preserve? **50,857 acres**

6. **TRAVEL** The distance between Dallas and Beaumont is about 290 miles. Henry drove from Dallas to Beaumont at 58 miles per hour. How many hours did it take Henry to reach Beaumont? **5 h**

7. **ANALYZE TABLES** The table lists the times that ferries leave the terminal every day. At what times will the next three ferries leave the terminal? **8:33 A.M., 8:39 A.M., 9:14 A.M.**

6:36 A.M.
7:11 A.M.
7:17 A.M.
7:52 A.M.
7:58 A.M.

8. **MONEY** The Wilsons bought a refrigerator and a stove for a total cost of $745. They will pay for the purchase in five equal payments. What will be the amount of each payment? **$149**

9. **MUSIC** Luanda practices playing the piano for 24 minutes each day. How many hours does she practice in one year? **146 h**

Copyright © Glencoe/McGraw-Hill, a division of The McGraw-Hill Companies, Inc.

NAME ______ DATE ______ PERIOD ____

1-2 Study Guide and Intervention

Prime Factors

Factors are the numbers that are multiplied to get a product. A product is the answer to a multiplication problem. A **prime number** is a whole number that has only 2 factors, 1 and the number itself. A **composite number** is a number greater than 1 with more than two factors.

Example 1 Tell whether each number is *prime, composite,* or *neither.*

Number	Factors	Prime or Composite?
15	1 × 15 3 × 5	Composite
17	1 × 17	Prime
1	1	Neither

Example 2 Find the prime factorization of 18.

18 is divisible by 2, because the ones digit is divisible by 2.
Circle the prime number, 2.
9 is divisible by 3, because the sum of the digits is divisible by 3.
Circle the prime numbers, 3 and 3.
The prime factorization of 18 is 2 × 3 × 3.

Exercises

Tell whether each number is *prime, composite,* or *neither.*

1. 7 **P**
2. 12 **C**
3. 29 **P**
4. 81 **C**
5. 18 **C**
6. 23 **P**
7. 54 **C**
8. 28 **C**
9. 120 **C**
10. 243 **C**
11. 61 **P**
12. 114 **C**

Find the prime factorization of each number.

13. 125 **5 × 5 × 5**
14. 44 **2 × 2 × 11**
15. 11 **11**
16. 56 **2 × 2 × 2 × 7**

NAME ______________________ DATE ____________ PERIOD _____

1-2 Practice
Prime Factors

Tell whether each number is *prime*, *composite*, or *neither*.

1. 24 **composite** 2. 1 **neither** 3. 13 **prime** 4. 25 **composite**

5. 91 **composite** 6. 0 **neither** 7. 181 **prime** 8. 145 **composite**

Find the prime factorization of each number.

9. 16 **$2 \times 2 \times 2 \times 2$**
10. 48 **$2 \times 2 \times 2 \times 2 \times 3$**
11. 66 **$2 \times 3 \times 11$**
12. 56 **$2 \times 2 \times 2 \times 7$**
13. 80 **$2 \times 2 \times 2 \times 2 \times 5$**
14. 95 **5×19**

15. Find the least prime number that is greater than 50. **53**

16. All odd numbers greater than 7 can be expressed as the sum of three prime numbers. Which three prime numbers have a sum of 43? Justify your answer. **Sample answer: 11, 13, and 19; 11 + 13 + 19 = 43**

17. GARDENING Julia wants to plant 24 tomato plants in rows. Each row will have the same number of plants in it. Find three possible numbers of rows and the number of plants in each row.
Sample answer: 2 rows of 12, 3 rows of 8, 4 rows of 6

18. SHOPPING Jamal bought boxes of nails that each cost the same. He spent a total of $42. Find three possible costs per box and the number of boxes that he could have purchased. **Sample answer: $2 and 21 boxes, $3 and 14 boxes, $6 and 7 boxes**

NAME ______________________ DATE ____________ PERIOD _____

1-3 Study Guide and Intervention
Powers and Exponents

A product of prime factors can be written using exponents and a base. Numbers expressed using exponents are called **powers**.

Powers	Words	Expression	Value
4^2	4 to the second power or 4 squared	4×4	16
5^6	5 to the sixth power	$5 \times 5 \times 5 \times 5 \times 5 \times 5$	15,625
7^4	7 to the fourth power	$7 \times 7 \times 7 \times 7$	2,401
9^3	9 to the third power or 9 cubed	$9 \times 9 \times 9$	729

Example 1 **Write $6 \times 6 \times 6$ using an exponent. Then find the value.**

The base is 6. Since 6 is a factor 3 times, the exponent is 3.
$6 \times 6 \times 6 = 6^3$ or 216

Example 2 **Write 2^4 as a product of the same factor. Then find the value.**

The base is 2. The exponent is 4. So, 2 is a factor 4 times.
$2^4 = 2 \times 2 \times 2 \times 2$ or 16

Example 3 **Write the prime factorization of 225 using exponents.**

The prime factorization of 225 can be written as $3 \times 3 \times 5 \times 5$, or $3^2 \times 5^2$.

Exercises

Write each product using an exponent. Then find the value.

1. $2 \times 2 \times 2 \times 2 \times 2$ **2^5; 32**
2. 9×9 **9^2; 81**
3. $3 \times 3 \times 3$ **3^3; 27**
4. $5 \times 5 \times 5$ **5^3; 125**
5. $3 \times 3 \times 3 \times 3 \times 3$ **3^5; 243**
6. 10×10 **10^2; 100**

Write each power as a product of the same factor. Then find the value.

7. 7^2 **7×7; 49**
8. 4^3 **$4 \times 4 \times 4$; 64**
9. 8^4 **$8 \times 8 \times 8 \times 8$; 4,096**
10. 5^5 **$5 \times 5 \times 5 \times 5 \times 5$; 3,125**
11. 2^8 **$2 \times 2 \times 2 \times 2 \times 2 \times 2 \times 2 \times 2$; 256**
12. 7^3 **$7 \times 7 \times 7$; 343**

Write the prime factorization of each number using exponents.

13. 40 **$2^3 \times 5$**
14. 75 **3×5^2**
15. 100 **$2^2 \times 5^2$**
16. 147 **3×7^2**

Lesson 1-3

Copyright © Glencoe/McGraw-Hill, a division of The McGraw-Hill Companies, Inc.

NAME ______________ DATE ________ PERIOD ____

1-3 Practice

Powers and Exponents

Write each product using an exponent.

1. 6×6 **6^2**
2. $10 \times 10 \times 10 \times 10$ **10^4**
3. $4 \times 4 \times 4 \times 4 \times 4$ **4^5**
4. $8 \times 8 \times 8 \times 8 \times 8 \times 8 \times 8 \times 8$ **8^8**
5. $5 \times 5 \times 5 \times 5 \times 5 \times 5$ **5^6**
6. $13 \times 13 \times 13$ **13^3**

Write each power as a product of the same factor. Then find the value.

7. 10^1 **10; 10**
8. 2^7 **$2 \times 2 \times 2 \times 2 \times 2 \times 2 \times 2$; 128**
9. 8^3 **$8 \times 8 \times 8$; 512**
10. 3^8 **$3 \times 3 \times 3 \times 3 \times 3 \times 3 \times 3 \times 3$; 6,561**
11. nine squared **9×9; 81**
12. four to the sixth power **$4 \times 4 \times 4 \times 4 \times 4 \times 4$; 4,096**

Write the prime factorization of each number using exponents.

13. 32 **2^5**
14. 100 **$2^2 \times 5^2$**
15. 63 **$3^2 \times 7$**
16. 99 **$3^2 \times 11$**
17. 52 **$2^2 \times 13$**
18. 147 **3×7^2**

19. **LABELS** A sheet of labels has 8 rows of labels with 8 labels in each row. How many total labels are on the sheet? Write your answer using exponents, and then find the value. **8^2; 64 labels**

20. **CANDLES** To find how much wax the candle mold holds, use the expression $s \times s \times s$, where s is the length of a side. Write this expression as a power. The amount of wax the mold holds is measured in cubic units. How many cubic units of wax does the mold hold? **s^3; 3,375 cubic units**

15 units
15 units
15 units

Copyright © Glencoe/McGraw-Hill, a division of The McGraw-Hill Companies, Inc.

NAME ______________ DATE ________ PERIOD ____

1-4 Study Guide and Intervention

Order of Operations

Order of Operations

1. Simplify the expressions inside grouping symbols, like parentheses.
2. Find the value of all powers.
3. Multiply and divide in order from left to right.
4. Add and subtract in order from left to right.

Example 1 **Find the value of $48 \div (3 + 3) - 2^2$.**

$48 \div (3 + 3) - 2^2 = 48 \div 6 - 2^2$ Simplify the expression inside the parentheses.
$= 48 \div 6 - 4$ Find 2^2.
$= 8 - 4$ Divide 48 by 6.
$= 4$ Subtract 4 from 8.

Example 2 **Write and solve an expression to find the total cost of planting flowers in the garden.**

Item	Cost Per Item	Number of Items Needed
pack of flowers	$4	5
bag of dirt	$3	1
bottle of fertilizer	$4	1

Words	cost of 5 flower packs	plus	cost of dirt	plus	cost of fertilizer
Expression	5 × $4	+	$3	+	$4

5 × $4 + $3 + $4 = $20 + $3 + $4
= $23 + $4
= $27

The total cost of planting flowers in the garden is $27.

Exercises

Find the value of each expression.

1. $7 + 2 \times 3$ **13**
2. $12 \div 3 + 5$ **9**
3. $16 - (4 + 5)$ **7**
4. $8 \times 8 \div 4$ **16**
5. $10 + 14 \div 2$ **17**
6. $3 \times 3 + 2 \times 4$ **17**
7. $80 - 8 \times 3^2$ **8**
8. $11 \times (9 - 2^2)$ **55**
9. $25 \div 5 + 6 \times (12 - 4)$ **53**

10. **GARDENING** Refer to Example 2 above. Suppose that the gardener did not buy enough flowers and goes back to the store to purchase four more packs. She also purchases a hoe for $16. Write an expression that shows the total amount she spent to plant flowers in her garden. **(4 + 5) × $4 + $3 + $4 + $16**

NAME ________________ DATE ________ PERIOD ____

1-4 Practice

Order of Operations

Find the value of each expression.

1. $34 + 17 - 5$ **46**
2. $25 - 14 + 3$ **14**
3. $42 + 6 \div 2$ **45**
4. $39 \times (15 \div 3) - 16$ **179**
5. $48 \div 8 + 5 \times (7 - 2)$ **31**
6. $64 \div (15 - 7) \times 2 - 9$ **7**
7. $(3 + 7) \times 6 + 4$ **64**
8. $9 + 8 \times 3 - (5 \times 2)$ **23**
9. $7^2 + 6 \times 2$ **61**
10. $34 - 8^2 \div 4$ **18**
11. $45 \div 3 \times 2^3$ **120**
12. $4 \times (5^2 - 12) - 6$ **46**
13. $78 - 2^4 \div (14 - 6) \times 2$ **74**
14. $9 + 7 \times (15 + 3) \div 3^2$ **23**
15. $13 + (4^3 \div 2) \times 5 - 17$ **156**
16. Using symbols, write the product of 18 and 7 plus 5. **18 × 7 + 5**

ART **For Exercises 17 and 18, use the following information.**
An art supply store sells posters for $9 each and picture frames for $15 each.

17. Write an expression for the total cost of 6 posters and 6 frames.
6 × $9 + 6 × $15 or 6 × ($9 + $15)

18. What is the total cost for 6 framed posters? **$144**

19. SCIENCE There are 24 students in a science class. Mr. Sato will give each pair of students 3 magnets. So far, Mr. Sato has given 9 pairs of students their 3 magnets. How many more magnets does Mr. Sato need so that each pair of students has exactly 3 magnets? **9 magnets**

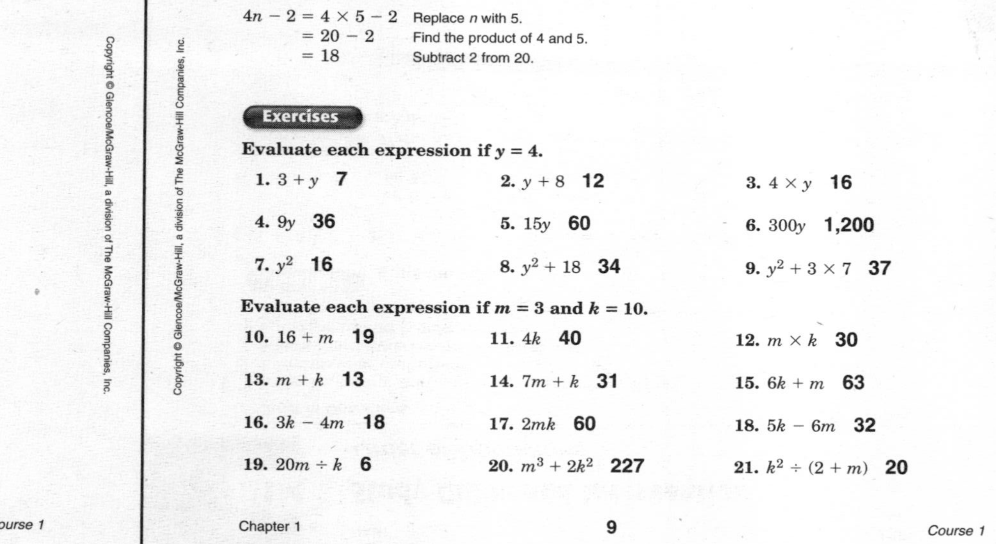

NAME ________________ DATE ________ PERIOD ____

1-5 Study Guide and Intervention

Algebra: Variables and Expressions

- A **variable** is a symbol, usually a letter, used to represent a number.
- Multiplication in algebra can be shown as $4n$, $4 \cdot n$, or $4 \times n$.
- **Algebraic expressions** are combinations of variables, numbers, and at least one operation.

Example 1 **Evaluate $35 + x$ if $x = 6$.**

$35 + x = 35 + 6$ Replace x with 6.
$= 41$ Add 35 and 6.

Example 2 **Evaluate $y + x$ if $x = 21$ and $y = 35$.**

$y + x = 35 + 21$ Replace x with 21 and y with 35.
$= 56$ Add 35 and 21.

Example 3 **Evaluate $4n + 3$ if $n = 2$.**

$4n + 3 = 4 \times 2 + 3$ Replace n with 2.
$= 8 + 3$ Find the product of 4 and 2.
$= 11$ Add 8 and 3.

Example 4 **Evaluate $4n - 2$ if $n = 5$.**

$4n - 2 = 4 \times 5 - 2$ Replace n with 5.
$= 20 - 2$ Find the product of 4 and 5.
$= 18$ Subtract 2 from 20.

Exercises

Evaluate each expression if $y = 4$.

1. $3 + y$ **7**
2. $y + 8$ **12**
3. $4 \times y$ **16**
4. $9y$ **36**
5. $15y$ **60**
6. $300y$ **1,200**
7. y^2 **16**
8. $y^2 + 18$ **34**
9. $y^2 + 3 \times 7$ **37**

Evaluate each expression if $m = 3$ and $k = 10$.

10. $16 + m$ **19**
11. $4k$ **40**
12. $m \times k$ **30**
13. $m + k$ **13**
14. $7m + k$ **31**
15. $6k + m$ **63**
16. $3k - 4m$ **18**
17. $2mk$ **60**
18. $5k - 6m$ **32**
19. $20m \div k$ **6**
20. $m^3 + 2k^2$ **227**
21. $k^2 \div (2 + m)$ **20**

Lesson 1–5

NAME ______________________ DATE __________ PERIOD ____

1-5 Practice

Algebra: Variables and Expressions

Evaluate each expression if $m = 6$ and $n = 12$.

1. $m + 5$ **11**
2. $n - 7$ **5**
3. $m \cdot 4$ **24**
4. $m + n$ **18**
5. $n - m$ **6**
6. $12 \div n$ **1**
7. $9 \cdot n$ **108**
8. $n \div m$ **2**
9. $2m + 5$ **17**
10. $4m - 17$ **7**
11. $36 - 6m$ **0**
12. $3n + 8$ **44**

Evaluate each expression if $a = 9$, $b = 3$, and $c = 12$.

13. $4a - 17$ **19**
14. $14 + 2c$ **38**
15. $c \div 2$ **6**
16. ac **108**
17. $c \div b$ **4**
18. $2ac$ **216**
19. $b^3 + c$ **39**
20. $19 + 6a \div 2$ **46**
21. $4b^2 \cdot 3$ **108**
22. $3c \div (2b^2)$ **2**
23. $c^2 - (3a)$ **117**
24. $ac \div (2b)$ **18**

25. **ANIMALS** A Gentoo penguin can swim at a rate of 17 miles per hour. How many miles can a penguin swim in 4 hours? Use the expression rt, where r represents rate and t represents time. **68 mi**

26. **CLOTHING** A company charges $6 to make a pattern for an order of T-shirts and $11 for each T-shirt it produces from the pattern. The expression 11n$ + \$6$ represents the cost of n T-shirts with the same pattern. Find the total cost for 5 T-shirts with the same pattern. **$61**

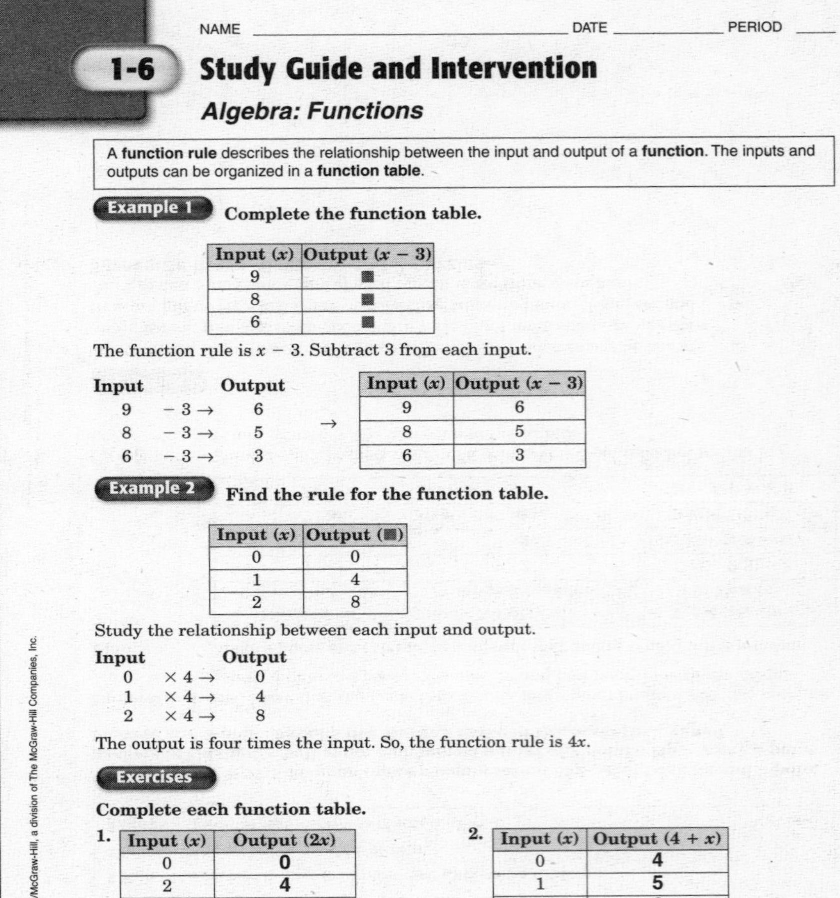

NAME ______________________ DATE __________ PERIOD ____

1-6 Study Guide and Intervention

Algebra: Functions

A **function rule** describes the relationship between the input and output of a **function**. The inputs and outputs can be organized in a **function table**.

Example 1 **Complete the function table.**

Input (x)	Output ($x - 3$)
9	■
8	■
6	■

The function rule is $x - 3$. Subtract 3 from each input.

Input		Output
9	$-3 \rightarrow$	6
8	$-3 \rightarrow$	5
6	$-3 \rightarrow$	3

→

Input (x)	Output ($x - 3$)
9	6
8	5
6	3

Example 2 **Find the rule for the function table.**

Input (x)	Output (■)
0	0
1	4
2	8

Study the relationship between each input and output.

Input		Output
0	$\times 4 \rightarrow$	0
1	$\times 4 \rightarrow$	4
2	$\times 4 \rightarrow$	8

The output is four times the input. So, the function rule is $4x$.

Exercises

Complete each function table.

1.

Input (x)	Output ($2x$)
0	**0**
2	**4**
4	**8**

2.

Input (x)	Output ($4 + x$)
0	**4**
1	**5**
4	**8**

Find the rule for each function table.

3.

Input (x)	Output (■)
1	3
2	4
5	7

$x + 2$

4.

Input (x)	Output (■)
2	1
6	3
10	5

$\frac{1}{2}x$

Lesson 1-6

NAME ______________________ DATE ____________ PERIOD _____

1-6 Practice

Algebra: Functions

Complete each function table.

1.

Input (x)	Output ($x + 6$)
0	**6**
3	**9**
7	**13**

2.

Input (x)	Output ($x - 1$)
1	**0**
4	**3**
8	**7**

3.

Input (x)	Output ($3x$)
0	**0**
2	**6**
4	**12**

4.

Input (x)	Output ($x \div 2$)
4	**2**
8	**4**
10	**5**

Find the rule for each function table.

5.

x	■
4	1
8	2
16	4

x ÷ 4

6.

x	■
12	8
13	9
15	11

x – 4

7.

x	■
2	1
6	3
10	5

x ÷ 2

8.

x	■
3	0
5	2
6	3
8	5
11	8

x – 3

9.

x	■
0	3
1	6
2	9
3	12
4	15

3x + 3

10.

x	■
2	5
4	13
6	21
8	29
10	37

4x – 3

11. **FOOD** A pizza place sells pizzas for $7 each plus a $4 delivery charge per order. If Pat orders 3 pizzas to be delivered, what will be his total cost?
$25

12. **MOVIES** A store sells used DVDs for $8 each and used videotapes for $6 each. Write a function rule to represent the total selling price of DVDs (d) and videotapes (v). Then use the function rule to find the price of 5 DVDs and 3 videotapes. **8*d* + 6*v*; $58**

NAME ______________________ DATE ____________ PERIOD _____

1-7 Study Guide and Intervention

Problem-Solving Investigation: Guess and Check

When solving problems, one strategy that is helpful to use is *guess and check*. Based on the information in the problem, you can make a guess of the solution. Then use computations to check if your guess is correct. You can repeat this process until you find the correct solution.

You can use guess and check, along with the following four-step problem solving plan to solve a problem.

1 Understand – Read and get a general understanding of the problem.

2 Plan – Make a plan to solve the problem and estimate the solution.

3 Solve – Use your plan to solve the problem.

4 Check – Check the reasonableness of your solution.

Example 1 SPORTS **Meagan made a combination of 2-point baskets and 3-point baskets in the basketball game. She scored a total of 9 points. How many 2-point baskets and 3-point baskets did Meagan make in the basketball game?**

Understand You know that she made both 2-point and 3-point baskets. You also know she scored a total of 9 points. You need to find how many of each she made.

Plan Make a guess until you find an answer that makes sense for the problem.

Solve

Number of 2-point baskets	Number of 3-point baskets	Total Number of Points
1	2	1(2) + 2(3) = 8
2	2	2(2) + 2(3) = 10
2	1	2(2) + 1(3) = 7
3	1	3(2) + 1(3) = 9

Check Three 2-point baskets result in 6 points. One 3-point basket results in 3 points. Since 6 + 3 is 9, the answer is correct.

Exercise

VIDEO GAMES Juan has 16 video games. The types of video games he has are sports games, treasure hunts, and puzzles. He has 4 more sports games than treasure hunts. He has 3 fewer puzzles than treasure hunts. Use guess and check to determine how many of each type of video game Juan has.
5 treasure hunts, 9 sports, and 2 puzzles

NAME ______________________ DATE __________ PERIOD ____

1-7 Practice

Problem-Solving Investigation: Guess and Check

Mixed Problem Solving

Use the guess and check strategy to solve Exercises 1 and 2.

1. MOVIES Tickets for the movies are $7 for adults and $4 for children. Fourteen people paid a total of $68 for tickets. How many were adults and how many were children? **4 adults and 10 children**

2. AGES Mei's mother is 4 times as old as Mei. Mei's grandmother is twice as old as Mei's mother. The sum of the three ages is 117. How old is Mei, her mother, and her grandmother? **Mei: 9 years old; mother: 36 years old; grandmother: 72 years old**

Use any strategy to solve Exercises 3–6. Some strategies are shown below.

Problem-Solving Strategies
• Guess and check.
• Find a pattern.

3. SWIMMING Brian is preparing for a swim meet. The table shows the number of laps he swam in the first four days of practice. If the pattern continues, how many laps will Brian swim on Friday?

Day	Mon.	Tues.	Wed.	Thurs.	Fri.
Laps	1	3	7	15	?

31 laps

4. ORDER OF OPERATIONS Use the symbols $+$, $-$, $\times$, and $\div$ to make the following math sentence true. Write each symbol only once. $\mathbf{8 \div 2 - 1 \times 3 + 4 = 5}$

8 ___ 2 ___ 1 ___ 3 ___ 4 = 5

5. PATTERNS Draw the next figure in the pattern.

6. MONEY Jason has $1.56 in change in his pocket. If there is a total of 19 coins, how many quarters, dimes, nickels, and pennies does he have? **3 quarters, 5 dimes, 5 nickels, and 6 pennies**

Copyright © Glencoe/McGraw-Hill, a division of The McGraw-Hill Companies, Inc.

NAME ______________________ DATE __________ PERIOD ____

1-8 Study Guide and Intervention

Algebra: Equations

An **equation** is a sentence that contains an **equals sign**, =. Some equations contain variables. When you replace a variable with a value that results in a true sentence, you **solve** the equation. The value for the variable is the **solution** of the equation.

Example 1 **Solve $m + 12 = 15$ mentally.**

$m + 12 = 15$ Think: What number plus 12 equals 15?
$3 + 12 = 15$ You know that 12 + 3 = 15.
$m = 3$

The solution is 3.

Example 2 **Solve $14 - p = 6$ using guess and check.**

Guess the value of p, then check it out.

Try 7.	Try 6.	Try 8.
$14 - p \stackrel{?}{=} 6$	$14 - p \stackrel{?}{=} 6$	$14 - p \stackrel{?}{=} 6$
$14 - 7 \neq 6$	$14 - 6 \neq 6$	$14 - 8 = 6$
no	no	yes

The solution is 8 because replacing p with 8 results in a true sentence.

Exercises

Identify the solution of each equation from the list given.

1. $k - 4 = 13$; 16, 17, 18 **17**
2. $31 + x = 42$; 9, 10, 11 **11**
3. $45 = 24 + k$; 21, 22, 23 **21**
4. $m - 12 = 15$; 27, 28, 29 **27**
5. $88 = 41 + s$; 46, 47, 48 **47**
6. $34 - b = 17$; 16, 17, 18 **17**
7. $69 - j = 44$; 25, 26, 27 **25**
8. $h + 19 = 56$; 36, 37, 38 **37**

Solve each equation mentally.

9. $j + 3 = 9$ **6**
10. $m - 5 = 11$ **16**
11. $23 + x = 29$ **6**
12. $31 - h = 24$ **7**
13. $18 = 5 + d$ **13**
14. $35 - a = 25$ **10**
15. $y - 26 = 3$ **29**
16. $14 + n = 19$ **5**
17. $100 = 75 + w$ **25**

Lesson 1–8

NAME ______________ DATE ________ PERIOD ____

1-8 Practice

Algebra: Equations

Identify the solution of each equation from the list given.

1. $h + 9 = 21$; 10, 11, 12 **12**
2. $45 - k = 27$; 17, 18, 19 **18**
3. $34 + p = 52$; 18, 19, 20 **18**
4. $t \div 6 = 9$; 52, 53, 54 **54**
5. $43 = 52 - s$; 8, 9, 10 **9**
6. $56 = 7q$; 7, 8, 9 **8**
7. $28 = r - 12$; 40, 41, 42 **40**
8. $30 \div w = 5$; 4, 5, 6 **6**
9. $y - 13 = 24$; 37, 38, 39 **37**

Solve each equation mentally.

10. $a + 6 = 11$ **5**
11. $k - 12 = 4$ **16**
12. $24 = 34 - j$ **10**
13. $9b = 36$ **4**
14. $f \div 7 = 8$ **56**
15. $7 + n = 18$ **11**
16. $45 \div m = 5$ **9**
17. $80 = 10d$ **8**
18. $25 - c = 15$ **10**
19. $17 = 9 + e$ **8**
20. $g \div 4 = 12$ **48**
21. $26 \div k = 2$ **13**

22. **ANIMALS** A whiptail lizard has a tail that is twice as long as its body. The equation $2b = 6$ describes the length of a certain whiptail lizard's tail in inches. If b is the length of the whiptail lizard's body, what is the length of this whiptail lizard's body? What is the total length of the lizard? **3 inches; 9 inches**

23. **SPORTS CAMP** There are 475 campers returning to sports camp this year. Last year, 525 campers attended sports camp. The equation $475 = 525 - c$ shows the decrease in the number of campers returning to camp from one year to the next. Find the number of campers who did not return to camp this year. **50 campers**

NAME ______________ DATE ________ PERIOD ____

1-9 Study Guide and Intervention

Algebra: Area Formulas

The **area** of a figure is the number of square units needed to cover a surface. You can use a formula to find the area of a rectangle. The formula for finding the area of a rectangle is $A = \ell \times w$. In this formula, A represents area, ℓ represents the length of the rectangle, and w represents the width of the rectangle.

Example 1 **Find the area of a rectangle with length 8 feet and width 7 feet.**

$A = \ell \times w$ Area of a rectangle
$A = 8 \times 7$ Replace ℓ with 8 and w with 7.
$A = 56$
The area is 56 square feet.

Example 2 **Find the area of a square with side length 5 inches.**

$A = s^2$ Area of a square
$A = 5^2$ Replace s with 5.
$A = 25$
The area is 25 square inches.

Exercises

Find the area of each figure.

1. **16 units²**
2. 5 ft, 8 ft **40 ft²**
3. 7 cm, 3 cm **21 cm²**
4. 6 yd, 6 yd **36 yd²**

5. What is the area of a rectangle with a length of 10 meters and a width of 7 meters? **70 m²**

6. What is the area of a square with a side length of 15 inches? **225 in²**

Copyright © Glencoe/McGraw-Hill, a division of The McGraw-Hill Companies, Inc.

NAME ________________ DATE ________ PERIOD ____

1-9 Practice

Algebra: Area Formulas

Find the area of each rectangle.

1. 9 m by 7 m — **63 m²**

2. 24 mm by 15 mm — **360 mm²**

3. 10 ft by 4 ft — **40 ft²**

4. Find the area of a rectangle with a length of 35 inches and a width of 21 inches. **735 in²**

Find the area of each square.

5. 8 ft by 8 ft — **64 ft²**

6. 2 cm by 2 cm — **4 cm²**

7. 13 in. by 13 in. — **169 in²**

8. What is the area of a square with a side length of 21 yards? **441 yd²**

Find the area of each shaded region.

10. 10 cm by 10 cm; 4 cm by 3 cm — **88 m²**

11. 14 yd by 12 yd; 6 yd by 6 yd — **132 yd²**

12. 23 ft by 21 ft; 18 ft by 8 ft — **339 ft²**

13. **REMODELING** The Crofts are covering the floor in their living room and in their bedroom with carpeting. The living room is 16 feet long and 12 feet wide. The bedroom is a square with 10 feet on each side. How many square feet of carpeting should the Crofts buy? **292 ft² of carpeting**

14. **GARDENING** The diagram shows a park's lawn with a sandy playground in the corner. If a bag of fertilizer feeds 5,000 square feet of lawn, how many bags of fertilizer are needed to feed the lawn area of the park? **4 bags**

150 ft
150 ft
50 ft
50 ft

NAME ________________ DATE ________ PERIOD ____

2-1 Study Guide and Intervention

Problem-Solving Investigation: Make a Table

When solving problems, one strategy that is helpful is to *make a table.* A table often makes it easy to clarify information in the problem. One type of table that is helpful to use is a *frequency table,* which shows the number of times each item or number appears.

You can use the *make a table* strategy, along with the following four-step problem-solving plan to solve a problem.

1 Understand – Read and get a general understanding of the problem.

2 Plan – Make a plan to solve the problem and estimate the solution.

3 Solve – Use your plan to solve the problem.

4 Check – Check the reasonableness of your solution.

Example 1 MOVIES **Carlos took a survey of the students in his class to find out what type of movie they preferred. Using C for comedy, A for action, D for drama, and M for animated, the results are shown below. How many more students like comedies than action movies?**

C A M M A C D C D C M A M M A C C D A C

Understand You need to find the number of students that chose comedies and the number of students that chose action. Then find the difference.

Plan Make a frequency table of the data.

Solve Draw and complete a frequency table.

7 people chose comedies and 5 people chose action. So, 7 − 5 or 2 more students chose comedy than action.

Check Go back to the list to verify there are 7 C's for comedy and 5 A's for action.

Favorite Type of Movie		
Movie Type	Tally	Frequency
comedy	卌 II	7
action	卌	5
drama	III	3
animated	卌	5

Exercise

GRADES The list below shows the quarterly grades for Mr. Vaquera's math class. Make a frequency table of the data. How many more students received a B than a D? **8**

B C A A B D C B A C B B
B D A C B B C A A B A B

Quarterly Grades		
Grade	Tally	Frequency
A	卌 II	7
B	卌 卌	10
C	卌	5
D	II	2

Lesson 2-1

NAME ______________________ DATE ____________ PERIOD _____

2-1 Practice

Problem-Solving Investigation: Make a Table

Mixed Problem Solving

Use the make a table strategy to solve Exercise 1.

1. BASKETBALL The winning scores for teams in the National Wheelchair Basketball Association junior division for a recent season are shown. Make a frequency table of the data. How many winning scores were between 21 and 25? **3 scores**

NWBA Jr. Div. Winning Scores					
25	26	34	16	33	18
34	26	24	33	12	23

NWBA Jr. Div. Winning Scores		
Scores	**Tally**	**Frequency**
11–15	|	1
16–20	||	2
21–25	|||	3
26–30	||	2
31–35	||||	4

Use any strategy to solve Exercises 2–5. Some strategies are shown below.

Problem-Solving Strategies
• Guess and check.
• Make a table.

2. MONEY Emelio has 9 coins that total \$2.21. He does not have a dollar coin. What are the coins? **Sample answer: 3 half dollars, 2 quarters, 1 dime, 2 nickels, 1 penny**

3. SCIENCE A biologist counted the birds she tagged and released each day for 20 days. Her counts were: 13, 14, 9, 16, 21, 8, 28, 25, 9, 13, 23, 16, 14, 9, 21, 25, 8, 10, 21, and 29. On how many days did she count between 6 and 10 birds or between 26 and 30 birds? **8 days**

4. TRAFFIC The table shows the types of vehicles seen passing a street corner. Make a frequency table of the data. How many fewer motorcycles than cars were seen? **5**

Types of Vehicles							
C	M	M	B	T	T	C	T
B	R	T	C	R	C	R	C
M	C	C	M	C	R	C	T

C = car B = bicycle T = truck
M = motorcycle R = recreational vehicle

Types of Vehicles		
Vehicle	**Tally**	**Frequency**
car	~~||||~~ ||||	9
bicycle	||	2
truck	~~||||~~	5
motorcycle	||||	4
RV	||||	4

5. MONEY Tonisha has \$0 in her savings account. She deposits \$40 every two weeks and withdraws \$25 every four weeks. What will be her balance at the end of 24 weeks? **(24 ÷ 2) × \$40 (24 ÷ 2) × \$25 = \$330**

NAME ______________________ DATE ____________ PERIOD _____

2-2 Study Guide and Intervention

Bar Graphs and Line Graphs

A **graph** is a visual way to display data. A **bar graph** is used to compare data. A **line graph** is used to show how data changes over a period of time.

Example 1 **Make a bar graph of the data. Compare the number of students in jazz class with the number in ballet class.**

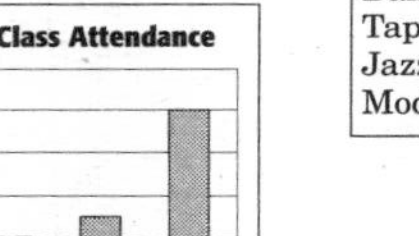
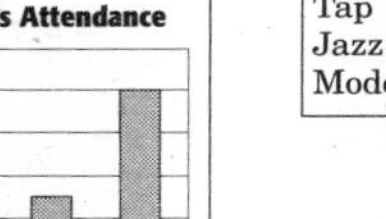
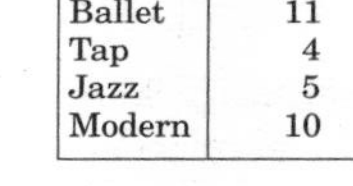

Dance Classes	
Style	**Students**
Ballet	11
Tap	4
Jazz	5
Modern	10

Step 1 Decide on the scale and interval.
Step 2 Label the horizontal and vertical axes.
Step 3 Draw bars for each style.
Step 4 Label the graph with a title.

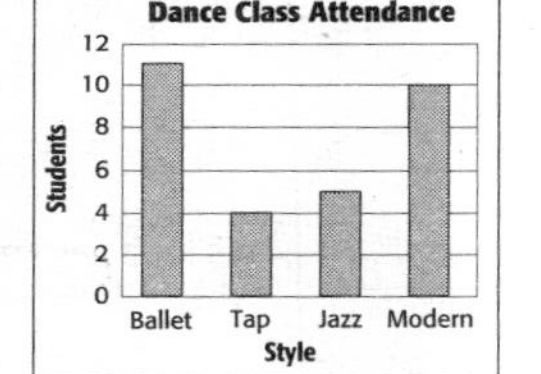

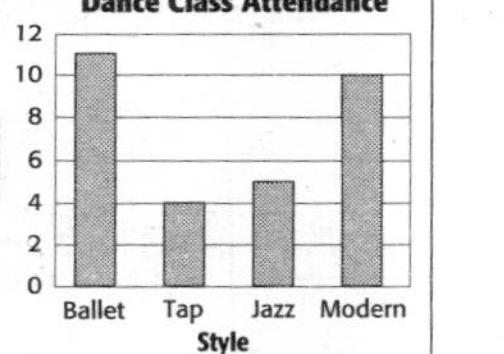

About twice as many students take ballet as take jazz.

Example 2 **Make a line graph of the data. Then describe the change in Gwen's allowance from 2003 to 2008.**

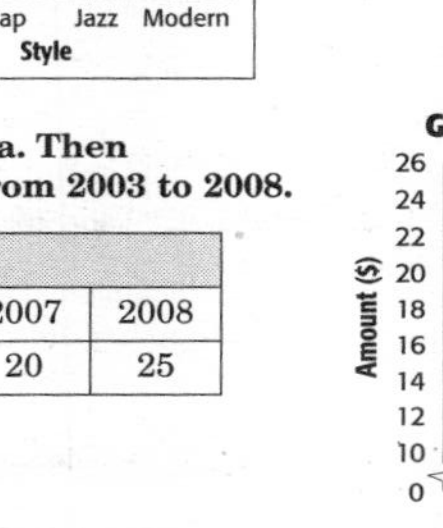

Gwen's Allowance						
Year	2003	2004	2005	2006	2007	2008
Amount (\$)	10	15	15	18	20	25

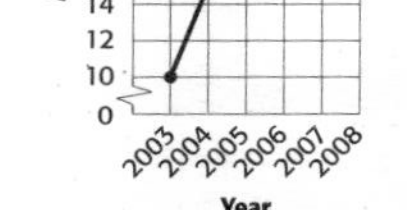

Step 1 Decide on the scale and interval.
Step 2 Label the horizontal and vertical axes.
Step 3 Draw and connect the points for each year.
Step 4 Label the graph with a title.

Gwen's allowance did not change from 2004 to 2005 and then increased from 2005 to 2008.

Exercises

Make the graph listed for each set of data.

1. bar graph **See students' work.**

Riding the Bus	
Student	**Time (min)**
Paulina	10
Omar	40
Ulari	20
Jacob	15
Amita	35

2. line graph **See students' work.**

Getting Ready for School	
Day	**Time (min)**
Monday	34
Tuesday	30
Wednesday	37
Thursday	20
Friday	25

Copyright © Glencoe/McGraw-Hill, a division of The McGraw-Hill Companies, Inc.

NAME ______________________ DATE ____________ PERIOD _____

2-2 Practice

Bar Graphs and Line Graphs

1. ANIMALS Make a bar graph of the data.

Vertebrates

Vertebrates	
Class	Number of Species
Amphibians	5,000
Birds	9,000
Fish	24,500
Mammals	9,000
Reptiles	8,000

Source: *The World Almanac for Kids*

For Exercises 2 and 3, refer to the bar graph you made in Exercise 1.

2. Which animal classes have the same number of species?
birds and mammals

3. Which animal class has about one third as many species as the fish class? **reptiles**

4. POPULATION Make a line graph of the data.

Population of the District of Columbia

Population of the District of Columbia	
Year	Population (thousands)
1960	764
1970	757
1980	638
1990	607
2000	572

Source: U.S. Census Bureau

For Exercises 5 and 6, refer to the line graph you made in Exercise 4.

5. Describe the change in the District of Columbia population from 1970 to 2000. **It decreased each year, including a sharp drop and then a steady decrease.**

6. What year showed the greatest change in population from the previous year? **1980**

BOOKS **For Exercises 7 and 8, refer to the table.**

Book Sales			
Week	Sales ($)	Week	Sales ($)
1	110	5	40
2	118	6	103
3	89	7	30
4	74	8	58

7. Choose an appropriate scale and interval for the data set.
Sample answer: scale: 0–120; interval: 20

8. Would this data set be best represented by a bar graph or a line graph? Explain your reasoning.
Sample answer: Line graph; a line graph will show changes in sales over time.

NAME ______________________ DATE ____________ PERIOD _____

2-3 Study Guide and Intervention

Interpret Line Graphs

Because they show trends over time, **line graphs** are often used to predict future events.

Example 1 **The graph shows the time Ruben spends each day practicing piano scales. Predict how much time he will spend practicing his scales on Friday.**

Piano Scale Practice Times

Continue the graph with a dotted line in the same direction until you reach a vertical position for Friday. By extending the graph, you see that Ruben will probably spend half an hour practicing piano scales on Friday.

Exercises

MONEY **Use the graph that shows the price of a ticket to a local high school football game over the last few years.**

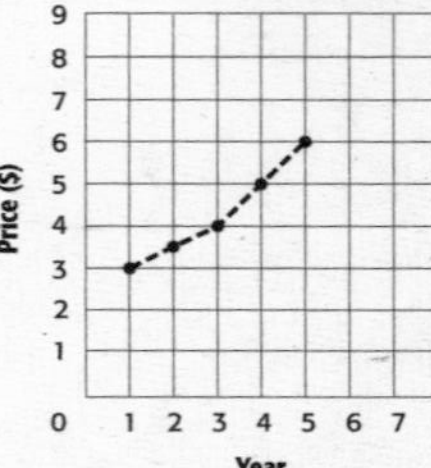
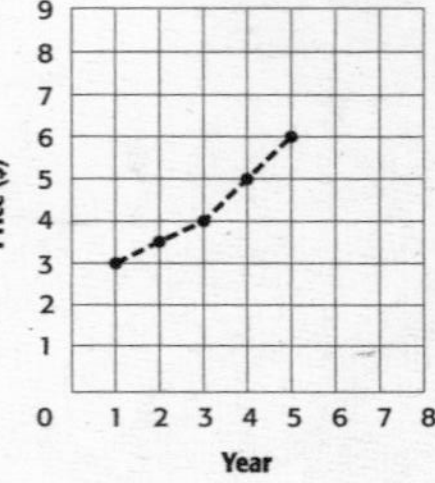

1. Has the price been increasing or decreasing? Explain. **Increasing; the graph rises as it goes from left to right.**

2. Predict the price of a ticket in year 6 if the trend continues.
about $7.00

3. In what year do you think the price will reach $9.00 if the trend continues?
around year 8

BANKS **Use the graph that shows the interest rate for a savings account over the last few years.**

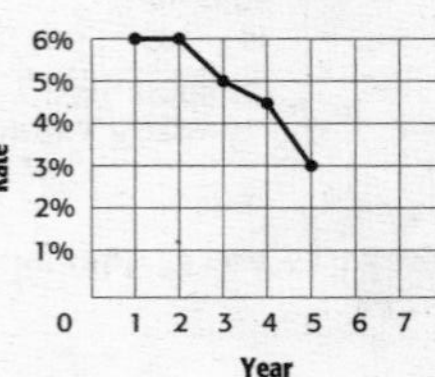

4. What does the graph tell you about interest rates?
They are decreasing.

5. If the trend continues, when will the interest rate reach 1 percent?
about year 7

Lesson 2–3

NAME ______________________ DATE __________ PERIOD ____

2-3 Practice
Interpret Line Graphs

SPORTS For Exercises 1–3, use the graph at the right.

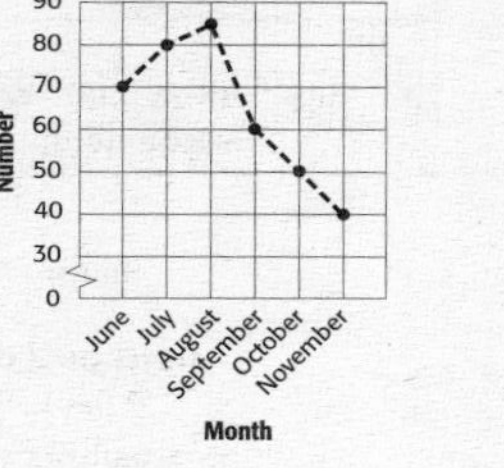

1. Describe the change in the number of swimsuits sold. **Sample answer: After gradually increasing, sales decreased sharply and then gradually.**
2. Predict the number of swimsuits sold in December. Explain your reasoning. **about 30; Sample answer: Sales decreased by 10 each month before December, so extend the graph forward from November to December by about 10.**
3. Predict the number of swimsuits sold in May. How did you reach this conclusion? **about 60; Sample answer: Extend the graph back from June to May.**

WEATHER For Exercises 4–7, use the graph at the right.

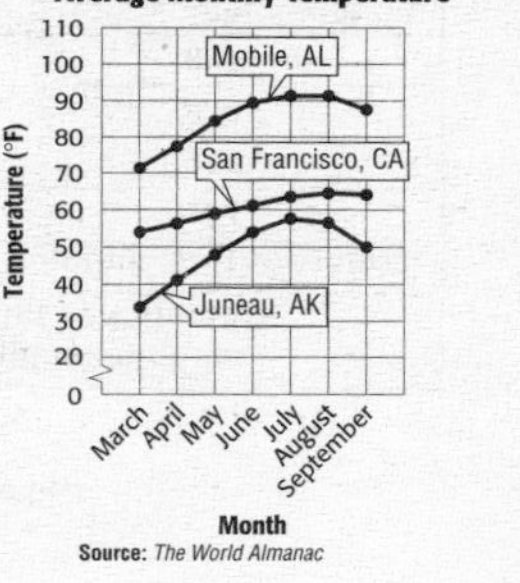

4. Predict the average temperature for Juneau in February. **about 25°**
5. Predict the average temperature for Mobile in October. **about 80°**
6. What do you think is the average temperature for San Francisco in October? **about 65°**
7. How much colder would you expect it to be in Juneau than in Mobile in October? **about 40° colder**

BASEBALL For Exercises 8–10, use the table that shows the number of games won by the Florida Gators men's baseball team from 2002 to 2007.

Florida Gators Baseball Statistics						
Year	2002	2003	2004	2005	2006	2007
Games Won	46	37	43	48	28	29

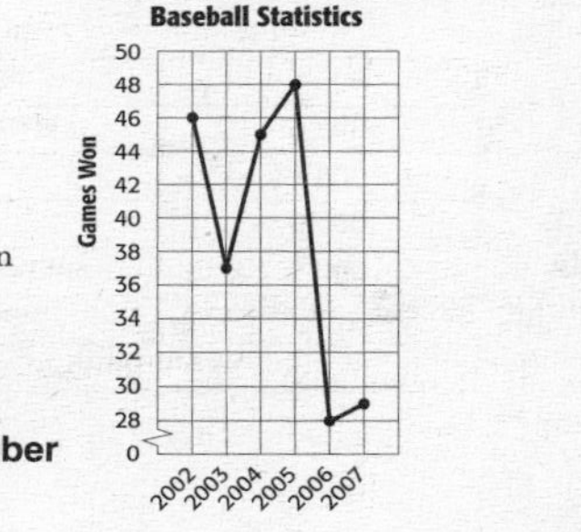

8. Make a line graph of the data.
9. In what year did the team have the greatest increase in the number of games won? **2004**
10. Explain the disadvantages of using this line graph to make a prediction about the number of games that the team will win in 2009. **Sample answer: The number of wins has been generally inconsistent.**

NAME ______________________ DATE __________ PERIOD ____

2-4 Study Guide and Intervention
Stem-and-Leaf Plots

Lesson 2–4

Sometimes it is hard to read data in a table. You can use a **stem-and-leaf plot** to display the data in a more readable way. In a stem-and-leaf plot, you order the data from least to greatest. Then you organize the data by place value.

Example 1 **Make a stem-and-leaf plot of the data in the table. Then write a few sentences that analyze the data.**

Money Earned Mowing Lawns ($)			
60	55	53	41
67	72	65	68
65	70	52	51

Step 1 Order the data from least to greatest.
41 51 52 53 55 60 65 65 67 68 70 72

Step 2 Draw a vertical line and write the tens digits from least to greatest to the left of the line.

Step 3 Write the ones digits to the right of the line with the corresponding stems.

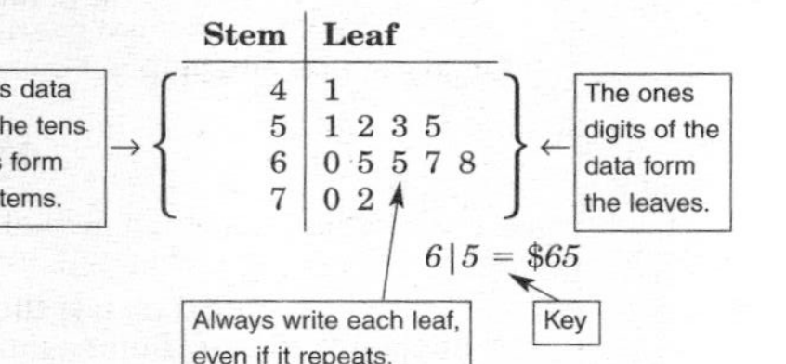

Stem	Leaf
4	1
5	1 2 3 5
6	0 5 5 7 8
7	0 2

$6|5 = \$65$

Step 4 Include a key that explains the stems and leaves.

By looking at the plot, it is easy to see that the least amount of money earned was \$41 and the greatest amount was \$72. You can also see that most of the data fall between \$51 and \$68.

Exercise

Make a stem-and-leaf plot for the set of data below. Write a few sentences that analyze the data.

Points scored: 34 44 51 48 55 41 47 22 55

Sample answer: The least number is 22 and the greatest number is 55. Most of the data fall between 41 and 55.

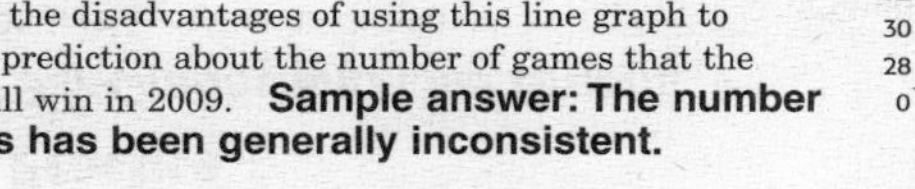

Stem	Leaf
2	2
3	4
4	1 4 7 8
5	1 5 5

$4|1 = 41$

NAME ______________ DATE ________ PERIOD ____

2-4 Practice
Stem-and-Leaf Plots

Make a stem-and-leaf plot for each set of data.

1. Minutes on the bus to school: 10, 5, 21, 30, 7, 12, 15, 21, 8, 12, 12, 20, 31, 10, 23, 31

Stem	Leaf
0	5 7 8
1	0 0 2 2 2 5
2	0 1 1 3
3	0 1 1

1|2 = 12 minutes

2. Employee's ages: 22, 52, 24, 19, 25, 36, 30, 32, 19, 26, 28, 33, 53, 24, 35, 26

Stem	Leaf
1	9 9
2	2 4 4 5 6 6 8
3	0 2 3 5 6
4	
5	2 3

2|4 = 24 years old

SHOPPING **For Exercises 3–5, use the stem-and-leaf plot at the right that shows costs for various pairs of jeans.**

Stem	Leaf
1	6 6 7 8 8 9 9 9 9
2	1 3 5
3	
4	2 2 3

2|3 = $23

3. How much is the most expensive pair of jeans? **$43**

4. How many pairs cost less than $20? **9**

5. Write a sentence or two that analyzes the data. **Sample answer: The least expensive jeans cost $16, and the most expensive cost $43. Jeans can be grouped into less expensive and more expensive groups, and there is a big gap between the groups. Most of the jeans cost less than $20.**

6. Construct a stem-and-leaf plot for the set of test scores 81, 55, 55, 62, 73, 49, 56, 91, 55, 64, 72, 62, 64, 53, 56, and 57. Then write sentences explaining how a teacher might use the plot. **Sample answer: A teacher can see where most of the scores were to determine how well students understood the material covered by the test. In this case, most students scored in the 50s and 60s, which indicates that the teacher may want to review the material again.**

Stem	Leaf
4	9
5	3 5 5 5 6 6 7
6	2 2 4 4
7	2 3
8	1
9	1

4|9 = 49

7. Display the amounts $104, $120, $99, $153, $122, $116, $114, $139, $102, $95, $123, $116, $152, $104 and $115 in a stem-and-leaf plot. (*Hint*: Use the hundreds and tens digits to form the stems.)

Stem	Leaf
9	5 9
10	2 4 4
11	4 5 6 6
12	0 2 3
13	9
14	
15	2 3

12|3 = $123

NAME ______________ DATE ________ PERIOD ____

2-5 Study Guide and Intervention
Line Plots

A **line plot** is a diagram that shows the frequency of data on a number line. A line plot is created by drawing a number line and then placing an × above a data value each time that data occurs.

Example 1 **Make a line plot of the data in the table at the right.**

Time Spent Traveling to School (minutes)						
5	6	3	10	12	15	5
10	5	8	12	5	5	8

Draw a number line. The smallest value is 3 minutes and the largest value is 15 minutes. So, you can use a scale of 0 to 15.

Put an × above the number that represents the travel time of each student in the table. Be sure to include a title.

0 5 10 15

Example 2 **How many students spend 5 minutes traveling to school each day?**

Locate 5 on the number line and count the number of ×'s above it. There are 5 students that travel 5 minutes to school each day.

Exercises

AGES **For Exercises 1–3, use the data below.**

Ages of Lifeguards at Brookville Swim Club					
16	18	16	20	22	18
18	17	18	25	17	19

1. Make a line plot of the data.

Ages of Lifeguards at Brookville Swim Club

15 16 17 18 19 20 21 22 23 24 25

2. How many of the lifeguards are 18 years old? **4**

3. What is the age difference between the oldest and youngest lifeguard at Brookville Swim Club? **9 years**

NAME ________________ DATE __________ PERIOD ____

2-5 Practice

Line Plots

PRESIDENTS For Exercises 1–4, use the line plot below. It shows the ages of the first ten Presidents of the United States when they first took office.

Age of First Ten Presidents at Inauguration

Years: 50 55 60 65 70

Source: *Time Almanac*

1. How many Presidents were 54 when they took office? **1**

2. Which age was most common among the first ten Presidents when they took office? **57 years**

3. How many Presidents were in their 60s when they first took office? **3**

4. What is the difference between the age of the oldest and youngest President represented in the line plot? **17 years**

5. EXERCISE Make a line plot for the set of data.

Miles Walked this Week			
16	21	11	24
8	14	16	11
21	10	8	14
11	24	12	18
18	27	11	14

5 10 15 20 25 30

BIRDS For Exercises 6 and 7, use the line plot below. It shows the number of mockingbirds each bird watcher saw on a bird walk.

20 25 30 35 40 45 50

6. How many more bird watchers saw 36 mockingbirds than saw 46 mockingbirds? **2 more bird watchers**

7. How many bird watchers are represented in the line plot? **21 bird watchers**

NAME ________________ DATE __________ PERIOD ____

2-6 Study Guide and Intervention

Mean

The **mean** is the most common measure of central tendency. It is an average, so it describes all of the data in a data set.

Example 1 **The picture graph shows the number of members on four different swim teams. Find the mean number of members for the four different swim teams.**

Swim Team Members	
Amberly	9 figures
Carlton	11 figures
Hamilton	6 figures
Westhigh	10 figures

Simplify an expression.

$$\text{mean} = \frac{9 + 11 + 6 + 10}{4}$$

$$= \frac{36}{4} \text{ or } 9$$

A set of data may contain very high or very low values. These values are called **outliers**.

Example 2 **Find the mean for the snowfall data with and without the outlier. Then tell how the outlier affects the mean of the data.**

Month	Snowfall (in.)
Nov.	20
Dec.	19
Jan.	20
Feb.	17
Mar.	4

Compared to the other values, 4 inches is low. So, it is an outlier.

mean with outlier

$$\text{mean} = \frac{20 + 19 + 20 + 17 + 4}{5} = \frac{80}{5} \text{ or } 16$$

mean without outlier

$$\text{mean} = \frac{20 + 19 + 20 + 17}{4} = \frac{76}{4} \text{ or } 19$$

With the outlier, the mean is less than the values of most of the data. Without the outlier, the mean is close in value to the data.

Exercises

SHOPPING For Exercises 1–3, use the bar graph at the right.

Jacket Prices

Price ($) by Jacket: A 22, B 25, C 28, D 9, E 21

1. Find the mean of the data. **$21**

2. Which jacket price is an outlier? **$9**

3. Find the mean of the data if the outlier is not included. **$24**

4. How does the outlier affect the mean of the data? **Sample answer: The outlier causes the mean to be less than the average price of the majority of the jackets.**

NAME ______________________ DATE ____________ PERIOD _____

2-6 Practice

Mean

Find the mean of the data represented in each model.

1.

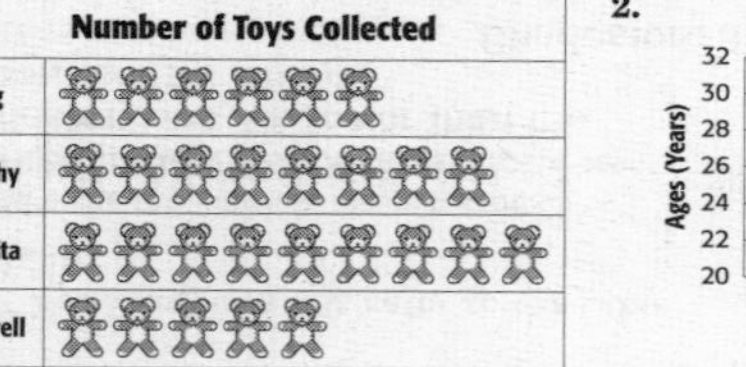

7 toys

2.

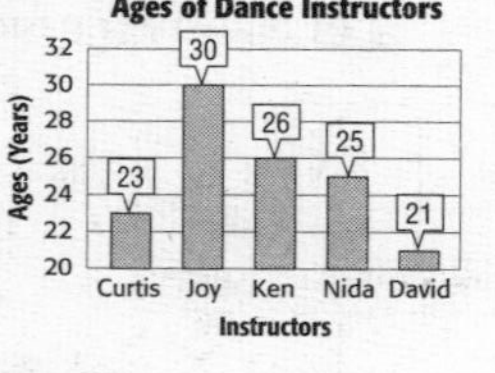

age 25

NATURE **For Exercises 3–6, use the table that shows the heights of the tallest waterfalls along Oregon's Columbia River Gorge.**

Falls	Height (ft)
Bridal Veil	153
Horsetail	176
Latourell	249
Metlako	150
Multnomah	620
Wahkeena	242

3. Find the mean of the data. **265 ft**

4. Identify the outlier. **620 ft**

5. Find the mean if Multnomah Falls is not included in the data set. **194 ft**

6. How does the outlier affect the mean of the data? **Sample answer: An outlier, such as this 620, that is much higher than the other values causes the mean of the data to be higher than the values in the table. So, the mean is less representative of the data.**

GARDENING **For Exercises 7–9, use the following information.**

Alan earned $23, $26, $25, $24, $23, $24, $6, $24, and $23 gardening.

7. What is the mean of the amounts he earned? **$22**

8. Which amount is an outlier? **$6**

9. How does the outlier affect the mean of the data? **Sample answer: This outlier, which is considerably lower than all the other values, causes the mean to be less than all the other values. Without the outlier, the mean would better represent the data.**

Find the mean for number of cans collected. Explain the method you used.

10. 57, 59, 60, 58, 58, 56 **58; Sample answer: Find compatible number pairs to average 58, e.g., 59 – 1 = 58, and 57 + 1 = 58.**

Copyright © Glencoe/McGraw-Hill, a division of The McGraw-Hill Companies, Inc.

NAME ______________________ DATE ____________ PERIOD _____

2-7 Study Guide and Intervention

Median, Mode, and Range

The **median** is the middle number of the data put in order, or the mean of the middle two numbers. The **mode** is the number or numbers that occur most often.

Example 1 **The table shows the costs of seven different books. Find the mean, median, and mode of the data.**

Book Costs ($)			
22	13	11	16
14	13	16	

mean: $\frac{22 + 13 + 11 + 16 + 14 + 13 + 16}{7} = \frac{105}{7}$ or 15

To find the median, write the data in order from least to greatest.
median: 11, 13, 13, (14), 16, 16, 22

To find the mode, find the number or numbers that occur most often.
mode: 11, (13, 13), 14, (16, 16), 22

The mean is $15. The median is $14. There are two modes, $13 and $16.

Whereas the measures of central tendency describe the average of a set of data, the **range** of a set of data describes how the data vary.

Example 2 **Find the range of the data in the stem-and-leaf plot. Then write a sentence describing how the data vary.**

Stem	Leaf
3	2
4	0
5	0 5
6	0 3

3 | 2 = 32°

The greatest value is 63. The least value is 32. So, the range is 63° − 32° or 31°. The range is large. It tells us that the data vary greatly in value.

Exercises

Find the mean, median, mode, and range of each set of data.

1. hours worked: 14, 13, 14, 16, 8
13; 14; 14; 8

2. points scored by football team: 29, 31, 14, 21, 31, 22, 20
24; 22; 31; 17

3.

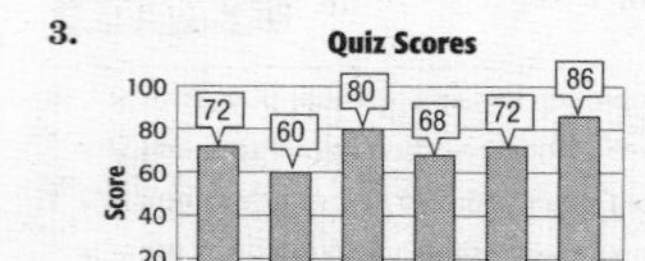

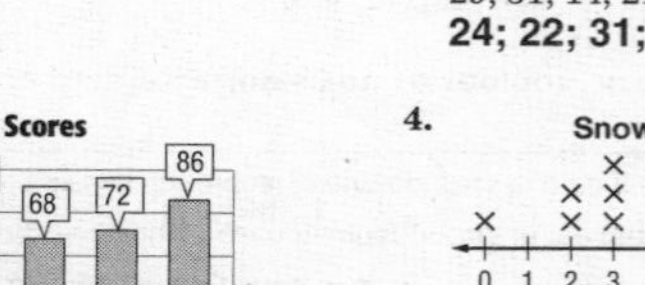

73; 72; 72; 26

4.

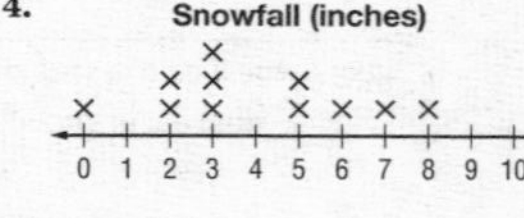

4; 3; 3; 8

NAME ______________________ DATE ____________ PERIOD _____

2-7 Practice

Median, Mode, and Range

Find the median, mode, and range for each set of data.

1. minutes spent practicing violin:
25, 15, 30, 25, 20, 15, 24
median: 24, mode: 15 and 25, range: 15

2. snow in inches:
40, 28, 24, 37, 43, 26, 30, 36
median: 33, mode: none, range: 19

Find the mean, median, mode, and range of the data represented in each statistical graph.

3. 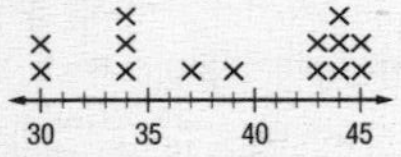
30
35
40
45
mean: 39, median: 41, modes: 34 and 44, range: 15

4.

Stem	Leaf
4	1 2 4 4
5	2 4
6	1 3 4 7 7 7 7 8 8
7	2 2 3
8	0 1 2 4 5 6

5|4 = $54

mean: $66, median: $67, mode: $67, range: $45

5. 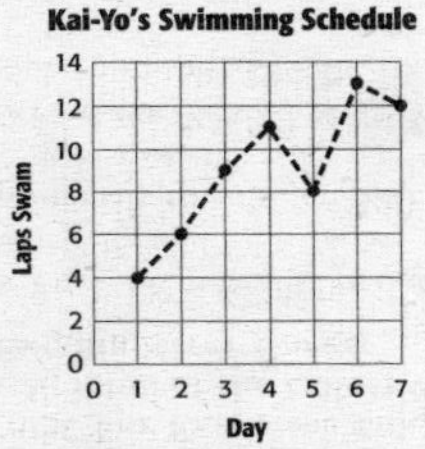
Kai-Yo's Swimming Schedule
Laps Swam
Day
mean: 9, median: 9, mode: none, range: 9

6. 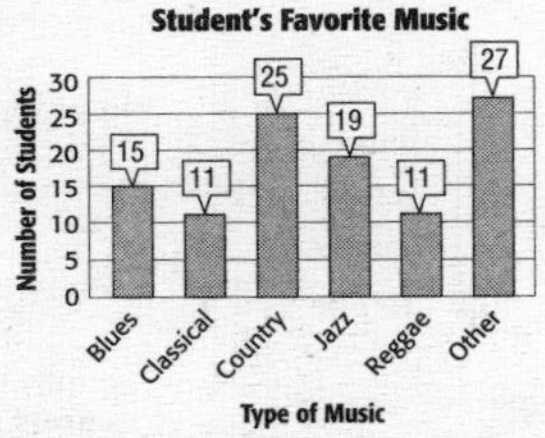
Student's Favorite Music
Number of Students
Type of Music
Blues
Classical
Country
Jazz
Reggae
Other
15
11
25
19
11
27
mean: 18, median: 17, mode: 11, range: 16

WEATHER For Exercises 7–9, refer to the table at the right.

Daily Low Temperatures (°F)	
Charleston	Atlanta
33 34 33 35	48 41 43 40
36 35 34	45 35 37

7. Compare the median low temperatures.
The median low temperature for Charleston was 7°F lower than the temperature for Atlanta.

8. Find the range for each data set. **Charleston: 3°F, Atlanta: 13°F**

9. Write a statement that compares the daily low temperatures for the two cities. **Charleston has a lower median temperature than Atlanta. The temperatures in Charleston did not vary as much as in Atlanta.**

Copyright © Glencoe/McGraw-Hill, a division of The McGraw-Hill Companies, Inc.

NAME ______________________ DATE ____________ PERIOD _____

2-8 Study Guide and Intervention

Selecting an Appropriate Display

Data can be displayed in many different ways, including the following:

- A **bar graph** shows the number of items in a specific category.
- A **line graph** shows change over a period of time.
- A **line plot** shows how many times each number occurs in the data.
- A **stem-and-leaf plot** lists all individual numerical data in a condensed form.

Example 1 **Which display allows you to see how art show ticket prices have changed since 2004.**

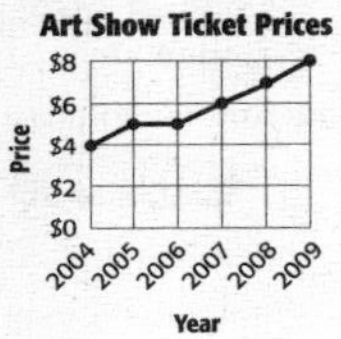
Art Show Ticket Prices
Price
Year

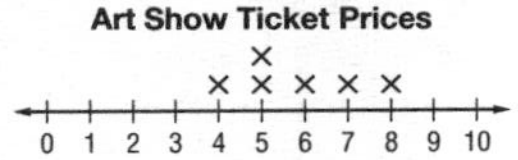
Art Show Ticket Prices

The line graph allows you to see how the art show ticket prices have increased since 2004.

Example 2 **What type of display would you use to show the results of a survey of students' favorite brand of tennis shoes.**

Since the data would list the number of students that chose each brand, or category, the data would best be displayed in a bar graph.

Exercises

1. **GRADES** Which display makes it easier to see how many students had test scores in the 80s? **stem-and-leaf plot**

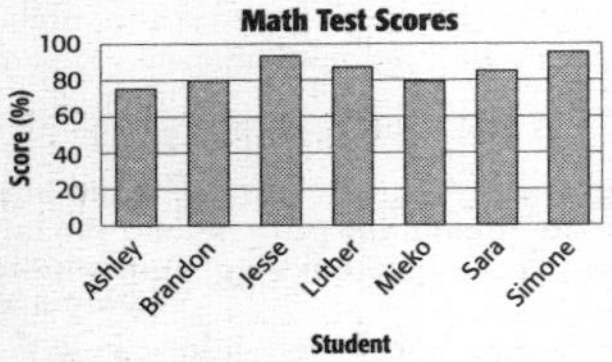
Math Test Scores
Score (%)
Student
Ashley
Brandon
Jesse
Luther
Mieko
Sara
Simone

Math Test Scores

Stem	Leaf
7	5 9
8	0 5 8
9	2 3

8|0 = 80%

2. **VOLLEYBALL** What type of display would you use to show the number of wins the school volleyball team had from 2000 to 2005? **bar graph**

Copyright © Glencoe/McGraw-Hill, a division of The McGraw-Hill Companies, Inc.

Copyright © Glencoe/McGraw-Hill, a division of The McGraw-Hill Companies, Inc.

NAME _______________ DATE _________ PERIOD _____

2-8 Practice

Selecting an Appropriate Display

1. FOOD Which display makes it easier to see the median cost of providing food stamps from 1998 to 2003? **stem-and-leaf plot**

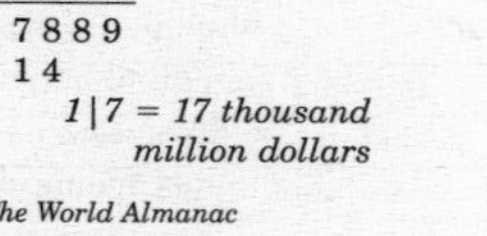

Source: *The World Almanac*

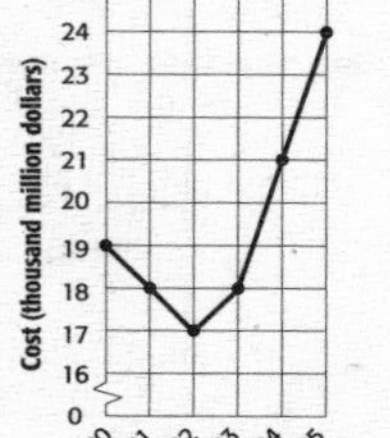

Select an appropriate type of display for data gathered about each situation. Sample answers are given.

2. the heights of buildings in town **stem-and-leaf plot or bar graph**
3. the number of cars a dealer sold each month over the past year **line graph**
4. the number of scores made by each team member in a basketball season **line plot**
5. OLYMPICS Select an appropriate type of display for the data. Then make a display.

Olympic Hammer Throw Winners

Year	Distance (m)	Year	Distance (m)
1968	73	1988	85
1972	76	1992	83
1976	78	1996	81
1980	82	2000	80
1984	78	2004	83

Olympic Hammer Throw Winners

Distance (m): 70, 75, 80, 85

6. GEOGRAPHY Display the data in the bar graph using another type of display. Compare the displays.

Active Volcanoes in Africa

Height (thousand ft); Erta-Ale, Fogo, Mt. Cameroon, Mt. Oku, Nyamuragira, Nyiragongo, Ol Doinyo Lengai

Source: *The World Almanac*

Height of Active Volcanoes in Africa

Thousands (ft): 1 2 3 4 5 6 7 8 9 10 11 12 13

Sample answer: The line plot allows you to see how many volcanoes are at each height. The bar graph, however, allows you to see the height of each volcano.

NAME _______________ DATE _________ PERIOD _____

2-9 Study Guide and Intervention

Integers and Graphing

Negative numbers represent data that are less than 0. A negative number is written with a − sign. **Positive numbers** represent data that are greater than 0. Positive numbers are written with a + sign or no sign at all.

Opposites are numbers that are the same distance from zero on a number line, but in opposite directions. The set of positive whole numbers, their opposites, and zero are called **integers**.

Example 1 Write an integer to show 3 degrees below zero. Then graph the integer on a number line.

Numbers *below zero* are negative numbers. The integer is −3.

Draw a number line. Then draw a dot at the location that represents −3.

−6 −5 −4 −3 −2 −1 0 1 2 3 4 5 6

Example 2 Make a line plot of the data represented in the table.

Draw a number line. Put an × above the number that represents each score in the table.

Rachel's Summer Golf Scores			
0	+3	−4	−2
+1	+3	−4	0
+1	−5	−2	+1

Rachel's Summer Golf Scores

−5 −4 −3 −2 −1 0 1 2 3 4 5

Exercises

Write an integer to represent each piece of data. Then graph the integer on the number line.

1. 4 degrees below zero **−4**
2. a gain of 2 points **+2 or 2**

−6 −5 −4 −3 −2 −1 0 1 2 3 4 5 6

3. BOOKS The table shows the change in the ranking from the previous week of the top ten best-selling novels. Make a line plot of the data.

Novel	A	B	C	D	E	F	G	H	I	J
Change in Ranking	+3	−2	0	+1	−2	0	+2	−4	+1	−2

Best-Selling Novels

−5 −4 −3 −2 −1 0 1 2 3 4 5

Lesson 2–9

NAME ______________ DATE ________ PERIOD ____

2-9 Practice
Integers and Graphing

Write an integer to represent each situation.

1. Bill drove 25 miles toward Tampa. **+25 or 25**
2. Susan lost $4. **−4**
3. Joe walked down 6 flights of stairs. **−6**
4. The baby gained 8 pounds. **+8 or 8**

Draw a number line from −10 to 10. Then graph each integer on the number line.

5. 2 6. 6 7. 10 8. 8
9. −7 10. −4 11. −9 12. −3

−10 −9 −8 −7 −6 −5 −4 −3 −2 −1 0 1 2 3 4 5 6 7 8 9 10

Write the opposite of each integer.

13. +8 **−8** 14. −5 **+5** 15. −2 **+2** 16. +9 **−9**
17. −11 **+11** 18. +21 **−21** 19. +10 **−10** 20. −7 **+7**

21. **SCIENCE** The average daytime surface temperature on the Moon is 260°F. Represent this temperature as an integer. **+260 or 260**
22. **GEOGRAPHY** The Salton Sea is a lake at 227 feet below sea level. Represent this altitude as an integer. **−227**
23. **WEATHER** The table below shows the extreme low temperatures for select cities. Make a line plot of the data. Then explain how the line plot can be used to determine whether more cities had extremes lower then zero degrees or greater than zero degrees.

Extreme Low Temperatures by City			
City	Temp. °F	City	Temp. °F
Mobile, AL	3	Boston, MA	−12
Wilmington, DE	−14	Jackson, MS	2
Jacksonville, FL	7	Raleigh, NC	−9
Savannah, GA	3	Portland, OR	−3
New Orleans, LA	11	Philadelphia, PA	−7
Baltimore, MD	−7	Charleston, SC	6

Source: *The World Almanac*

Sample answer: By counting the number of Xs for temperatures above 0 and Xs below 0, you can determine that the number of cities is equal at 6.

Extreme Low Temperatures in Selected Cities

−15 −10 −5 0 5 10 15

Temperature (°F)

NAME ______________ DATE ________ PERIOD ____

3-1 Study Guide and Intervention
Representing Decimals

Decimals can be written in standard form and expanded form.

Standard form is the usual way to write a decimal, such as 3.52. **Expanded form** is a sum of the products of each digit and its place, such as (3 × 1) + (5 × 0.1) + (2 × 0.01).

Example 1 Write 128.0732 in word form.

Place-Value Chart							
thousands	hundreds	tens	ones	tenths	hundredths	thousandths	ten-thousandths
0	1	2	8 •	0	7	3	2

In words, 128.0732 is *one hundred twenty-eight and seven hundred thirty-two ten-thousandths.*

Example 2 Write *ninety-nine and two hundred seven thousandths* in standard form and expanded form.

Place-Value Chart							
thousands	hundreds	tens	ones	tenths	hundredths	thousandths	ten-thousandths
0	0	9	9 •	2	0	7	0

Standard form: 99.207
Expanded form: (9 × 10) + (9 × 1) + (2 × 0.1) + (0 × 0.01) + (7 × 0.001)

Exercises

Write each decimal in word form.

1. 2.3 **two and three tenths**
2. 0.68 **sixty-eight hundredths**
3. 32.501 **thirty-two and five hundred one thousandths**
4. 0.0036 **thirty-six ten-thousandths**

Write each decimal in standard form and in expanded form.

5. twenty and two hundredths **standard: 20.02; expanded: (2 × 10) + (0 × 1) + (0 × 0.1) + (2 × 0.01)**
6. seven and five tenths **standard: 7.5; expanded: (7 × 1) + (5 × 0.1)**
7. three hundred four ten-thousandths **standard: 0.0304; expanded: (0 × 0.1) + (3 × 0.01) + (0 × 0.001) + (4 × 0.0001)**
8. eleven thousandths **standard: 0.011; expanded: (0 × 0.1) + (1 × 0.01) + (1 × 0.001)**

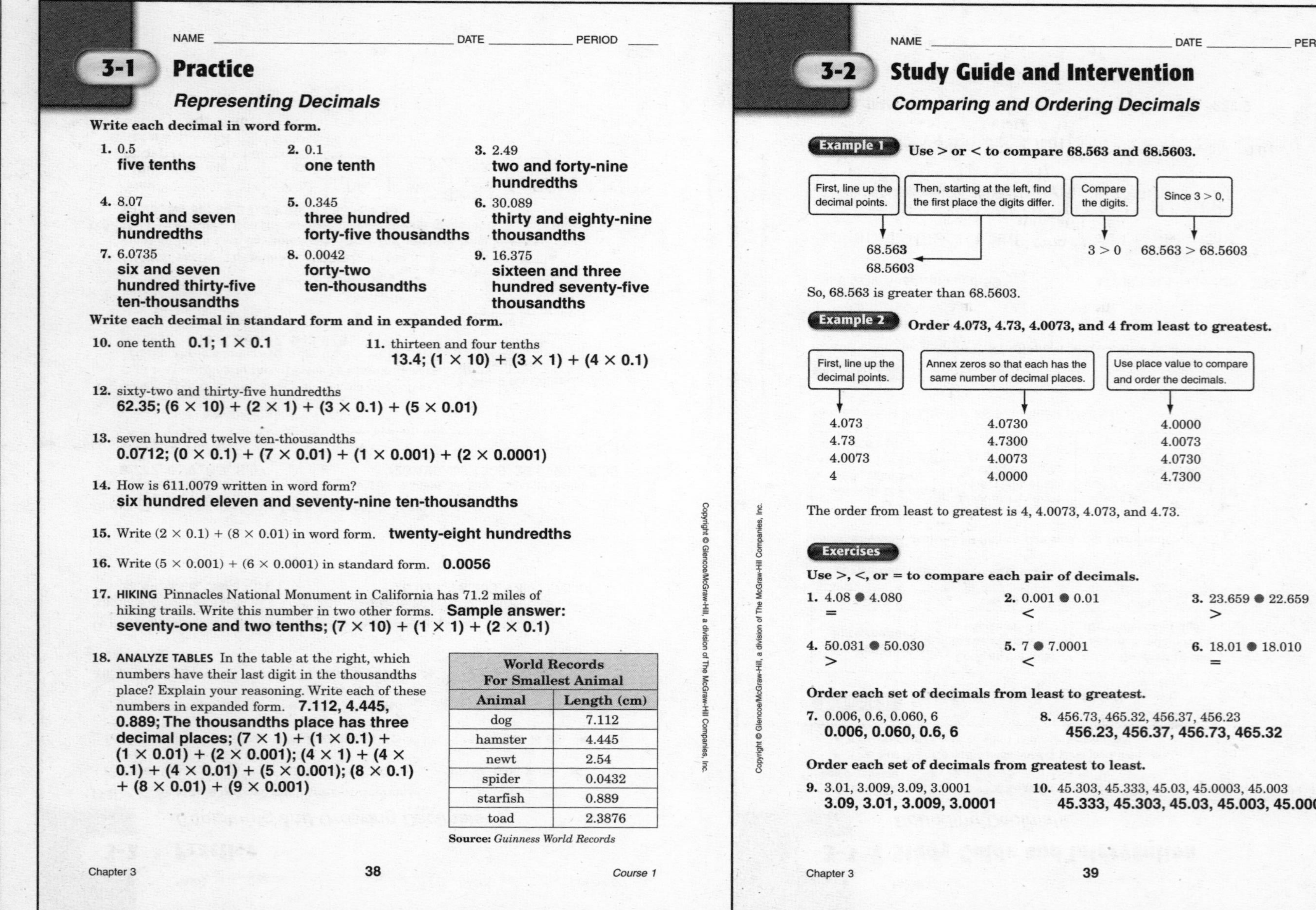

NAME ______________ DATE ________ PERIOD ____

3-1 Practice
Representing Decimals

Write each decimal in word form.

1. 0.5 **five tenths**
2. 0.1 **one tenth**
3. 2.49 **two and forty-nine hundredths**
4. 8.07 **eight and seven hundredths**
5. 0.345 **three hundred forty-five thousandths**
6. 30.089 **thirty and eighty-nine thousandths**
7. 6.0735 **six and seven hundred thirty-five ten-thousandths**
8. 0.0042 **forty-two ten-thousandths**
9. 16.375 **sixteen and three hundred seventy-five thousandths**

Write each decimal in standard form and in expanded form.

10. one tenth **0.1; 1 × 0.1**
11. thirteen and four tenths **13.4; (1 × 10) + (3 × 1) + (4 × 0.1)**
12. sixty-two and thirty-five hundredths **62.35; (6 × 10) + (2 × 1) + (3 × 0.1) + (5 × 0.01)**
13. seven hundred twelve ten-thousandths **0.0712; (0 × 0.1) + (7 × 0.01) + (1 × 0.001) + (2 × 0.0001)**
14. How is 611.0079 written in word form? **six hundred eleven and seventy-nine ten-thousandths**
15. Write (2 × 0.1) + (8 × 0.01) in word form. **twenty-eight hundredths**
16. Write (5 × 0.001) + (6 × 0.0001) in standard form. **0.0056**
17. **HIKING** Pinnacles National Monument in California has 71.2 miles of hiking trails. Write this number in two other forms. **Sample answer: seventy-one and two tenths; (7 × 10) + (1 × 1) + (2 × 0.1)**
18. **ANALYZE TABLES** In the table at the right, which numbers have their last digit in the thousandths place? Explain your reasoning. Write each of these numbers in expanded form. **7.112, 4.445, 0.889; The thousandths place has three decimal places; (7 × 1) + (1 × 0.1) + (1 × 0.01) + (2 × 0.001); (4 × 1) + (4 × 0.1) + (4 × 0.01) + (5 × 0.001); (8 × 0.1) + (8 × 0.01) + (9 × 0.001)**

World Records For Smallest Animal

Animal	Length (cm)
dog	7.112
hamster	4.445
newt	2.54
spider	0.0432
starfish	0.889
toad	2.3876

Source: *Guinness World Records*

Copyright © Glencoe/McGraw-Hill, a division of The McGraw-Hill Companies, Inc.

NAME ______________ DATE ________ PERIOD ____

3-2 Study Guide and Intervention
Comparing and Ordering Decimals

Example 1 **Use $>$ or $<$ to compare 68.563 and 68.5603.**

First, line up the decimal points. → 68.563 / 68.5603
Then, starting at the left, find the first place the digits differ.
Compare the digits. → $3 > 0$
Since $3 > 0$, → $68.563 > 68.5603$

So, 68.563 is greater than 68.5603.

Example 2 **Order 4.073, 4.73, 4.0073, and 4 from least to greatest.**

First, line up the decimal points.	Annex zeros so that each has the same number of decimal places.	Use place value to compare and order the decimals.
4.073	4.0730	4.0000
4.73	4.7300	4.0073
4.0073	4.0073	4.0730
4	4.0000	4.7300

The order from least to greatest is 4, 4.0073, 4.073, and 4.73.

Exercises

Use $>$, $<$, or $=$ to compare each pair of decimals.

1. 4.08 ● 4.080 **$=$**
2. 0.001 ● 0.01 **$<$**
3. 23.659 ● 22.659 **$>$**
4. 50.031 ● 50.030 **$>$**
5. 7 ● 7.0001 **$<$**
6. 18.01 ● 18.010 **$=$**

Order each set of decimals from least to greatest.

7. 0.006, 0.6, 0.060, 6 **0.006, 0.060, 0.6, 6**
8. 456.73, 465.32, 456.37, 456.23 **456.23, 456.37, 456.73, 465.32**

Order each set of decimals from greatest to least.

9. 3.01, 3.009, 3.09, 3.0001 **3.09, 3.01, 3.009, 3.0001**
10. 45.303, 45.333, 45.03, 45.0003, 45.003 **45.333, 45.303, 45.03, 45.003, 45.0003**

NAME ______________________ DATE ____________ PERIOD ____

3-2 Practice

Comparing and Ordering Decimals

Use >, <, or = to compare each pair of decimals.

1. 8.8 ● 8.80 **=**
2. 0.3 ● 3.0 **<**
3. 0.06 ● 0.6 **<**
4. 5.10 ● 5.01 **>**
5. 4.42 ● 4.24 **>**
6. 0.009 ● 0.9 **<**
7. 0.305 ● 0.315 **<**
8. 7.006 ● 7.060 **<**
9. 8.408 ● 8.044 **>**
10. 91.77 ● 91.770 **=**
11. 7.2953 ● 7.2593 **>**
12. 0.0826 ● 0.0286 **>**

Order each set of decimals from least to greatest.

13. 33.6, 34.01, 33.44, 34
33.44, 33.6, 34, 34.01

14. 78.203, 78.34, 78.023, 78.23
78.023, 78.203, 78.23, 78.34

Order each set of decimals from greatest to least.

15. 8.7, 8.77, 8.07, 8.777
8.777, 8.77, 8.7, 8.07

16. 26.0999, 26.199, 25.99, 26.1909
26.199, 26.1909, 26.0999, 25.99

17. LIBRARY Books in the library are placed on shelves in order according to their Dewey Decimal numbers. Arrange these numbers in order from least to greatest. **943.6, 943.67, 943.678**

Book Number
943.678
943.6
943.67

18. ANALYZE TABLES The following table shows the amount of money Sonia spent on lunch each day this week. Order the amounts from least to greatest and then find the median amount she spent on lunch.
$4.23, $4.38, $4.39, $4.45, $4.53; $4.39

Day	Mon.	Tue.	Wed.	Thu.	Fri.
Amount Spent ($)	4.45	4.39	4.23	4.53	4.38

Copyright © Glencoe/McGraw-Hill, a division of The McGraw-Hill Companies, Inc.

NAME ______________________ DATE ____________ PERIOD ____

3-3 Study Guide and Intervention

Rounding Decimals

To round a decimal, first underline the digit to be rounded. Then look at the digit to the right of the place being rounded.

- If the digit is 4 or less, the underlined digit remains the same.
- If the digit is 5 or greater, add 1 to the underlined digit.

Example 1 **Round 6.58 to the nearest tenth.**

Underline the digit to be rounded.	Look at the digit to the right of the underlined digit.	Since the digit to the right is 8, add one to the underlined digit.
6.5̲8	6.5̲8	6.6

To the nearest tenth, 6.58 rounds to 6.6.

Example 2 **Round 86.943 to the nearest hundredth.**

Underline the digit to be rounded.	Look at the digit to the right of the underlined digit.	Since the digit is 3 and 3 < 5, the digit 4 remains the same.
86.94̲3	86.94̲3	86.94

To the nearest hundredth, 86.943 rounds to 86.94.

Exercises

Round each decimal to the indicated place-value position.

1. 3.21; tenths **3.2**
2. 2.0505; thousandths **2.051**
3. 6.5892; hundredths **6.59**
4. 235.709; hundredths **235.71**
5. 0.0914; thousandths **0.091**
6. 34.35; tenths **34.4**
7. 500.005; hundredths **500.01**
8. 2.5134; tenths **2.5**
9. 0.0052; thousandths **0.005**
10. 0.0052; hundredths **0.01**
11. 131.1555; thousandths **131.156**
12. 232.88; tenths **232.9**

Copyright © Glencoe/McGraw-Hill, a division of The McGraw-Hill Companies, Inc.

NAME ______________ DATE ________ PERIOD ____

3-3 Practice

Rounding Decimals

Round each decimal to the indicated place-value position.

1. 8.239; tenths **8.2**
2. 3.666; tenths **3.7**
3. 4.47; ones **4**
4. 10.86; ones **11**
5. 3.299; hundredths **3.30**
6. 20.687; hundredths **20.69**
7. 2.3654; thousandths **2.365**
8. 69.0678; thousandths **69.068**
9. 5.58214; hundredths **5.58**
10. 468.09156; thousandths **468.092**
11. $46.49; tens **$50**
12. 1,358.761; tens **1,360**

13. LANGUAGES In the United States, about 1.64 million people speak French as their primary language. Round this number to the nearest million. **2 million**

14. SHOPPING The price of a pound of cooked shrimp was $3.29. How much was this to the nearest dollar? **$3**

15. COMPUTERS Crystal has filled up 13.57 gigabytes of her computer's hard drive. Round this amount to the nearest tenth of a gigabyte. **13.6 GB**

16. CURRENCY Recently, one Canadian dollar was equal to 0.835125 U.S. dollars. Round this amount of U.S. dollars to the nearest cent. **$0.84**

CALCULATOR A calculator will often show the results of a calculation with a very long decimal. Round each of the numbers on the calculator displays to the nearest thousandth.

17. 35.67381216 **35.674**

18. 1342.409448 **1,342.409**

19. .5235728864 **0.524**

20. RACING The table shows the times for a canoe paddling race at summer camp. Will it help to round these times to the nearest tenth before listing them in in order from least to greatest? Explain. **No; if you round the times, some of them will have the same value.**

Canoe Race	
Team	**Time (h)**
Cougars	1.751
Moose	1.824
Jack Rabbits	1.665
Bears	1.739

NAME ______________ DATE ________ PERIOD ____

3-4 Study Guide and Intervention

Estimating Sums and Differences

Estimation Methods	
Rounding	Estimate by rounding each decimal to the nearest whole number that is easy for you to add or subtract mentally.
Clustering	Estimate by rounding a group of close numbers to the same number.
Front-End Estimation	Estimate by adding or subtracting the values of the digits in the front place..

Example 1 **Estimate 14.07 + 43.22 using front-end estimation.**

Add the front digits.

```
  14.07
+ 43.22
  5
```

Add the next digits.

```
  14.07
+ 43.22
  57.00
```

An estimate for 14.07 + 43.22 is 57.

Example 2 **Use clustering to estimate $7.62 + $7.89 + $8.01 + $7.99.**

To use clustering, round each addend to the same number.

```
  7.62  →    8.00
  7.89  →    8.00
  8.01  →    8.00
+ 7.99  →  + 8.00
            32.00
```

An estimate for $7.62 + $7.89 + $8.01 + $7.99 is $32.

Exercises **1-9. Sample answers given.**

Estimate using rounding.

1. 59.118 + 17.799 **59 + 18 = 77**
2. $45.85 + $6.82 **$46 + $7 = $53**
3. 4.65 + 4.44 **5 + 4 = 9**

Estimate using clustering.

4. $0.99 + $1.15 + $0.52 **1 + 1 + 1 = 3**
5. 3.65 + 4.02 + 3.98 **4 + 4 + 4 = 12**
6. 6.87 + 6.97 + 7.39 **7 + 7 + 7 = 21**

Estimate using front-end estimation.

7. 81.23 + 5.51 **81 + 5 = 86**
8. 42.06 + 17.39 **42 + 17 = 59**
9. 754.23 − 23.17 **754 − 23 = 731**

Lesson 3–4

NAME ______________________ DATE ____________ PERIOD _____

3-4 Practice

Estimating Sums and Differences

Estimate using rounding.

1. 68.99 + 22.31 **70 + 20 = 90**
2. 39.57 + 18.34 **40 + 20 = 60**
3. 81.25 – 23.16 **80 – 20 = 60**
4. 21.56 – 19.62 **22 – 20 = 2**
5. 5.69 + 3.47 + 8.02 **6 + 3 + 8 = 17**
6. 6.6 + 1.22 + 5.54 **7 + 1 + 6 = 14**

Estimate using clustering.

7. \$4.56 + \$4.79 + \$5.21 + \$5.38 **4 × \$5 = \$20**
8. 9.7325 + 9.55 + 10.333 **3 × 10 = 30**
9. 39.8 + 39.6 + 40.21 + 40.47 **4 × 40 = 160**
10. \$69.72 + \$70.44 + \$70.59 + \$69.56 **4 × \$70 = \$280**

Estimate using front-end estimation.

11. 34.87 – 29.12 **10**
12. 69.45 – 44.8 **20**
13. \$78.69 + \$31.49 **\$100**
14. \$258.32 + \$378.60 **\$500**

15. SHOPPING Miriam bought a basketball for \$24.99 and basketball shoes for \$47.79. About how much did Miriam spend on the ball and shoes?
Sample answer: \$25 + \$50 = \$75

16. PRECIPITATION Albuquerque gets an average of 6.35 inches of precipitation a year. Phoenix gets an average of 6.82 inches a year. About how many more inches of precipitation does Phoenix get than Albuquerque using rounding and using front-end estimation?
Rounding: 7 – 6 = 1 in.; Front-end estimation: 6 – 6 = 0 in.

NAME ______________________ DATE ____________ PERIOD _____

3-5 Study Guide and Intervention

Adding and Subtracting Decimals

To add or subtract decimals, line up the decimal points then add or subtract digits in the same place-value position. Estimate first so you know if your answer is reasonable.

Example 1 **Find the sum of 61.32 + 8.26.**

First, estimate the sum using front-end estimation.

61.32 + 8.26 → 61 + 8 = 69

$$\begin{array}{r} 61.32 \\ +\ 8.26 \\ \hline 69.58 \end{array}$$

Since the estimate is close, the answer is reasonable.

Example 2 **Find 2.65 – 0.2.**

Estimate: 2.65 – 0.2 → 3 – 0 = 3

$$\begin{array}{r} 2.65 \\ -\ 0.20 \\ \hline 2.45 \end{array}$$ Annex a zero.

Since the estimate is close, the answer is reasonable.

Exercises

Find each sum or difference.

1. 2.3 + 4.1 = **6.4**
2. \$13.67 – 7.19 = **\$6.48**
3. 0.0123 – 0.0028 = **0.0095**
4. 132.346 + 0.486 = **132.832**
5. 113.7999 + 6.2001 = **120**
6. 0.0058 – 0.0026 = **0.0032**
7. \$5.63 + 4.10 = **\$9.73**
8. 5.00921 – 4.00013 = **1.00908**
9. 0.2 + 5.64 + 9.005 **14.845**
10. 12.36 – 4.081 **8.279**
11. 216.8 – 34.055 **182.745**
12. 4.62 + 3.415 + 2.4 **10.435**

Lesson 3–5

NAME ______________ DATE ________ PERIOD ____

3-5 Practice

Adding and Subtracting Decimals

Find each sum.

1. 5.4 + 6.5 **11.9**
2. 6.0 + 3.8 **9.8**
3. 3.65 + 4 **7.65**
4. 52.47 + 13.21 **65.68**
5. 91.64 + 19.5 **111.14**
6. 0.675 + 28 **28.675**

Find each difference.

7. 7.8 – 4.5 **3.3**
8. 69 – 12.88 **56.12**
9. 17.46 – 6.79 **10.67**
10. 74 – 59.29 **14.71**
11. 87.31 – 25.09 **62.22**
12. 19.75 – 12.98 **6.77**

ALGEBRA **Evaluate each expression if $a = 219.6$ and $b = 12.024$.**

13. $a - b$ **207.576**
14. $b + a$ **231.624**
15. $a - 13.45 - b$ **194.126**

Find the value of each expression.

16. $4.3 + 6 \times 7$ **46.3**
17. $3^2 - 2.55$ **6.45**
18. $19.7 - 4^2$ **3.7**

19. BIKE RIDING The table shows the distances the members of two teams rode their bicycles for charity.

Distances Ridden for Charity			
Lori's Team		Tati's Team	
Lori	13.8 mi	Tati	13.6 mi
Marcus	11.8 mi	Luis	15.1 mi
Hassan	15.4 mi		

a. How many total miles did Lori's team ride? **41 mi**

b. How many more miles did Lori's team ride than Tati's team?
12.3 mi

NAME ______________ DATE ________ PERIOD ____

3-6 Study Guide and Intervention

Multiplying Decimals by Whole Numbers

When you multiply a decimal by a whole number, you multiply the numbers as if you were multiplying all whole numbers. Then you use estimation or you count the number of decimal places to decide where to place the decimal point. If there are not enough decimal places in the product, annex zeros to the left.

Example 1 **Find 6.25 × 5.**

Method 1 Use estimation.

Round 6.25 to 6.
6.25 × 5 → 6 × 5 or 30

```
 1 2
 6.25
×   5
31.25
```

Since the estimate is 30 place the decimal point after 31.

Method 2 Count decimal places.

```
 6.25
×   5
31.25
```

There are two places to the right of the decimal point.

Count the same number of decimal places from right to left.

Example 2 **Find 3 × 0.0047.**

```
    2
0.0047
×    3
0.0141
```

There are four decimal places.

Annex a zero on the left of 141 to make four decimal places.

Example 3 **Find 6.3 × 1,000.**

Method 1 Use paper and pencil.

```
  1,000
  × 6.3
  3 000
 60 000
6,300.0
```

Method 2 Use mental math.
Move the decimal point to the right the same number of zeros that are in 1,000 or 3 places.
6.3 × 1,000 = 6,300

Exercises

Multiply.

1. 8.03 × 3 **24.09**
2. 6 × 12.6 **75.6**
3. 2 × 0.012 **0.024**
4. 0.0008 × 9 **0.0072**
5. 2.32 × 10 **23.2**
6. 6.8 × 100 **680**
7. 5.2 × 1000 **5,200**
8. 1.412 × 100 **141.2**

NAME ______________________ DATE ____________ PERIOD _____

3-6 Practice

Multiplying Decimals by Whole Numbers

Multiply.

1. 0.8×6 **4.8**
2. 0.7×4 **2.8**
3. 1.9×5 **9.5**
4. 3.4×9 **30.6**
5. 6×3.4 **20.4**
6. 5.2×9 **46.8**
7. 0.6×6 **3.6**
8. 4×0.8 **3.2**
9. 5×0.05 **0.25**
10. 3×0.029 **0.087**
11. 0.0027×15 **0.0405**
12. 0.0186×92 **1.7112**

ALGEBRA Evaluate each expression.

13. $5.02h$ if $h = 36$ **180.72**
14. $72.33j$ if $j = 3$ **216.99**
15. $21k$ if $k = 24.09$ **505.89**

Multiply.

16. 4.23×100 **423**
17. $3.7 \times 1{,}000$ **3,700**
18. 2.6×10 **26**
19. $4.2 \times 1{,}000$ **4,200**
20. 1.23×100 **123**
21. $5.14 \times 1{,}000$ **5,140**
22. 6.7×10 **67**
23. $7.89 \times 1{,}000$ **7,890**

24. **SHOPPING** Basketballs sell for $27.99 each at the Super D and for $21.59 each at the Bargain Spot. If the coach buys a dozen basketballs, how much can he save by buying them at the Bargain Spot? Justify your answer. **$76.80; $27.99 × 12 = $335.88, $21.59 × 12 = $259.08, $335.88 − $259.08 = $76.80**

25. **SCHOOL** Jaimie purchases 10 pencils at the school bookstore. They cost $0.30 each. How much did she spend on pencils? **$3.00**

NAME ______________________ DATE ____________ PERIOD _____

3-7 Study Guide and Intervention

Multiplying Decimals

When you multiply a decimal by a decimal, multiply the numbers as if you were multiplying all whole numbers. To decide where to place the decimal point, find the sum of the number of decimal places in each factor. The product has the same number of decimal places.

Example 1 **Find 5.2 × 6.13.**

Estimate: 5 × 6 or 30

```
    5.2  ←— one decimal place
 × 6.13  ←— two decimal places
    156
     52
   312
 31.876  ←— three decimal places
```

The product is 31.876. Compared to the estimate, the product is reasonable.

Example 2 **Evaluate $0.023t$ if $t = 2.3$.**

$0.023t = 0.023 \times 2.3$ Replace t with 2.3.

```
  0.023  ←— three decimal places
  × 2.3  ←— one decimal place
     69
    46
 0.0529  ←— Annex a zero to make four decimal places.
```

Exercises

Multiply.

1. 7.2×2.1 **15.12**
2. 4.3×8.5 **36.55**
3. 2.64×1.4 **3.696**
4. 14.23×8.21 **116.8283**
5. 5.01×11.6 **58.116**
6. 9.001×4.2 **37.8042**

ALGEBRA Evaluate each expression if $x = 5.07$, $y = 1.5$, and $z = 0.403$.

7. $3.2x + y$ **17.724**
8. $yz + x$ **5.6745**
9. $z \times 7.06 - y$ **1.34518**

NAME ______________________ DATE ____________ PERIOD ____

3-7 Practice

Multiplying Decimals

Multiply.

1. 0.3 × 0.9 **0.27**
2. 2.6 × 1.7 **4.42**
3. 1.09 × 5.4 **5.886**
4. 17.2 × 12.86 **221.192**
5. 0.56 × 0.03 **0.0168**
6. 4.9 × 0.02 **0.098**
7. 2.07 × 2.008 **4.15656**
8. 26.02 × 2.006 **52.19612**

ALGEBRA Evaluate each expression if $r = 0.034$, $s = 4.05$, and $t = 2.6$.

9. $5.027 + 4.68r$ **5.18612**
10. $2.9s - 3.7t$ **2.125**
11. $4.13s + r$ **16.7605**
12. rst **0.35802**

13. **MINING** A mine produces 42.5 tons of coal per hour. How much coal will the mine produce in 9.5 hours? **403.75 tons**

14. **SHOPPING** Ms. Morgan bought 3.5 pounds of bananas at $0.51 a pound and 4.5 pounds of pineapple at $1.19 a pound. How much did she pay for the bananas and pineapple? **$7.14**

Copyright © Glencoe/McGraw-Hill, a division of The McGraw-Hill Companies, Inc.

NAME ______________________ DATE ____________ PERIOD ____

3-8 Study Guide and Intervention

Dividing Decimals by Whole Numbers

When you divide a decimal by a whole number, place the decimal point in the quotient above the decimal point in the dividend. Then divide as you do with whole numbers.

Example 1 **Find 8.73 ÷ 9.**

Estimate: 9 ÷ 9 = 1

```
   0.97   ← Place the decimal point directly above the decimal point in the quotient.
 9)8.73
  −0
   87
  −81     ← Divide as with whole numbers.
    63
   −63
     0
```

8.73 ÷ 9 = 0.97 Compared to the estimate, the quotient is reasonable.

Example 2 **Find 8.58 ÷ 12.**

Estimate: 10 ÷ 10 = 1

```
    0.715  ← Place the decimal point.
 12)8.580  ← Annex a zero to continue dividing.
   −84
     18
    −12
      60
     −60
       0
```

8.58 ÷ 12 = 0.715 Compared to the estimate, the quotient is reasonable.

Exercises

Divide.

1. 9.2 ÷ 4 **2.3**
2. 4.5 ÷ 5 **0.9**
3. 8.6 ÷ 2 **4.3**
4. 2.89 ÷ 4 **0.7225**
5. 3.2 ÷ 4 **0.8**
6. 7.2 ÷ 3 **2.4**
7. 7.5 ÷ 5 **1.5**
8. 3.25 ÷ 5 **0.65**

NAME ______________________ DATE ____________ PERIOD _____

3-8 Practice

Dividing Decimals by Whole Numbers

Divide. Round to the nearest tenth if necessary.

1. 25.2 ÷ 4 **6.3**

2. 147.2 ÷ 8 **18.4**

3. 5.69 ÷ 7 **0.8**

4. 13.28 ÷ 3 **4.4**

5. 22.5 ÷ 15 **1.5**

6. 65.28 ÷ 12 **5.44**

7. 243.83 ÷ 32 **7.6**

8. 654.29 ÷ 19 **34.4**

9. **WEATHER** What is the average January precipitation in Arches National Park? Round to the nearest hundredth if necessary. **0.48 in.**

January Precipitation in Arches National Park

Year	1997	1998	1999	2000	2001	2002	2003	2004
Precipitation (in.)	1.09	0.013	0.54	0.80	0.89	0.24	0.11	0.16

Source: National Park Service

10. **SHOPPING** A 3-pack of boxes of juice costs $1.09. A 12-pack of boxes costs $4.39. A case of 24 boxes costs $8.79. Which is the best buy? Explain your reasoning.
3-pack; the cost for each box of juice is about $0.36 in the 3-pack, but the cost for each box in both the 12-pack and the 24-pack is about $0.37.

NAME ______________________ DATE ____________ PERIOD _____

3-9 Study Guide and Intervention

Dividing by Decimals

When you divide a decimal by a decimal, multiply both the divisor and the dividend by the same power of ten. Then divide as with whole numbers.

Example 1 **Find 10.14 ÷ 5.2.**

Estimate: 10 ÷ 5 = 2

Multiply by 10 to make a whole number.

5.2)10.14 → 52)101.40 — quotient 1.95

Multiply by the same number, 10.

```
     1.95
52)101.40    Place the decimal point.
  - 52       Divide as with whole numbers.
    494
  - 468
     260     Annex a zero to continue.
   - 260
       0
```

10.14 divided by 5.2 is 1.95. Compare to the estimate.
Check: 1.95 × 5.2 = 10.14 ✓

Example 2 **Find 4.09 ÷ 0.02.**

0.02)4.00 → 2)409.0

Multiply each by 100.

```
   204.5
2)409.0     Place the decimal point.
 - 4        Divide.
   00
  - 0
    09
   - 8
    10      Write a zero in the dividend
  - 10      and continue to divide.
     0
```

4.09 ÷ 0.02 is 204.5.
Check: 204.5 × 0.02 = 4.09 ✓

Exercises

Divide.

1. 9.8 ÷ 1.4 **7**

2. 4.41 ÷ 2.1 **2.1**

3. 16.848 ÷ 0.72 **23.4**

4. 8.652 ÷ 1.2 **7.21**

5. 0.5 ÷ 0.001 **500**

6. 9.594 ÷ 0.06 **159.9**

Lesson 3–9

NAME ______________________ DATE ____________ PERIOD ____

3-9 Practice

Dividing by Decimals

Divide.

1. 12.92 ÷ 3.4
3.8

2. 22.47 ÷ 0.7
32.1

3. 0.025 ÷ 0.5
0.05

4. 7.224 ÷ 0.08
90.3

5. 0.855 ÷ 9.5
0.09

6. 0.9 ÷ 0.12
7.5

7. 3.0084 ÷ 0.046
65.4

8. 0.0868 ÷ 0.007
12.4

9. **WHALES** After its first day of life, a baby blue whale started growing. It grew 47.075 inches. If the average baby blue whale grows at a rate of 1.5 inches a day, for how many days did the baby whale grow, to the nearest tenth of a day? **31.4 days**

10. **LIZARDS** The two largest lizards in the United States are the Gila Monster and the Chuckwalla. The average Gila Monster is 0.608 meter long. The average Chuckwalla is 0.395 meters long. How many times longer is the Gila Monster than the Chuckwalla to the nearest hundredth? **1.54 times longer**

Copyright © Glencoe/McGraw-Hill, a division of The McGraw-Hill Companies, Inc.

NAME ______________________ DATE ____________ PERIOD ____

3-10 Study Guide and Intervention

Problem-Solving Investigation: Reasonable Answers

When solving problems, one strategy that is helpful is to *determine reasonable answers.* If you are solving a problem with big numbers, or a problem with information that you are unfamiliar with, it may be helpful to look back at your answer to determine if it is reasonable.

You can use the *determine reasonable answers* strategy, along with the following four-step problem solving plan to solve a problem.

1 Understand – Read and get a general understanding of the problem.

2 Plan – Make a plan to solve the problem and estimate the solution.

3 Solve – Use your plan to solve the problem.

4 Check – Check the reasonableness of your solution.

Example ANIMALS **The average height of a male chimpanzee is 1.2 meters, and the average height of a female chimpanzee is 1.1 meters. What is a reasonable height in feet of a male chimpanzee?**

Understand We know the average height in meters of a male chimpanzee.

We need to find a reasonable height in feet.

Plan One meter is very close to one yard. One yard is equal to 3 feet. So, estimate how many feet would be in 1.2 yards.

Solve 1.2 yards would be more than 3 feet, but less than 6 feet.

So, a reasonable average height of a male chimpanzee is about 4 feet.

Check Since 1.2 yd = 3.6 ft, the answer of 4 feet is reasonable.

Exercise

SHOPPING Alexis wants to buy 2 bracelets for $6.95 each, 1 pair of earrings for $4.99, and 2 necklaces for $8.95 each. Does she need $40 or will $35 be more reasonable? Explain. **$40; 2 × 7 + 5 + 2 × 9 = $37**

Lesson 3–10

NAME ______________ DATE __________ PERIOD ____

3-10 Practice

Problem-Solving Investigation: Reasonable Answers

Mixed Problem Solving

Use the determine reasonable answers strategy to solve Exercises 1 and 2.

1. LIFE EXPECTANCY Use the graph below to determine whether 80, 85, or 90 years is a reasonable prediction of the life expectancy of a person born in 2020.
80 years

Life Expectancy at Birth in the U.S.

Age at Death (years): 0, 40, 45, 50, 55, 60, 65, 70, 75, 80, 85, 90, 95, 100

Year: 1900, 1920, 1940, 1960, 1980, 2000, 2020

2. SNACKS Paolo is stocking up on after-school snacks. He wants to buy 2 pounds of bananas at $0.79 per pound, 2 cans of mixed nuts at $3.89 a can, and a bottle of apple juice at $1.19 a bottle. Does he need to bring $20 to the store or will $15 be enough? Explain your reasoning.
$15; 2 × $1 + 2 × $4 + $1.20 < $15

Use any strategy to solve Exercises 3–6. Some strategies are shown below.

Problem-Solving Strategies
• Solve a simpler problem.
• Draw a diagram.
• Determine reasonable answers.

3. CARVINGS In how many ways can Kwan line up her carvings of a duck, a gull, and a pelican on a shelf? **6 ways**

4. CARNIVAL There are 56 students in the sixth grade. Ms. Rockwell's class is sponsoring a carnival for the sixth graders at the school. The class has spent $40 on decorations and $10 on publicity. To pay for the expenses, an entrance fee of $0.75 is being considered. Is this a reasonable amount to charge?
Sample answer: No; even if all 56 students came, there would not be enough to cover expenses. 56 × $0.75 = $42 and $42 < $40 + $10

5. PARKS The four largest national parks in the United States are in Alaska. The largest is Wrangell-St. Elias at 8.3 million acres. The fourth largest is Katmai at 1.48 million acres. How many times larger is Wrangell-St. Elias than Katmai to the nearest tenth million?
Division; 8.3 ÷ 1.48 is about 5.6, so Wrangell-St. Elias is about 5.6 times larger.

6. RACING Hector ran in the city charity race for four years. His times in minutes were: 14.8, 22.3, 26.7, and 31.9. What was his mean time for the four years to the nearest tenth minute?
Addition followed by division; (14.8 + 22.3 + 26.7 + 31.9) ÷ 4 = 23.9 min

NAME ______________ DATE __________ PERIOD ____

4-1 Study Guide and Intervention

Greatest Common Factor

The **greatest common factor (GCF)** of two or more numbers is the greatest of the common factors of the numbers. To find the GCF, you can make a list or use prime factors.

Example 1 **Find the GCF of 12 and 30.**

Make an organized list of the factors for each number.

12: 1 × 12, 2 × 6, 3 × 4
30: 1 × 30, 2 × 15, 3 × 10, 5 × 6

The common factors are 1, 2, 3, and 6. The greatest is 6. The GCF of 12 and 30 is 6.

Example 2 **Find the GCF of 18 and 27 by using prime factors.**

Write the prime factorizations of 18 and 27.

18 → 2 · 9 → 2 · ③ · ③

27 → 3 · 9 → ③ · ③ · 3

The common prime factors are 3 and 3. So, the GCF of 18 and 27 is 3 × 3 or 9.

Exercises

Find the GCF of each set of numbers by making a list.

1. 8 and 12
8: 1, 2, 4, 8
12: 1, 2, 3, 4, 6, 12
GCF: 4

2. 10 and 15
10: 1, 2, 5, 10
15: 1, 3, 5, 15
GCF: 5

3. 81 and 27
81: 1, 3, 9, 27, 81
27: 1, 3, 9, 27
GCF: 27

Find the GCF of each set of numbers by using prime factors.

4. 15 and 20
15 = 3 × 5
20 = 2 × 2 × 5
GCF: 5

5. 6 and 12
6 = 2 × 3
12 = 2 × 2 × 3
GCF: 6

6. 28 and 42
28 = 2 × 2 × 7
42 = 2 × 3 × 7
GCF: 14

Find the GCF of each set of numbers.

7. 21 and 9 **3**

8. 15 and 7 **1**

9. 54 and 81 **27**

10. 30 and 45 **15**

11. 44 and 55 **11**

12. 35, 20, and 15 **5**

Copyright © Glencoe/McGraw-Hill, a division of The McGraw-Hill Companies, Inc.

NAME ______________________ DATE ____________ PERIOD ____

4-1 Practice

Greatest Common Factor

Identify the common factors of each set of numbers.

1. 12 and 20 **1, 2, 4**
2. 12, 24, 36 **1, 2, 3, 4, 6, 12**
3. 15, 33, 45 **1, 3**

Find the GCF of each set of numbers.

4. 12 and 30 **6**
5. 50 and 40 **10**
6. 20 and 27 **1**
7. 28, 42, 56 **14**
8. 14, 56, 63 **7**
9. 9, 21, 60 **3**

Find three numbers whose GCF is the indicated value.

10. 3 **Sample answer: 3, 9, 12**
11. 16 **Sample answer: 16, 32, 48**
12. 18 **Sample answer: 18, 36, 54**

TOYS **For Exercises 13 and 14, use the following information.**

A store is organizing toys into bins. The toys must be put into bins such that each bin contains the same number of toys without mixing the toys.

Toys to Place in Bins	
Toy	Number of Toys
airplanes	36
boats	72
cars	60

13. What is the greatest number of toys that can be put in a bin? **12 toys**

14. How many bins are needed for each type of toy? **airplanes: 3 bins; boats: 6 bins; cars: 5 bins**

Copyright © Glencoe/McGraw-Hill, a division of The McGraw-Hill Companies, Inc.

NAME ______________________ DATE ____________ PERIOD ____

4-2 Study Guide and Intervention

Simplifying Fractions

Fractions that have the same value are **equivalent fractions**. To find equivalent fractions, you can multiply or divide the numerator and denominator by the same nonzero number.

Example 1 **Replace the ● with a number so that $\frac{1}{2} = \frac{●}{10}$.**

Since $2 \times 5 = 10$, multiply the numerator and denominator by 5.

$$\frac{1}{2} = \frac{●}{10} \quad (\times 5) \qquad \frac{1}{2} = \frac{5}{10} \quad (\times 5)$$

When the GCF of the numerator and denominator is 1, the fraction is in simplest form. To write a fraction in simplest form, you can divide the numerator and denominator by the GCF.

Example 2 **Write $\frac{12}{30}$ in simplest form.**

The GCF of 12 and 30 is 6.

$$\frac{12}{30} = \frac{2}{5} \quad (\div 6)$$

Divide the numerator and denominator by the GCF, 6.

The GCF of 2 and 5 is 1, so $\frac{2}{5}$ is in simplest form.

Exercises

Replace each ● with a number so the fractions are equivalent.

1. $\frac{1}{5} = \frac{●}{15}$ **3**
2. $\frac{12}{18} = \frac{2}{●}$ **3**
3. $\frac{●}{14} = \frac{27}{42}$ **9**

Write each fraction in simplest form. If the fraction is already in simplest form, write *simplest form*.

4. $\frac{6}{30}$ $\mathbf{\frac{1}{5}}$
5. $\frac{2}{3}$ **simplest form**
6. $\frac{6}{8}$ $\mathbf{\frac{3}{4}}$
7. $\frac{21}{28}$ $\mathbf{\frac{3}{4}}$
8. $\frac{15}{30}$ $\mathbf{\frac{1}{2}}$
9. $\frac{7}{10}$ **simplest form**

NAME ______________________ DATE ____________ PERIOD _____

4-2 Practice

Simplifying Fractions

Replace each ● with a number so the fractions are equivalent.

1. $\frac{1}{3} = \frac{●}{9}$ **3**
2. $\frac{1}{4} = \frac{●}{16}$ **4**
3. $\frac{●}{2} = \frac{8}{16}$ **1**
4. $\frac{●}{8} = \frac{9}{24}$ **3**
5. $\frac{1}{2} = \frac{16}{●}$ **32**
6. $\frac{12}{21} = \frac{4}{●}$ **7**
7. $\frac{30}{36} = \frac{●}{6}$ **5**
8. $\frac{28}{42} = \frac{●}{3}$ **2**

Write each fraction in simplest form. If the fraction is already in simplest form, write *simplest form*.

9. $\frac{7}{28}$ $\mathbf{\frac{1}{4}}$
10. $\frac{9}{15}$ $\mathbf{\frac{3}{5}}$
11. $\frac{10}{42}$ $\mathbf{\frac{5}{21}}$
12. $\frac{12}{42}$ $\mathbf{\frac{2}{7}}$
13. $\frac{17}{28}$ **simplest form**
14. $\frac{24}{64}$ $\mathbf{\frac{3}{8}}$

Write two fractions that are equivalent to the given fraction.

15. $\frac{3}{10}$ **Sample answer: $\frac{6}{20}$ and $\frac{12}{40}$**
16. $\frac{7}{13}$ **Sample answer: $\frac{14}{26}$ and $\frac{21}{39}$**
17. $\frac{15}{33}$ **Sample answer: $\frac{5}{11}$ and $\frac{30}{66}$**

18. **ANIMALS** In Ms Reyes' class, 4 out of the 30 students had guinea pigs as pets. Express this fraction in simplest form. $\mathbf{\frac{2}{15}}$

19. **ANALYZE GRAPHS** The bar graph shows the number of titles held by the top seven women Wimbledon tennis champions. In simplest form, what fraction of the number of titles is held by Steffi Graf? $\mathbf{\frac{1}{7}}$

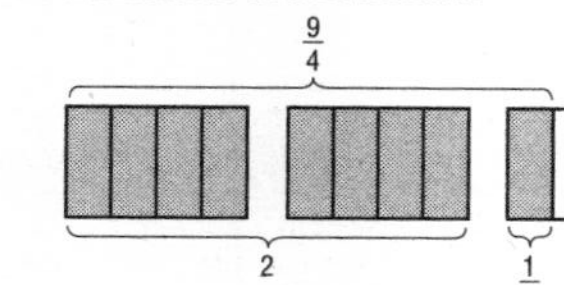

Source: United States Tennis Association

NAME ______________________ DATE ____________ PERIOD _____

4-3 Study Guide and Intervention

Mixed Numbers and Improper Fractions

Lesson 4–3

The number $2\frac{2}{3}$ is a mixed number. A **mixed number** indicates the sum of a whole number and a fraction. The number $\frac{5}{3}$ is an improper fraction. **Improper fractions** have values that are greater than or equal to 1. Mixed numbers can be written as mixed numbers or as improper fractions.

Example 1 **Write $2\frac{1}{3}$ as an improper fraction.**

$2\frac{1}{3} \rightarrow 2 \times \frac{3}{3} + \frac{1}{3} = \frac{7}{3}$ Think: $2 \times 3 = 6$ and $6 + 1 = 7$

Check: Use a model.

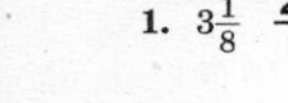
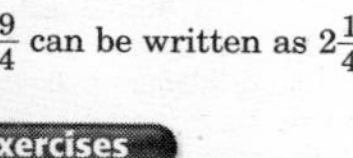
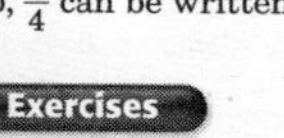

$\frac{7}{3} = 2 + \frac{1}{3}$ or $2\frac{1}{3}$ ✓

Example 2 **Write $\frac{9}{4}$ as a mixed number.**

Divide 9 by 4. Use the remainder as the numerator of the fraction.

$$4\overline{)9}\ = 2\frac{1}{4}, \quad 9 - 8 = 1$$

$\frac{9}{4}$ 2 $\frac{1}{4}$

So, $\frac{9}{4}$ can be written as $2\frac{1}{4}$.

Exercises

Write each mixed number as an improper fraction.

1. $3\frac{1}{8}$ $\mathbf{\frac{25}{8}}$
2. $2\frac{4}{5}$ $\mathbf{\frac{14}{5}}$
3. $2\frac{1}{2}$ $\mathbf{\frac{5}{2}}$
4. $1\frac{2}{3}$ $\mathbf{\frac{5}{3}}$
5. $2\frac{1}{9}$ $\mathbf{\frac{19}{9}}$
6. $3\frac{7}{10}$ $\mathbf{\frac{37}{10}}$
7. $2\frac{3}{8}$ $\mathbf{\frac{19}{8}}$
8. $1\frac{3}{4}$ $\mathbf{\frac{7}{4}}$

Write each improper fraction as a mixed number or a whole number.

9. $\frac{7}{4}$ $\mathbf{1\frac{3}{4}}$
10. $\frac{5}{3}$ $\mathbf{1\frac{2}{3}}$
11. $\frac{3}{2}$ $\mathbf{1\frac{1}{2}}$
12. $\frac{11}{8}$ $\mathbf{1\frac{3}{8}}$
13. $\frac{22}{5}$ $\mathbf{4\frac{2}{5}}$
14. $2\frac{15}{15}$ **3**
15. $\frac{25}{4}$ $\mathbf{6\frac{1}{4}}$
16. $\frac{16}{3}$ $\mathbf{5\frac{1}{3}}$

NAME ______________ DATE ________ PERIOD ____

4-3 Practice

Mixed Numbers and Improper Fractions

Write each mixed number as an improper fraction.

1. $4\frac{2}{3}$ **$\frac{14}{3}$**
2. $2\frac{1}{2}$ **$\frac{5}{2}$**
3. $5\frac{3}{7}$ **$\frac{38}{7}$**
4. $3\frac{5}{6}$ **$\frac{23}{6}$**
5. $6\frac{1}{4}$ **$\frac{25}{4}$**
6. $5\frac{3}{5}$ **$\frac{28}{5}$**
7. $8\frac{1}{9}$ **$\frac{73}{9}$**
8. $6\frac{3}{4}$ **$\frac{27}{4}$**

9. **SNAKES** The garden snake that Fumiko measured was $7\frac{3}{4}$ inches long. Write the length as an improper fraction. **$\frac{31}{4}$**

10. Express *four and seven eighths* as an improper fraction. **$\frac{39}{8}$**

Write each improper fraction as a mixed number or a whole number.

11. $\frac{13}{4}$ **$3\frac{1}{4}$**
12. $\frac{11}{10}$ **$1\frac{1}{10}$**
13. $\frac{10}{3}$ **$3\frac{1}{3}$**
14. $\frac{23}{7}$ **$3\frac{2}{7}$**
15. $6\frac{14}{14}$ **7**
16. $\frac{8}{8}$ **1**

17. **TREES** A nursery is growing trees. Find the height of each tree in terms of feet. Write your answer as a mixed number in simplest form.
apricot $6\frac{1}{12}$; peach: $5\frac{1}{6}$; pear: $4\frac{1}{2}$; plum: $5\frac{2}{3}$

Trees in Nursery

Tree	Height (in.)
Apricot	73
Peach	62
Pear	54
Plum	68

Copyright © Glencoe/McGraw-Hill, a division of The McGraw-Hill Companies, Inc.

NAME ______________ DATE ________ PERIOD ____

4-4 Study Guide and Intervention

Problem-Solving Investigation: Make an Organized List

When solving problems, one strategy that is helpful is to *make an organized list.* A list of all the possible combinations based on the information in the problem will help you solve the problem.

You can use the *make an organized list* strategy, along with the following four-step problem solving plan to solve a problem.

1 Understand – Read and get a general understanding of the problem.
2 Plan – Make a plan to solve the problem and estimate the solution.
3 Solve – Use your plan to solve the problem.
4 Check – Check the reasonableness of your solution.

Example 1 ELECTIONS **Tyler, McKayla, and Kareem are running for student council office. The three positions they could be elected for are president, treasurer, and secretary. How many possible ways could the three of them be elected?**

Understand You know that there are three positions and three students to fill the positions. You need to know the number of possible arrangements for them to be elected.

Plan Make a list of all the different possible arrangements. Use T for Tyler, M for McKayla, and K for Kareem.

Solve

President	T	T	K	K	M	M
Treasurer	M	K	M	T	T	K
Secretary	K	M	T	M	K	T

Check Check the answer by seeing if each student is accounted for in each situation.

Exercise

SHOPPING Khuan has to stop by the photo store, the gas station, the grocery store, and his grandmother's house. How many different ways can Khuan make the stops? **24**

NAME ________________ DATE ________ PERIOD ____

4-4 Practice

Problem-Solving Investigation: Make an Organized List

Mixed Problem Solving

Use the make an organized list strategy to solve Exercises 1 and 2.

1. FLAGS Randy wants to place the flag of each of 3 countries in a row on the wall for an international fair. How many arrangements are possible? **6**

2. KITES A store sells animal kites, box kites, and diamond kites in four different colors. How many combinations of kite type and color are possible? **12**

Use any strategy to solve Exercises 3–7. Some strategies are shown below.

Problem-Solving Strategies
• Make a table.
• Guess and check.

3. SHIRTS A mail-order company sells 4 styles of shirts in 6 different colors. How many combinations of style and color are possible? **24**

4. PATTERNS If the pattern continues, how many small squares are in the fifth figure of this pattern? **25**

5. FOOD Is $6 enough money to buy a head of lettuce for $0.99, two pounds of tomatoes for $2.38, and two pounds of avocados for $2.78?
No, $6 is not enough.

6. MONEY Nikki earns $45 a week pet sitting. How much does she earn each year?
$2,340

7. WRITING The number of magazine articles Nora sold in her first four years is shown. At this rate, how many articles will she sell in the fifth year?

Year	Number Sold
1	2
2	4
3	7
4	11
5	?

16

NAME ________________ DATE ________ PERIOD ____

4-5 Study Guide and Intervention

Least Common Multiple

A **multiple** of a number is the product of the number and any counting number. The multiples of 2 are below.

$1 \times 2 = 2$ $2 \times 2 = 4$ $3 \times 2 = 6$ $4 \times 2 = 8$ $5 \times 2 = 10$

The smallest number that is a multiple of two or more whole numbers is the **least common multiple (LCM)** of the numbers.

Example 1 **Identify the first three common multiples of 3 and 6.**

Step 1 List the multiples of each number.

multiples of 3: 3, 6, 9, 12, 15, 18, …

multiples of 6: 6, 12, 18, 24, 30, …

Step 2 Identify the first three common multiples from the list.

The first three common multiples of 3 and 6 are 6, 12, and 18.

Example 2 **Find the LCM of 6 and 15 by using prime factors.**

Step 1 Write the prime factorization of each number.

6 → 2×3 15 → 3×5

Step 2 Identify all common prime factors.

$6 = 2 \times 3$

$15 = 3 \times 5$

Step 3 Find the product of all of the prime factors using each common prime factor once and any remaining factors.

The LCM is $2 \times 3 \times 5$ or 30.

Exercises

Identify the first three common multiples of each set of numbers.

1. 2 and 4 **4, 8, and 12**
2. 5 and 10 **10, 20, and 30**
3. 2 and 7 **14, 28, and 42**

Find the LCM of each set of numbers.

4. 5 and 6 **30**
5. 6 and 9 **18**
6. 4 and 10 **20**
7. 9 and 27 **27**
8. 4 and 6 **12**
9. 5 and 7 **35**

Lesson 4–5

Copyright © Glencoe/McGraw-Hill, a division of The McGraw-Hill Companies, Inc.

NAME ______________ DATE ________ PERIOD ____

4-5 Practice

Least Common Multiple

Identify the first three common multiples of each set of numbers.

1. 4 and 5 **20, 40, 60**
2. 1 and 9 **9, 18, 27**
3. 3 and 4 **12, 24, 36**
4. 4, 6, and 8 **24, 48, 72**

Find the LCM of each set of numbers.

5. 3 and 5 **15**
6. 8 and 12 **24**
7. 3, 5, and 6 **30**
8. 6, 12, and 15 **60**
9. PATTERNS List the next four common multiples after the LCM of 3 and 8. **48, 72, 96, 120**
10. E-MAIL Alberto gets newsletters by e-mail. He gets one for sports every 5 days, one for model railroads every 10 days, and one for music every 8 days. If he got all three today, how many more days will it be until he gets all three newsletters on the same day? **40 days**

Copyright © Glencoe/McGraw-Hill, a division of The McGraw-Hill Companies, Inc.

NAME ______________ DATE ________ PERIOD ____

4-6 Study Guide and Intervention

Comparing and Ordering Fractions

To compare two fractions,

- Find the **least common denominator (LCD)** of the fractions; that is, find the least common multiple of the denominators.
- Write an equivalent fraction for each fraction using the LCD.
- Compare the numerators.

Example 1 **Replace ● with <, >, or = to make $\frac{1}{3}$ ● $\frac{5}{12}$ true.**

- The LCM of 3 and 12 is 12. So, the LCD is 12.
- Rewrite each fraction with a denominator of 12.

$\frac{1}{3} = \frac{●}{12}$ (× 4), so $\frac{1}{3} = \frac{4}{12}$. $\frac{5}{12} = \frac{5}{12}$

- Now, compare. Since $4 < 5$, $\frac{4}{12} < \frac{5}{12}$. So $\frac{1}{3} < \frac{5}{12}$.

Example 2 **Order $\frac{1}{6}, \frac{2}{3}, \frac{1}{4}$, and $\frac{3}{8}$ from least to greatest.**

The LCD of the fractions is 24. So, rewrite each fraction with a denominator of 24.

$\frac{1}{6} = \frac{●}{24}$ (× 4), so $\frac{1}{6} = \frac{4}{24}$. $\frac{2}{3} = \frac{●}{24}$ (× 8), so $\frac{2}{3} = \frac{16}{24}$.

$\frac{1}{4} = \frac{●}{24}$ (× 6), so $\frac{1}{4} = \frac{6}{24}$. $\frac{3}{8} = \frac{●}{24}$ (× 3), so $\frac{3}{8} = \frac{9}{24}$.

The order of the fractions from least to greatest is $\frac{1}{6}, \frac{1}{4}, \frac{3}{8}, \frac{2}{3}$.

Exercises

Replace each ● with <, >, or = to make a true sentence.

1. $\frac{5}{12}$ ● $\frac{3}{8}$ >
2. $\frac{6}{8}$ ● $\frac{3}{4}$ =
3. $\frac{2}{7}$ ● $\frac{1}{6}$ >

Order the fractions from least to greatest.

4. $\frac{3}{4}, \frac{3}{8}, \frac{1}{2}, \frac{1}{4}$ **$\frac{1}{4}, \frac{3}{8}, \frac{1}{2}, \frac{3}{4}$**
5. $\frac{2}{3}, \frac{1}{6}, \frac{5}{18}, \frac{7}{9}$ **$\frac{1}{6}, \frac{5}{18}, \frac{2}{3}, \frac{7}{9}$**
6. $\frac{1}{2}, \frac{5}{6}, \frac{5}{8}, \frac{5}{12}$ **$\frac{5}{12}, \frac{1}{2}, \frac{5}{8}, \frac{5}{6}$**

Lesson 4–6

NAME ______________________ DATE ____________ PERIOD ____

4-6 Practice

Comparing and Ordering Fractions

Replace each ● with <, >, or = to make a true statement.

1. $\frac{11}{21}$ ● $\frac{2}{3}$ **<**

2. $\frac{1}{2}$ ● $\frac{9}{18}$ **=**

3. $2\frac{3}{8}$ ● $2\frac{8}{24}$ **>**

4. $6\frac{2}{3}$ ● $6\frac{12}{15}$ **<**

5. $5\frac{3}{4}$ ● $5\frac{8}{12}$ **>**

6. $\frac{2}{3}$ ● $\frac{10}{18}$ **>**

7. $\frac{18}{14}$ ● $1\frac{2}{7}$ **=**

8. $\frac{11}{12}$ ● $2\frac{1}{3}$ **<**

9. $\frac{34}{18}$ ● $1\frac{5}{6}$ **>**

Order the fractions from least to greatest.

10. $\frac{3}{5}, \frac{1}{4}, \frac{1}{2}, \frac{2}{5}$ $\mathbf{\frac{1}{4}, \frac{2}{5}, \frac{1}{2}, \frac{3}{5}}$

11. $\frac{7}{9}, \frac{13}{18}, \frac{5}{6}, \frac{2}{3}$ $\mathbf{\frac{2}{3}, \frac{13}{18}, \frac{7}{9}, \frac{5}{6}}$

12. $6\frac{3}{4}, 6\frac{1}{2}, 6\frac{5}{6}, 6\frac{3}{8}$ $\mathbf{6\frac{3}{8}, 6\frac{1}{2}, 6\frac{3}{4}, 6\frac{5}{6}}$

13. $2\frac{2}{3}, 2\frac{6}{15}, 2\frac{3}{5}, 2\frac{4}{9}$ $\mathbf{2\frac{6}{15}, 2\frac{4}{9}, 2\frac{3}{5}, 2\frac{2}{3}}$

14. MUSIC Ramundus is making a xylophone. So far, he has bars that are $1\frac{3}{4}$ feet, $1\frac{7}{12}$ feet, and $1\frac{2}{3}$ feet long. What is the length of the longest bar? **$1\frac{3}{4}$ ft**

15. DANCE Alana practiced dancing for $\frac{11}{4}$ hours on Monday, $\frac{19}{8}$ hours on Wednesday, and $2\frac{3}{5}$ hours on Friday. On which day did she practice the closest to 2 hours? Explain your reasoning. **Wednesday; First, write each fraction as a mixed number. Second, find the LCD, which is 40. Third, write each mixed number with a denominator of 40. Next, compare the mixed numbers. Since $\frac{19}{8} = 2\frac{3}{8} = 2\frac{15}{40}$ is the smallest, it is closest to 2 hours.**

NAME ______________________ DATE ____________ PERIOD ____

4-7 Study Guide and Intervention

Writing Decimals as Fractions

Decimals like 0.58, 0.12, and 0.08 can be written as fractions.
To write a decimal as a fraction, you can follow these steps.
1. Identify the place value of the last decimal place.
2. Write the decimal as a fraction using the place value as the denominator.

Example 1 **Write 0.5 as a fraction in simplest form.**

$0.5 = \frac{5}{10}$ 0.5 means five tenths.

$= \frac{5^{1}}{10_{2}}$ Simplify. Divide the numerator and denominator by the GCF, 5.

$= \frac{1}{2}$ So, in simplest form, 0.5 is $\frac{1}{2}$.

Example 2 **Write 0.35 as a fraction in simplest form.**

$0.35 = \frac{35}{100}$ 0.35 means 35 hundredths.

$= \frac{35^{7}}{100_{20}}$ Simplify. Divide the numerator and denominator by the GCF, 5.

$= \frac{7}{20}$ So, in simplest form, 0.35 is $\frac{7}{20}$.

Example 3 **Write 4.375 as a mixed number in simplest form.**

$4.375 = 4\frac{375}{1,000}$ 0.375 means 375 thousandths.

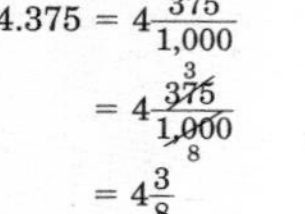

$= 4\frac{375^{3}}{1,000_{8}}$ Simplify. Divide by the GCF, 125.

$= 4\frac{3}{8}$

Exercises

Write each decimal as a fraction or mixed number in simplest form.

1. 0.9 $\mathbf{\frac{9}{10}}$

2. 0.8 $\mathbf{\frac{4}{5}}$

3. 0.27 $\mathbf{\frac{27}{100}}$

4. 0.75 $\mathbf{\frac{3}{4}}$

5. 0.34 $\mathbf{\frac{17}{50}}$

6. 0.125 $\mathbf{\frac{1}{8}}$

7. 0.035 $\mathbf{\frac{7}{200}}$

8. 0.008 $\mathbf{\frac{1}{125}}$

9. 1.4 $\mathbf{1\frac{2}{5}}$

10. 3.6 $\mathbf{3\frac{3}{5}}$

11. 6.28 $\mathbf{6\frac{7}{25}}$

12. 2.65 $\mathbf{2\frac{13}{20}}$

13. 12.05 $\mathbf{12\frac{1}{20}}$

14. 4.004 $\mathbf{4\frac{1}{250}}$

15. 23.205 $\mathbf{23\frac{41}{200}}$

16. 51.724 $\mathbf{51\frac{181}{250}}$

NAME ________________ DATE __________ PERIOD ____

4-7 Practice

Writing Decimals as Fractions

Write each decimal as a fraction in simplest form.

1. 0.5 $\frac{1}{2}$	2. 0.8 $\frac{4}{5}$	3. 0.9 $\frac{9}{10}$
4. 0.75 $\frac{3}{4}$	5. 0.48 $\frac{12}{25}$	6. 0.72 $\frac{18}{25}$
7. 0.625 $\frac{5}{8}$	8. 0.065 $\frac{13}{200}$	9. 0.002 $\frac{1}{500}$

Write each decimal as a mixed number in simplest form.

10. 3.6 $3\frac{3}{5}$	11. 10.4 $10\frac{2}{5}$	12. 2.11 $2\frac{11}{100}$
13. 29.15 $29\frac{3}{20}$	14. 7.202 $7\frac{101}{500}$	15. 23.535 $23\frac{107}{200}$

16. DISTANCE The library is 0.96 mile away from Theo's home. Write this distance as a fraction in simplest form.
$\frac{24}{25}$ mile

17. INSECTS A Japanese beetle has a length between 0.3 and 0.5 inch. Find two lengths that are within the given span. Write them as fractions in simplest form.
Sample answer: $\frac{2}{5}$ and $\frac{9}{20}$

Copyright © Glencoe/McGraw-Hill, a division of The McGraw-Hill Companies, Inc.

NAME ________________ DATE __________ PERIOD ____

4-8 Study Guide and Intervention

Writing Fractions as Decimals

Fractions whose denominators are factors of 10, 100, or 1,000 can be written as decimals using equivalent fractions. Any fraction can also be written as a decimal by dividing the numerator by the denominator.

Example 1 **Write $\frac{3}{5}$ as a decimal.**

Since 5 is a factor of 10, write an equivalent fraction with a denominator of 10.

$$\frac{3}{5} = \frac{6}{10} \quad (\times 2)$$

$$= 0.6$$

Therefore, $\frac{3}{5} = 0.6$.

Example 2 **Write $\frac{3}{8}$ as a decimal.**

Divide.

```
    0.375
 8 )3.000
   -2 4
     60
    -56
      40
     -40
       0
```

Therefore, $\frac{3}{8} = 0.375$.

Exercises

Write each fraction or mixed number as a decimal.

1. $\frac{3}{10}$ **0.3**	2. $\frac{3}{4}$ **0.75**	3. $\frac{1}{4}$ **0.25**	4. $\frac{3}{5}$ **0.6**
5. $\frac{1}{8}$ **0.125**	6. $2\frac{1}{4}$ **2.25**	7. $\frac{6}{20}$ **0.3**	8. $\frac{9}{25}$ **0.36**
9. $1\frac{3}{8}$ **1.375**	10. $1\frac{5}{8}$ **1.625**	11. $3\frac{5}{16}$ **3.3125**	12. $4\frac{9}{20}$ **4.45**

NAME ______________________ DATE ____________ PERIOD _____

4-8 Practice

Writing Fractions as Decimals

Write each fraction or mixed number as a decimal.

1. $\frac{4}{5}$ **0.8**
2. $\frac{7}{20}$ **0.35**
3. $\frac{13}{250}$ **0.052**
4. $\frac{7}{8}$ **0.875**
5. $\frac{3}{16}$ **0.1875**
6. $\frac{11}{32}$ **0.34375**
7. $9\frac{29}{40}$ **9.725**
8. $7\frac{29}{80}$ **7.3625**
9. $4\frac{11}{32}$ **4.34375**

Replace each ● with <, >, or = to make a true sentence.

10. $\frac{1}{4}$ ● 0.2 >
11. $\frac{13}{20}$ ● 0.63 >
12. 0.5 ● $\frac{3}{5}$ <

13. DISTANCE River Road is $11\frac{4}{5}$ miles long. Prairie Road is 14.9 miles long. How much longer is Prairie Road than River Road? **3.1 mi**

14. ANIMALS The table shows lengths of different pond insects. Using decimals, name the insect having the smallest length and the insect having the greatest length.
Smallest: Springtail; greatest: Water Treader

Pond Insects				
Insect	Deer Fly	Spongilla Fly	Springtail	Water Treader
Length (in.)	$\frac{2}{5}$	$\frac{3}{10}$	$\frac{3}{20}$	$\frac{1}{2}$

Source: *Golden Nature Guide to Pond Life*

Copyright © Glencoe/McGraw-Hill, a division of The McGraw-Hill Companies, Inc.

NAME ______________________ DATE ____________ PERIOD _____

4-9 Study Guide and Intervention

Algebra: Ordered Pairs and Functions

Lesson 4–9

A **coordinate plane** is formed when two number lines intersect at their zero points. This intersection is called the **origin**. The horizontal number line is called the ***x*-axis**. The vertical number line is called the ***y*-axis**.

An **ordered pair** is used to name a point on a coordinate plane. The first number in the ordered pair is the ***x*-coordinate**, and the second number is the ***y*-coordinate**.

Example 1 **Write the ordered pair that names point A.**

Start at the origin. Move right along the x-axis until you are under point A. The x-coordinate is 4.

Then move up until you reach point A. The y-coordinate is 1.

So, point A is named by the ordered pair (4, 1).

Example 2 **Graph the point $W(2, 4)$.**

Start at the origin. Move 2 units to the right along the x-axis.

Then move 4 units up to locate the point. Draw a dot and label the point W.

Exercises

Use the coordinate plane at the right to name the ordered pair for each point.

1. J **(1, 1)**
2. K **(4, 2)**
3. L **(5, 4)**
4. M **(2, 4)**

Graph and label each point on the coordinate plane.

5. $S(1, 3)$

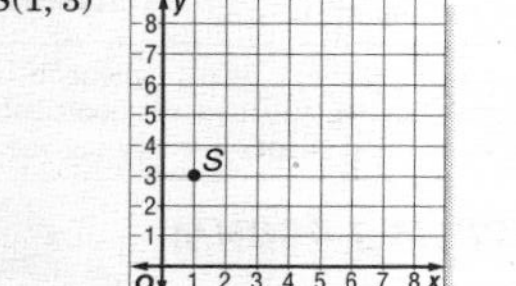

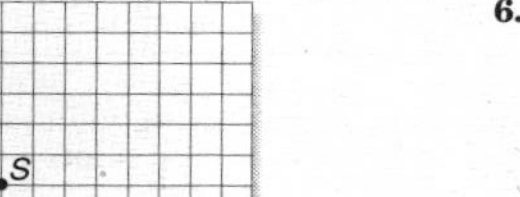

6. $T(4, 0)$

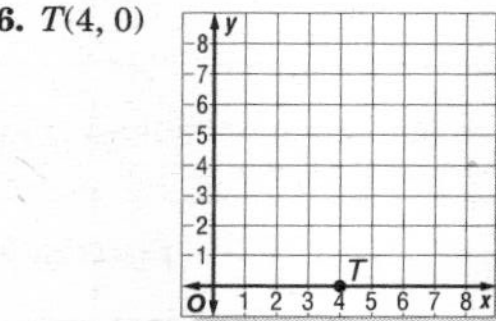

Copyright © Glencoe/McGraw-Hill, a division of The McGraw-Hill Companies, Inc.

NAME ______________ DATE ________ PERIOD ____

4-9 Practice

Algebra: Ordered Pairs and Functions

Use the coordinate plane at the right to name the ordered pair for each point.

1. A **(3, 5)**
2. B **(4, 0)**
3. C **(0, 4)**
4. D **(1, 2)**
5. F **(0, 0)**
6. G **(6, 5)**
7. H **(4.5, 6)**
8. J **(7, 4.5)**
9. K **(2, 6.5)**
10. M **(5.25, 3)**

Graph and label each point on the coordinate plane at the right.

11. N (4, 3)
12. P (0, 4)
13. R $(2, 4\frac{1}{2})$
14. S $(1\frac{3}{4}, 2)$
15. T (2.75, 4)
16. W (3, 1.5)
17. A $(4\frac{1}{4}, 1)$
18. B $(1, 3\frac{3}{4})$

CAR WASH For Exercises 19 and 20, use the following information.

A car wash can wash four cars in one hour. The table shows the total number of cars washed in 0, 1, 2, and 3 hours.

Hours	0	1	2	3
Cars Washed	0	4	8	12

19. List this information as ordered pairs (number of hours, number of cars washed). **(0, 0), (1, 4), (2, 8), (3, 12)**

20. Graph the ordered pairs on the coordinate plane at the right. Then describe the graph. **Sample answer: The points appear to be in a straight line.**

21. **GEOMETRY** A square drawn on a coordinate plane has the following ordered pairs: (2, 2.5), (2, 6.5), and (6, 2.5). What is the ordered pair of the fourth point? **(6, 6.5)**

Copyright © Glencoe/McGraw-Hill, a division of The McGraw-Hill Companies, Inc.

NAME ______________ DATE ________ PERIOD ____

5-1 Study Guide and Intervention

Rounding Fractions and Mixed Numbers

Use these guidelines to round fractions and mixed numbers to the nearest half.

Rounding Fractions and Mixed Numbers		Example
Round up	When the numerator is almost as large as the denominator, round up to the next whole number.	$\frac{7}{8}$ rounds to 1.
Round to $\frac{1}{2}$	When the numerator is about half of the denominator, round the fraction to $\frac{1}{2}$.	$4\frac{3}{7}$ rounds to $4\frac{1}{2}$.
Round down	When the numerator is much smaller than the denominator, round down to the previous whole number.	$\frac{1}{5}$ rounds to 0.

Example 1 **Round $2\frac{3}{8}$ to the nearest half.**

The numerator of $\frac{3}{8}$ is about half of the denominator. So, $2\frac{3}{8}$ rounds to $2\frac{1}{2}$.

$2\frac{3}{8}$

2 $2\frac{1}{2}$ 3

Round up when it is better for a measure to be too large than too small. Round down when it is better for a measure to be too small than too large.

Example 2 **MUSIC You have $4\frac{1}{2}$ minutes left on a CD you are making for a friend. Should you choose a song that is 5 minutes long or a song that is 4 minutes long?**

In order for the entire song to be recorded, you should round down the number of minutes left on the CD and choose the song that is 4 minutes long.

Exercises

Round each number to the nearest half.

1. $\frac{2}{5}$ $\mathbf{\frac{1}{2}}$
2. $\frac{1}{18}$ **0**
3. $\frac{6}{13}$ $\mathbf{\frac{1}{2}}$
4. $6\frac{2}{9}$ **6**
5. $5\frac{4}{7}$ $\mathbf{5\frac{1}{2}}$
6. $8\frac{4}{5}$ **9**
7. $4\frac{1}{7}$ **4**
8. $\frac{2}{7}$ **0**

Tell whether each number should be rounded up or down.

9. the weight of a package you are mailing **up**

10. the length of a rug for your bathroom **down**

NAME ______________ DATE ________ PERIOD ____

5-1 Practice

Rounding Fractions and Mixed Numbers

Round each number to the nearest half.

1. $8\frac{1}{7}$ **8**
2. $\frac{11}{12}$ **1**
3. $4\frac{3}{8}$ **$4\frac{1}{2}$**
4. $2\frac{2}{3}$ **$2\frac{1}{2}$**
5. $6\frac{5}{9}$ **$6\frac{1}{2}$**
6. $2\frac{3}{10}$ **$2\frac{1}{2}$**
7. $\frac{7}{12}$ **$\frac{1}{2}$**
8. $3\frac{5}{6}$ **4**
9. $1\frac{5}{16}$ **$1\frac{1}{2}$**
10. $\frac{11}{16}$ **$\frac{1}{2}$**
11. $7\frac{5}{24}$ **7**
12. $5\frac{25}{32}$ **6**

Find the length of each item to the nearest half inch.

13. **$3\frac{1}{2}$ in.**

14. **$1\frac{1}{2}$ in.**

15. **3 in.**

16. **$2\frac{1}{2}$ in.**

17. **STORAGE** Mike is moving and is packing his books. His largest book is $12\frac{1}{3}$ inches long. He can choose from two boxes. One box is $12\frac{2}{5}$ inches long and the other box is $12\frac{2}{9}$ inches long. Which size box should Mike use? Why? **In order for the book to fit in the box, Mike should use the $12\frac{2}{5}$-inch box since $12\frac{2}{5}$ rounds to $12\frac{1}{2}$ inches and $12\frac{2}{9}$ rounds to 12 inches.**

18. **CRAFTS** Gloria is covering the top of a table with colored paper for displaying her pottery. The top of the table is $6\frac{1}{4}$ feet by $3\frac{5}{8}$ feet. To the nearest half foot, how large must the paper be? **$6\frac{1}{2}$ ft by 4 ft**

NAME ______________ DATE ________ PERIOD ____

5-2 Study Guide and Intervention

Problem-Solving Investigation: Act It Out

When solving problems, one strategy that is helpful is to *act it out.* By using paper and pencil, a model, fraction strips, or any manipulative, you can often act out the problem situation. Then by using your model, you can determine an answer to the situation.

You can use the *act it out* strategy, along with the following four-step problem-solving plan to solve a problem.

1 Understand – Read and get a general understanding of the problem.

2 Plan – Make a plan to solve the problem and estimate the solution.

3 Solve – Use your plan to solve the problem.

4 Check – Check the reasonableness of your solution.

Example 1 **HOBBIES This fall, Patrick is going to play one sport and take music lessons. He is deciding between playing football, cross country, or soccer. He is also deciding between guitar lessons or piano lessons. How many possible combinations are there of a sport and music lesson for Patrick?**

Understand You know the three sports he is choosing from: football, cross country, and soccer. You also know the music lessons he is choosing from: guitar and piano. You need to determine how many possible combinations there are.

Plan Start by choosing one sport, and pairing it with each of the two music lessons. Then do this for each sport.

Solve

football, guitar	cross country, guitar	soccer, guitar
football, piano	cross country, piano	soccer, piano

So, there are 6 possible combinations of a sport and music lessons.

Check You can multiply the number of sport choices by the number of music lesson choices. $3 \times 2 = 6$

Exercise

WOOD WORK Darnell and his dad are making wooden picture frames. Each picture frame uses $1\frac{1}{4}$ feet of wood. If they have a total of $8\frac{1}{2}$ feet of wood, how many picture frames can they make? **6 picture frames**

NAME ________________ DATE ________ PERIOD ____

5-2 Practice

Problem-Solving Investigation: Act It Out

Mixed Problem Solving

Use the act it out strategy to solve Exercises 1 and 2.

1. FITNESS Brad jumps 4 feet forward and then 2 feet backward. How many sets will he have jumped when he reaches 16 feet? **8 sets**

2. SEWING Dion's grandmother is making a quilt using four small squares put together to form one large square block. How many different blocks can she make using one each of red, green, blue, and yellow small squares? Show the possible arrangements. **24 blocks**

Y B / G R

R G / B Y	G R / B Y	B R / G Y	Y R / G B
R G / Y B	G R / Y B	B R / Y G	Y R / B G
R B / G Y	G B / R Y	B G / R Y	Y G / R B
R B / Y G	G B / Y R	B G / Y R	Y G / B R
R Y / G B	G Y / R B	B Y / R G	Y B / R G
R Y / B G	G Y / B R	B Y / G R	

Use any strategy to solve Exercises 3–6. Some strategies are shown below.

Problem-Solving Strategies
• Use make a table.
• Use act it out.

3. ANIMALS Nine birds are sitting on a power line. Three more birds arrive at the same time five of the birds fly off. How many birds are sitting on the power line now? **7 birds**

4. MONEY Ping bought a pair of running shoes for \$7 less than the regular price. If he paid \$29, what was the regular price? **\$36**

5. FOOD Elena bought three bags of dried fruit that weighed $1\frac{7}{10}$ pounds, $3\frac{1}{4}$ pounds, and $2\frac{3}{5}$ pounds. About how much fruit did she buy? **about 8 lb.**

6. PATTERNS What number is missing in the pattern
. . . , 654, 533, □, 291, . . . ? **412**

Copyright © Glencoe/McGraw-Hill, a division of The McGraw-Hill Companies, Inc.

NAME ________________ DATE ________ PERIOD ____

5-3 Study Guide and Intervention

Adding and Subtracting Fractions with Like Denominators

Fractions with the same denominator are called **like fractions**.
- To add like fractions, add the numerators. Use the same denominator in the sum.
- To subtract like fractions, subtract the numerators. Use the same denominator in the difference.

Example 1 **Find the sum of $\frac{3}{5}$ and $\frac{3}{5}$.**

Estimate $\frac{1}{2} + \frac{1}{2} = 1$

$\frac{3}{5} + \frac{3}{5} = \frac{3+3}{5}$ Add the numerators.

$= \frac{6}{5}$ Simplify.

$= 1\frac{1}{5}$ Write the improper fraction as a mixed number.

Compared to the estimate, the answer is reasonable.

Example 2 **Find the difference of $\frac{3}{4}$ and $\frac{1}{4}$.**

Estimate $1 - 0 = 1$

$\frac{3}{4} - \frac{1}{4} = \frac{3-1}{4}$ Subtract the numerators.

$= \frac{2}{4}$ or $\frac{1}{2}$ Simplify.

Compared to the estimate, the answer is reasonable.

Exercises

Add or subtract. Write in simplest form.

1. $\frac{1}{9} + \frac{4}{9}$ **$\frac{5}{9}$**
2. $\frac{9}{11} - \frac{7}{11}$ **$\frac{2}{11}$**
3. $\frac{9}{10} + \frac{5}{10}$ **$1\frac{2}{5}$**
4. $\frac{11}{12} - \frac{9}{12}$ **$\frac{1}{6}$**
5. $\frac{4}{7} + \frac{5}{7}$ **$1\frac{2}{7}$**
6. $\frac{4}{9} - \frac{1}{9}$ **$\frac{1}{3}$**
7. $\frac{7}{8} + \frac{5}{8}$ **$1\frac{1}{2}$**
8. $\frac{6}{7} - \frac{4}{7}$ **$\frac{2}{7}$**
9. $\frac{3}{4} + \frac{3}{4}$ **$1\frac{1}{2}$**
10. $\frac{4}{5} - \frac{1}{5}$ **$\frac{3}{5}$**
11. $\frac{5}{6} + \frac{1}{6}$ **1**
12. $\frac{7}{10} - \frac{1}{10}$ **$\frac{3}{5}$**

Lesson 5–3

NAME ______________________ DATE ____________ PERIOD _____

5-3 Practice

Adding and Subtracting Fractions with Like Denominators

Add or subtract. Write in simplest form.

1. $\frac{3}{7}+\frac{6}{7}$ **$1\frac{2}{7}$**
2. $\frac{2}{5}+\frac{4}{5}$ **$1\frac{1}{5}$**
3. $\frac{3}{4}+\frac{3}{4}$ **$1\frac{1}{2}$**
4. $\frac{2}{3}+\frac{2}{3}$ **$1\frac{1}{3}$**
5. $\frac{5}{8}+\frac{7}{8}$ **$1\frac{1}{2}$**
6. $\frac{11}{16}+\frac{7}{16}$ **$1\frac{1}{8}$**
7. $\frac{7}{8}-\frac{3}{8}$ **$\frac{1}{2}$**
8. $\frac{3}{10}-\frac{1}{10}$ **$\frac{1}{5}$**
9. $\frac{11}{15}-\frac{6}{15}$ **$\frac{1}{3}$**
10. $\frac{7}{9}-\frac{4}{9}$ **$\frac{1}{3}$**
11. $\frac{9}{11}-\frac{6}{11}$ **$\frac{3}{11}$**
12. $\frac{17}{18}-\frac{5}{18}$ **$\frac{2}{3}$**
13. $\frac{5}{7}+\frac{1}{7}+\frac{6}{7}$ **$1\frac{5}{7}$**
14. $\frac{9}{10}+\frac{9}{10}-\frac{3}{10}$ **$1\frac{1}{2}$**
15. $\frac{11}{12}-\frac{7}{12}+\frac{5}{12}$ **$\frac{3}{4}$**

Write an addition or subtraction expression for each model. Then add or subtract.

16. **$\frac{4}{8}+\frac{2}{8}=\frac{6}{8}$ or $\frac{3}{4}$**

17. **$\frac{4}{5}-\frac{2}{5}=\frac{2}{5}$**

18. **WEATHER** In January through March, Death Valley gets a total of about $\frac{21}{25}$ inch of precipitation. In April through June, it gets a total of about $\frac{6}{25}$ inch. How much more precipitation occurs in January through March? **$\frac{3}{5}$ in.**

19. **ANALYZE GRAPHS** What part of the school population likes basketball, baseball, or football? How much larger is this than the part of the student population that prefers soccer? **$\frac{9}{12}$ or $\frac{3}{4}$; $\frac{6}{12}$ or $\frac{1}{2}$**

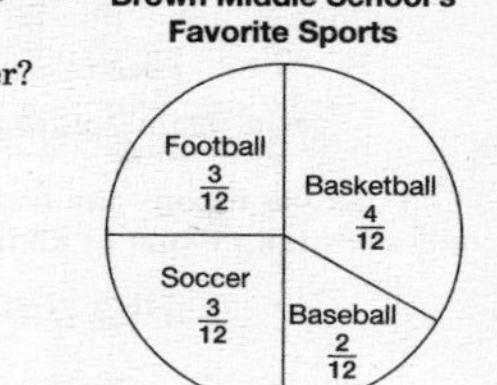

NAME ______________________ DATE ____________ PERIOD _____

5-4 Study Guide and Intervention

Adding and Subtracting Fractions with Unlike Denominators

To find the sum or difference of two fractions with unlike denominators, rename the fractions using the least common denominator (LCD). Then add or subtract and simplify.

Example 1 **Find $\frac{1}{3}+\frac{5}{6}$.**

The LCD of $\frac{1}{3}$ and $\frac{5}{6}$ is 6.

Write the problem. → Rename using the LCD, 6. → Add the fractions.

$$\frac{1}{3} + \frac{5}{6} \rightarrow \frac{1\times2}{3\times2}=\frac{2}{6},\ +\frac{5\times1}{6\times1}=\frac{5}{6} \rightarrow \frac{2}{6}+\frac{5}{6}=\frac{7}{6} \text{ or } 1\frac{1}{6}$$

Example 2 **Find $\frac{2}{3}-\frac{1}{4}$.**

The LCD of $\frac{2}{3}$ and $\frac{1}{4}$ is 12.

Write the problem. → Rename using the LCD, 12. → Subtract the fractions.

$$\frac{2}{3} - \frac{1}{4} \rightarrow \frac{2\times4}{3\times4}=\frac{8}{12},\ -\frac{1\times3}{4\times3}=\frac{3}{12} \rightarrow \frac{8}{12}-\frac{3}{12}=\frac{5}{12}$$

Example 3 **Evaluate $x-y$ if $x=\frac{1}{2}$ and $y=\frac{2}{5}$.**

$x-y=\frac{1}{2}-\frac{2}{5}$ — Replace x with $\frac{1}{2}$ and y with $\frac{2}{5}$.

$=\frac{1\times5}{2\times5}-\frac{2\times2}{5\times2}$ — Rename $\frac{1}{2}$ and $\frac{2}{5}$ using the LCD, 10.

$=\frac{5}{10}-\frac{4}{10}$ — Simplify.

$=\frac{1}{10}$ — Subtract the numerators.

Exercises

Add or subtract. Write in simplest form.

1. $\frac{1}{6}+\frac{1}{2}$ **$\frac{2}{3}$**
2. $\frac{2}{3}-\frac{1}{2}$ **$\frac{1}{6}$**
3. $\frac{1}{4}+\frac{7}{8}$ **$1\frac{1}{8}$**
4. $\frac{9}{10}-\frac{3}{5}$ **$\frac{3}{10}$**
5. $\frac{2}{7}+\frac{1}{2}$ **$\frac{11}{14}$**
6. $\frac{5}{6}-\frac{1}{12}$ **$\frac{3}{4}$**
7. $\frac{7}{10}+\frac{1}{2}$ **$1\frac{1}{5}$**
8. $\frac{4}{9}-\frac{1}{3}$ **$\frac{1}{9}$**

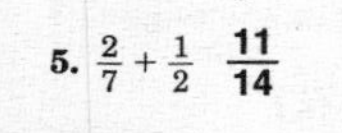

9. Evaluate $x+y$ if $x=\frac{1}{12}$ and $y=\frac{1}{6}$. **$\frac{1}{4}$**
10. Evaluate $a+b$ if $a=\frac{1}{2}$ and $b=\frac{3}{4}$. **$1\frac{1}{4}$**

Lesson 5–4

NAME ________________ DATE ________ PERIOD ____

5-4 Practice

Adding and Subtracting Fractions with Unlike Denominators

Add or subtract. Write in simplest form.

1. $\frac{3}{4} + \frac{1}{8}$ **$\frac{7}{8}$**

2. $\frac{1}{2} + \frac{1}{3}$ **$\frac{5}{6}$**

3. $\frac{11}{12} - \frac{2}{3}$ **$\frac{1}{4}$**

4. $\frac{7}{10} - \frac{1}{2}$ **$\frac{1}{5}$**

5. $\frac{1}{6} + \frac{3}{10}$ **$\frac{7}{15}$**

6. $\frac{3}{4} + \frac{1}{6}$ **$\frac{11}{12}$**

7. $\frac{3}{5} - \frac{1}{4}$ **$\frac{7}{20}$**

8. $\frac{6}{7} - \frac{3}{4}$ **$\frac{3}{28}$**

9. $\frac{6}{7} + \frac{1}{3}$ **$1\frac{4}{21}$**

10. $\frac{9}{10} + \frac{3}{5}$ **$1\frac{1}{2}$**

11. $\frac{11}{12} - \frac{3}{4}$ **$\frac{1}{6}$**

12. $\frac{7}{11} - \frac{1}{2}$ **$\frac{3}{22}$**

ALGEBRA Evaluate each expression.

13. $a + b$ if $a = \frac{3}{5}$ and $b = \frac{5}{8}$ **$1\frac{9}{40}$**

14. $c - d$ if $c = \frac{9}{10}$ and $d = \frac{5}{6}$ **$\frac{1}{15}$**

15. **ANIMALS** A newborn panda at the San Diego zoo grew about $\frac{9}{16}$ pound the first week and about $\frac{5}{8}$ pound the second week. How much more did the panda grow the second week? Justify your answer.

$\frac{1}{16}$ lb; The LCD of $\frac{5}{8}$ and $\frac{9}{16}$ is 16, so $\frac{5}{8} - \frac{9}{16} = \frac{10}{16} - \frac{9}{16}$ or $\frac{1}{16}$ lb.

16. **EXERCISES** Every day Kim does leg muscle exercises for $\frac{3}{7}$ of an hour and foot muscle exercises for $\frac{2}{3}$ of an hour. Which exercises does she spend the most time doing and by how much?

foot muscle exercises; $\frac{5}{21}$ h

Copyright © Glencoe/McGraw-Hill, a division of The McGraw-Hill Companies, Inc.

NAME ________________ DATE ________ PERIOD ____

5-5 Study Guide and Intervention

Adding and Subtracting Mixed Numbers

To add or subtract mixed numbers:
1. Add or subtract the fractions.
2. Then add or subtract the whole numbers.
3. Rename and simplify if necessary.

Example 1 **Find $2\frac{1}{3} + 4\frac{1}{4}$.**

The LCD of $\frac{1}{3}$ and $\frac{1}{4}$ is 12.

Write the problem.

$$2\frac{1}{3} + 4\frac{1}{4}$$

Rename the fractions using the LCD, 12.

$$2\frac{1 \times 4}{3 \times 4} = 2\frac{4}{12} \qquad + 4\frac{1 \times 3}{4 \times 3} = +4\frac{3}{12}$$

Add the fractions. Then add the whole numbers.

$$2\frac{4}{12} + 4\frac{3}{12} = 6\frac{7}{12}$$

So, $2\frac{1}{3} + 4\frac{1}{4} = 6\frac{7}{12}$.

Example 2 **Find $6\frac{1}{2} - 2\frac{1}{3}$.**

The LCD of $\frac{1}{2}$ and $\frac{1}{3}$ is 6.

Write the problem.

$$6\frac{1}{2} - 2\frac{1}{3}$$

Rename the fractions using the LCD, 6.

$$6\frac{1 \times 3}{2 \times 3} = 6\frac{3}{6} \qquad - 2\frac{1 \times 2}{3 \times 2} = -2\frac{2}{6}$$

Subtract the fractions. Then subtract the whole numbers.

$$6\frac{3}{6} - 2\frac{2}{6} = 4\frac{1}{6}$$

So, $6\frac{1}{2} - 2\frac{1}{3} = 4\frac{1}{6}$.

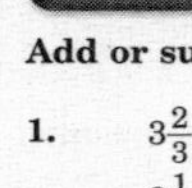

Exercises

Add or subtract. Write in simplest form.

1. $3\frac{2}{3} - 2\frac{1}{3}$ **$1\frac{1}{3}$**

2. $4\frac{3}{4} + 1\frac{3}{4}$ **$6\frac{1}{2}$**

3. $5\frac{1}{2} + 4\frac{1}{3}$ **$9\frac{5}{6}$**

4. $6\frac{7}{8} - 3\frac{1}{2}$ **$3\frac{3}{8}$**

5. $3\frac{2}{3} - 1\frac{1}{2}$ **$2\frac{1}{6}$**

6. $4\frac{2}{3} + 2\frac{1}{4}$ **$6\frac{11}{12}$**

7. $5\frac{1}{3} - 2\frac{1}{4}$ **$3\frac{1}{12}$**

Lesson 5–5

NAME ______________ DATE ________ PERIOD ____

5-5 Practice

Adding and Subtracting Mixed Numbers

Add or subtract. Write in simplest form.

1. $5 - 3\frac{4}{7}$ **$1\frac{3}{7}$**
2. $8 - 2\frac{3}{8}$ **$5\frac{5}{8}$**
3. $7\frac{7}{8} - 3\frac{3}{8}$ **$4\frac{1}{2}$**
4. $8\frac{5}{7} - 4\frac{3}{7}$ **$4\frac{2}{7}$**
5. $9\frac{3}{4} - 2\frac{3}{8}$ **$7\frac{3}{8}$**
6. $6\frac{2}{3} - 1\frac{1}{6}$ **$5\frac{1}{2}$**
7. $8\frac{1}{4} + 2\frac{4}{5}$ **$11\frac{1}{20}$**
8. $10\frac{2}{3} + 8\frac{7}{10}$ **$19\frac{11}{30}$**
9. $5\frac{9}{10} + 3\frac{1}{2}$ **$9\frac{2}{5}$**
10. $3\frac{5}{6} + 10\frac{5}{8}$ **$14\frac{11}{24}$**
11. $8\frac{5}{6} - 3\frac{1}{3}$ **$5\frac{1}{2}$**
12. $9\frac{6}{7} - 2\frac{5}{14}$ **$7\frac{1}{2}$**

ALGEBRA. **Evaluate each expression if $a = 3\frac{5}{6}$, $b = 2\frac{2}{3}$, and $c = 1\frac{1}{4}$.**

13. $a + b$ **$6\frac{1}{2}$**
14. $a + c$ **$5\frac{1}{12}$**
15. $b - c$ **$1\frac{5}{12}$**
16. $a - c$ **$2\frac{7}{12}$**

17. COOKING A punch recipe calls for $4\frac{1}{4}$ cups pineapple juice, $2\frac{2}{3}$ cups orange juice, and $3\frac{1}{2}$ cups cranberry juice. How much juice is needed to make the punch?
$10\frac{5}{12}$ cups

18. ANALYZE TABLES The wingspans of two butterflies and a moth are shown. How much greater is the longest wingspan than the shortest wingspan? Justify your answer.
$\frac{7}{16}$ in.; Sample answer: Rename the mixed numbers using the LCD of 16: $1\frac{3}{8} = 1\frac{6}{16}$, $1\frac{13}{16}$, $1\frac{3}{4} = 1\frac{12}{16}$. The greatest of these is $1\frac{13}{16}$ and the least is $1\frac{6}{16}$. The difference between these wingspans is $1\frac{13}{16} - 1\frac{6}{16}$ or $\frac{7}{16}$ in.

Butterfly and Moth Wingspans	
Butterfly or Moth	**Width (in.)**
American Snout butterfly	$1\frac{3}{8}$
Garden Tiger moth	$1\frac{13}{16}$
Milbert's Tortoiseshell butterfly	$1\frac{3}{4}$

NAME ______________ DATE ________ PERIOD ____

5-6 Study Guide and Intervention

Estimating Products of Fractions

Numbers that are easy to divide mentally are called **compatible numbers**. One way to estimate products involving fractions is to use compatible numbers.

Example 1 **Estimate $\frac{2}{3} \times 8$.**

Estimate $\frac{2}{3} \times 8$. Make it easier by finding $\frac{1}{3} \times 8$ first.

$\frac{1}{3} \times 9 = ?$ Change 8 to 9 since 3 and 9 are compatible numbers.

$\frac{1}{3} \times 9 = 3$ $\frac{1}{3}$ of 9, or 9 divided by 3, is 3.

$\frac{2}{3} \times 9 = 6$ Since $\frac{1}{3}$ of 9 is 3, $\frac{2}{3}$ of 9 is 2×3 or 6.

So, $\frac{2}{3} \times 8$ is about 6.

You can estimate the product of fractions by rounding to 0, $\frac{1}{2}$, or 1.

Example 2 **Estimate $\frac{1}{3} \times \frac{5}{6}$.**

$\frac{1}{3} \times \frac{5}{6} \to \frac{1}{2} \times 1 = \frac{1}{2}$.

So, $\frac{1}{3} \times \frac{5}{6}$ is about $\frac{1}{2}$.

You can estimate the product of mixed numbers by rounding to the next whole number.

Example 3 **Estimate $3\frac{1}{4} \times 5\frac{7}{8}$.**

Since $3\frac{1}{4}$ rounds to 3 and $5\frac{7}{8}$ rounds to 6, $3\frac{1}{4} \times 5\frac{7}{8} \to 3 \times 6 = 18$.

So, $3\frac{1}{4} \times 5\frac{7}{8}$ is about 18.

Exercises **1–12. Sample answers given.**

Estimate each product. Show how you found your estimate.

1. $\frac{1}{5} \times 24$ **$\frac{1}{5} \times 25 = 5$**
2. $\frac{7}{8} \times \frac{3}{5}$ **$1 \times \frac{1}{2} = \frac{1}{2}$**
3. $7\frac{2}{7} \times 5\frac{3}{4}$ **$7 \times 6 = 42$**
4. $\frac{4}{7} \times 20$ **$\frac{4}{7} \times 21 = 12$**
5. $\frac{5}{8} \times 19$ **$\frac{2}{3} \times 18 = 12$**
6. $2\frac{4}{5} \times 6\frac{1}{12}$ **$3 \times 6 = 18$**
7. $\frac{1}{9} \times \frac{1}{12}$ **$0 \times 0 = 0$**
8. $3\frac{7}{8} \times 10\frac{1}{10}$ **$4 \times 10 = 40$**
9. $\frac{11}{12} \times \frac{6}{7}$ **$1 \times 1 = 1$**
10. $\frac{3}{8} \times 17$ **$\frac{3}{8} \times 16 = 6$**
11. $4\frac{7}{8} \times 2\frac{9}{10}$ **$5 \times 3 = 15$**
12. $\frac{11}{12} \times \frac{1}{3}$ **$1 \times \frac{1}{2} = \frac{1}{2}$**

Copyright © Glencoe/McGraw-Hill, a division of The McGraw-Hill Companies, Inc.

NAME ______________________ DATE ____________ PERIOD _____

5-6 Practice

Estimating Products of Fractions

Estimate each product. Sample answers are given.

1. $\frac{1}{3} \times 28$
$\frac{1}{3} \times 27 = 9$

2. $\frac{1}{7} \times 20$
$\frac{1}{7} \times 21 = 3$

3. $\frac{1}{9}$ of 83
$\frac{1}{9}$ of $81 = 9$

4. $\frac{1}{6}$ of 23
$\frac{1}{6}$ of $24 = 4$

5. $\frac{2}{3} \times 76$
$\frac{2}{3} \times 75 = 50$

6. $\frac{3}{8} \times 15$
$\frac{3}{8} \times 16 = 6$

7. $\frac{2}{5}$ of 37
$\frac{2}{5}$ of $35 = 14$

8. $\frac{2}{3}$ of 11
$\frac{2}{3}$ of $12 = 8$

9. $\frac{3}{5} \times \frac{2}{9}$
$\frac{1}{2} \times 0 = 0$

10. $\frac{7}{8} \times \frac{4}{5}$
$1 \times 1 = 1$

11. $\frac{10}{19} \times \frac{3}{8}$
$\frac{1}{2} \times \frac{1}{2} = \frac{1}{4}$

12. $\frac{3}{4} \times \frac{3}{7}$
$1 \times \frac{1}{2} = \frac{1}{2}$

13. $\frac{6}{7} \times \frac{1}{4}$
$1 \times 0 = 0$

14. $2\frac{9}{10} \times 6\frac{1}{4}$
$3 \times 6 = 18$

15. $4\frac{3}{8} \times 7\frac{2}{7}$
$4 \times 7 = 28$

Estimate the area of each rectangle. Sample answers are given.

16.
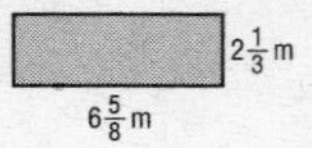

$7 \times 2 = 14$ m^2

17.
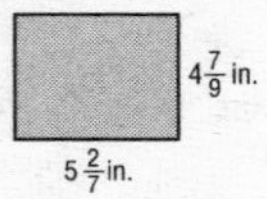

$5 \times 5 = 25$ in^2

SCULPTURE Trevor is using the recipe for a sculpture carving material shown at the right.

Girostone Recipe
1 cup vermiculite
$\frac{1}{4}$ cup cement
$\frac{1}{8}$ cup sand
water to form thick paste

18. About how many cups of cement would he need to make $\frac{4}{9}$ batch of the recipe?
Sample answer: $\frac{1}{2} \times \frac{1}{4} = \frac{1}{8}$ cup cement

19. About how many cups of sand would he need to make $1\frac{6}{7}$ batches of the recipe?
Sample answer: $2 \times \frac{1}{8} = \frac{1}{4}$ cup sand

NAME ______________________ DATE ____________ PERIOD _____

5-7 Study Guide and Intervention

Multiplying Fractions

Type of Product	What To Do	Example
two fractions	Multiply the numerators. Then multiply the denominators.	$\frac{2}{3} \times \frac{4}{5} = \frac{2 \times 4}{3 \times 5} = \frac{8}{15}$
fraction and a whole number	Rename the whole number as an improper fraction. Multiply the numerators. Then multiply the denominators.	$\frac{3}{11} \times 6 = \frac{3}{11} \times \frac{6}{1} = \frac{18}{11} = 1\frac{7}{11}$

Example 1 **Find $\frac{2}{5} \times \frac{3}{4}$.** **Estimate:** $\frac{1}{2} \times 1 = \frac{1}{2}$

$\frac{2}{5} \times \frac{3}{4} = \frac{2 \times 3}{5 \times 4}$ Multiply the numerators. Multiply the denominators.

$= \frac{6}{20}$ or $\frac{3}{10}$ Simplify. Compare to the estimate.

Example 2 **Find $\frac{4}{9} \times 8$.** **Estimate:** $\frac{1}{2} \times 8 = 4$

$\frac{4}{9} \times 8 = \frac{4}{9} \times \frac{8}{1}$ Write 8 as $\frac{8}{1}$.

$= \frac{4 \times 8}{9 \times 1}$ Multiply.

$= \frac{32}{9}$ or $3\frac{5}{9}$ Simplify. Compare to the estimate.

Example 3 **Find $\frac{2}{5} \times \frac{3}{8}$.** **Estimate:** $\frac{1}{2} \times \frac{1}{2} = \frac{1}{4}$

$\frac{2}{5} \times \frac{3}{8} = \frac{\overset{1}{\cancel{2}} \times 3}{5 \times \underset{4}{\cancel{8}}}$ Divide both the numerator and denominator by the common factor, 2.

$= \frac{3}{20}$ Simplify. Compare to the estimate.

Exercises

Multiply.

1. $\frac{1}{4} \times \frac{5}{6}$ **$\frac{5}{24}$**
2. $\frac{3}{7} \times \frac{3}{4}$ **$\frac{9}{28}$**
3. $4 \times \frac{1}{5}$ **$\frac{4}{5}$**
4. $\frac{5}{12} \times 2$ **$\frac{5}{6}$**
5. $\frac{3}{5} \times 10$ **6**
6. $\frac{2}{3} \times \frac{3}{8}$ **$\frac{1}{4}$**
7. $\frac{1}{7} \times \frac{1}{7}$ **$\frac{1}{49}$**
8. $\frac{2}{9} \times \frac{1}{2}$ **$\frac{1}{9}$**

NAME ______________________ DATE __________ PERIOD ____

5-7 Practice
Multiplying Fractions

Multiply.

1. $\frac{1}{4} \times \frac{3}{5}$ **$\frac{3}{20}$**
2. $\frac{7}{8} \times \frac{1}{3}$ **$\frac{7}{24}$**
3. $\frac{1}{2} \times \frac{3}{4}$ **$\frac{3}{8}$**
4. $\frac{2}{3} \times \frac{2}{9}$ **$\frac{4}{27}$**
5. $\frac{1}{3} \times 11$ **$3\frac{2}{3}$**
6. $\frac{1}{2} \times 12$ **6**
7. $\frac{5}{6} \times 21$ **$17\frac{1}{2}$**
8. $\frac{3}{4} \times 10$ **$7\frac{1}{2}$**
9. $\frac{1}{4} \times \frac{4}{5}$ **$\frac{1}{5}$**
10. $\frac{4}{9} \times \frac{3}{8}$ **$\frac{1}{6}$**
11. $\frac{7}{10} \times \frac{4}{21}$ **$\frac{2}{15}$**
12. $\frac{3}{5} \times \frac{5}{12}$ **$\frac{1}{4}$**
13. $\frac{1}{3} \times \frac{1}{4} \times \frac{1}{5}$ **$\frac{1}{60}$**
14. $\frac{3}{4} \times \frac{3}{8} \times \frac{2}{3}$ **$\frac{3}{16}$**
15. $\frac{2}{3} \times \frac{12}{17} \times \frac{1}{4}$ **$\frac{2}{17}$**

ALGEBRA Evaluate each expression if $a = \frac{4}{5}$, $b = \frac{1}{2}$, and $c = \frac{2}{7}$.

16. bc **$\frac{1}{7}$**
17. abc **$\frac{4}{35}$**
18. $ab + \frac{3}{5}$ **1**

19. **PRESIDENTS** By 2005, 42 different men had been President of the United States. Of these men, $\frac{2}{21}$ had no children. How many presidents had no children?
4 presidents

NAME ______________________ DATE __________ PERIOD ____

5-8 Study Guide and Intervention
Multiplying Mixed Numbers

To multiply mixed numbers, write the mixed numbers as improper fractions, and then multiply as with fractions.

Example 1 **Find $2\frac{1}{4} \times 1\frac{2}{3}$.** **Estimate:** 2 × 2 = 4.

$2\frac{1}{4} \times 1\frac{2}{3} = \frac{9}{4} \times \frac{5}{3}$ Write mixed numbers as improper fractions.

$= \frac{\overset{3}{\cancel{9}} \times 5}{4 \times \underset{1}{\cancel{3}}}$ Divide the numerator and denominator by their common factor, 3.

$= \frac{15}{4}$ or $3\frac{3}{4}$ Simplify. Compare to the estimate.

Example 2 **If $a = 1\frac{1}{3}$ and $b = 2\frac{1}{4}$, what is the value of ab?**

$ab = 1\frac{1}{3} \times 2\frac{1}{4}$ Replace a with $1\frac{1}{3}$ and b with $2\frac{1}{4}$.

$= \frac{4}{3} \times \frac{9}{4}$ Write mixed numbers as improper fractions.

$= \frac{\overset{1}{\cancel{4}}}{\underset{1}{\cancel{3}}} \times \frac{\overset{3}{\cancel{9}}}{\underset{1}{\cancel{4}}}$ Divide the numerator and denominator by their common factors, 3 and 4.

$= \frac{3}{1}$ or 3 Simplify.

Exercises

Multiply. Write in simplest form.

1. $\frac{1}{3} \times 1\frac{1}{3}$ **$\frac{4}{9}$**
2. $1\frac{1}{5} \times \frac{3}{4}$ **$\frac{9}{10}$**
3. $3 \times 1\frac{3}{5}$ **$4\frac{4}{5}$**
4. $\frac{2}{3} \times 3\frac{1}{2}$ **$2\frac{1}{3}$**
5. $9 \times 1\frac{1}{6}$ **$10\frac{1}{2}$**
6. $2\frac{4}{9} \times \frac{4}{11}$ **$\frac{8}{9}$**
7. $2\frac{1}{2} \times 1\frac{1}{3}$ **$3\frac{1}{3}$**
8. $1\frac{1}{4} \times \frac{3}{5}$ **$\frac{3}{4}$**
9. $8 \times 1\frac{1}{4}$ **10**
10. $\frac{3}{8} \times 2\frac{1}{2}$ **$\frac{15}{16}$**
11. $4 \times 1\frac{1}{8}$ **$4\frac{1}{2}$**
12. $1\frac{1}{9} \times 3$ **$3\frac{1}{3}$**

13. **ALGEBRA** Evaluate $5x$ if $x = 1\frac{2}{3}$. **$8\frac{1}{3}$**

14. **ALGEBRA** If $t = 2\frac{3}{8}$, what is $4t$? **$9\frac{1}{2}$**

Copyright © Glencoe/McGraw-Hill, a division of The McGraw-Hill Companies, Inc.

NAME ______________ DATE ________ PERIOD ____

5-8 Practice

Multiplying Mixed Numbers

Multiply. Write in simplest form.

1. $\frac{4}{5} \times 3\frac{1}{8}$ **$2\frac{1}{2}$**
2. $\frac{9}{10} \times 3\frac{1}{3}$ **3**
3. $1\frac{3}{5} \times \frac{3}{5}$ **$\frac{24}{25}$**
4. $2\frac{5}{8} \times \frac{2}{3}$ **$1\frac{3}{4}$**
5. $\frac{2}{3} \times 3\frac{1}{4}$ **$2\frac{1}{6}$**
6. $3\frac{3}{4} \times 2\frac{2}{3}$ **10**
7. $1\frac{1}{4} \times 2\frac{2}{3}$ **$3\frac{1}{3}$**
8. $5\frac{1}{3} \times 2\frac{1}{4}$ **12**
9. $2\frac{1}{5} \times 1\frac{1}{4}$ **$2\frac{3}{4}$**
10. $5\frac{1}{2} \times 4\frac{1}{3}$ **$23\frac{5}{6}$**
11. $\frac{2}{9} \times \frac{3}{4} \times 2\frac{1}{4}$ **$\frac{3}{8}$**
12. $1\frac{1}{2} \times 2\frac{1}{6} \times 1\frac{1}{5}$ **$3\frac{9}{10}$**

ALGEBRA Evaluate each expression if $f = \frac{6}{7}$, $g = 1\frac{3}{4}$, and $h = 2\frac{2}{3}$.

13. fg **$1\frac{1}{2}$**
14. $\frac{3}{8}h$ **1**
15. gh **$4\frac{2}{3}$**

16. **LUMBER** A lumber yard has a scrap sheet of plywood that is $23\frac{3}{4}$ inches by $41\frac{1}{5}$ inches. What is the area of the plywood?
$978\frac{1}{2}$ in^2

17. **LANDSCAPING** A planter box in the city plaza measures $3\frac{2}{3}$ feet by $4\frac{1}{8}$ feet by $2\frac{1}{2}$ feet. Find the volume of the planter box.
$37\frac{13}{16}$ ft^3

Copyright © Glencoe/McGraw-Hill, a division of The McGraw-Hill Companies, Inc.

NAME ______________ DATE ________ PERIOD ____

5-9 Study Guide and Intervention

Dividing Fractions

When the product of two numbers is 1, the numbers are called **reciprocals**.

Example 1 **Find the reciprocal of 8.**

Since $8 \times \frac{1}{8} = 1$, the reciprocal of 8 is $\frac{1}{8}$.

Example 2 **Find the reciprocal of $\frac{5}{9}$.**

Since $\frac{5}{9} \times \frac{9}{5} = 1$, the reciprocal of $\frac{5}{9}$ is $\frac{9}{5}$.

You can use reciprocals to divide fractions. To divide by a fraction, multiply by its reciprocal.

Example 3 **Find $\frac{2}{3} \div \frac{4}{5}$.**

$\frac{2}{3} \div \frac{4}{5} = \frac{2}{3} \times \frac{5}{4}$ Multiply by the reciprocal, $\frac{5}{4}$.

$= \frac{\overset{1}{\cancel{2}} \times 5}{3 \times \underset{2}{\cancel{4}}}$ Divide 2 and 4 by the GCF, 2.

$= \frac{5}{6}$ Multiply numerators and denominators.

Exercises

Find the reciprocal of each number.

1. 2 **$\frac{1}{2}$**
2. $\frac{1}{6}$ **6**
3. $\frac{4}{11}$ **$\frac{11}{4}$**
4. $\frac{3}{5}$ **$\frac{5}{3}$**

Divide. Write in simplest form.

5. $\frac{1}{3} \div \frac{2}{5}$ **$\frac{5}{6}$**
6. $\frac{1}{9} \div \frac{1}{2}$ **$\frac{2}{9}$**
7. $\frac{2}{3} \div \frac{1}{4}$ **$2\frac{2}{3}$**
8. $\frac{1}{2} \div \frac{3}{4}$ **$\frac{2}{3}$**
9. $\frac{4}{5} \div 2$ **$\frac{2}{5}$**
10. $\frac{4}{5} \div \frac{1}{10}$ **8**
11. $\frac{5}{12} \div \frac{5}{6}$ **$\frac{1}{2}$**
12. $\frac{9}{10} \div 3$ **$\frac{3}{10}$**
13. $\frac{3}{4} \div \frac{7}{12}$ **$1\frac{2}{7}$**
14. $\frac{9}{10} \div 9$ **$\frac{1}{10}$**
15. $\frac{2}{3} \div \frac{5}{8}$ **$1\frac{1}{15}$**
16. $4 \div \frac{7}{9}$ **$5\frac{1}{7}$**

Lesson 5–9

NAME ______________ DATE ________ PERIOD ____

5-9 Practice
Dividing Fractions

Find the reciprocal of each number.

1. $\frac{2}{7}$ $\mathbf{\frac{7}{2}}$
2. $\frac{1}{9}$ **9**
3. $\frac{3}{8}$ $\mathbf{\frac{8}{3}}$
4. 2 $\mathbf{\frac{1}{2}}$
5. 12 $\mathbf{\frac{1}{12}}$

Divide. Write in simplest form.

6. $\frac{2}{3} \div \frac{1}{6}$ **4**
7. $\frac{1}{2} \div \frac{2}{5}$ $\mathbf{1\frac{1}{4}}$
8. $\frac{2}{3} \div \frac{1}{4}$ $\mathbf{2\frac{2}{3}}$
9. $\frac{3}{4} \div \frac{1}{10}$ $\mathbf{7\frac{1}{2}}$
10. $2 \div \frac{1}{4}$ **8**
11. $8 \div \frac{2}{5}$ **20**
12. $3 \div \frac{4}{5}$ $\mathbf{3\frac{3}{4}}$
13. $2 \div \frac{5}{8}$ $\mathbf{3\frac{1}{5}}$
14. $\frac{3}{7} \div 3$ $\mathbf{\frac{1}{7}}$
15. $\frac{4}{5} \div 10$ $\mathbf{\frac{2}{25}}$
16. $\frac{7}{9} \div 14$ $\mathbf{\frac{1}{18}}$
17. $\frac{5}{7} \div 4$ $\mathbf{\frac{5}{28}}$

ALGEBRA **Find the value of each expression if $h = \frac{3}{8}$, $j = \frac{1}{3}$, and $k = \frac{1}{4}$.**

18. $h \div k$ $\mathbf{1\frac{1}{2}}$
19. $k \div j - h$ $\mathbf{\frac{3}{8}}$
20. $h \div j + k$ $\mathbf{1\frac{3}{8}}$

21. INSECTS An average ant is $\frac{1}{4}$ inch long. An average aphid is $\frac{3}{32}$ inch long. How many times longer is an average ant than an average aphid?
$2\frac{2}{3}$ times longer

NAME ______________ DATE ________ PERIOD ____

5-10 Study Guide and Intervention
Dividing Mixed Numbers

To divide mixed numbers, express each mixed number as an improper fraction. Then divide as with fractions.

Example 1 **Find $2\frac{2}{3} \div 1\frac{1}{5}$.** **Estimate:** $3 \div 1 = 3$

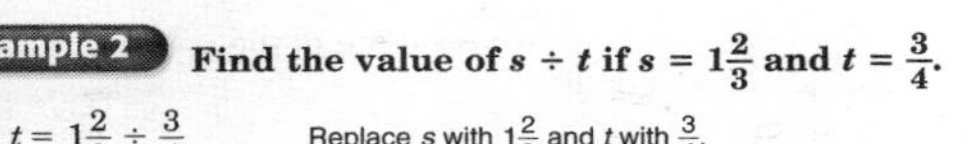

$2\frac{2}{3} \div 1\frac{1}{5} = \frac{8}{3} \div \frac{6}{5}$ Write mixed numbers as improper fractions.

$= \frac{8}{3} \times \frac{5}{6}$ Multiply by the reciprocal, $\frac{5}{6}$.

$= \frac{\overset{4}{\cancel{8}} \times 5}{3 \times \underset{3}{\cancel{6}}}$ Divide 8 and 6 by the GCF, 2.

$= \frac{20}{9}$ or $2\frac{2}{9}$ Simplify. Compare to the estimate.

Example 2 **Find the value of $s \div t$ if $s = 1\frac{2}{3}$ and $t = \frac{3}{4}$.**

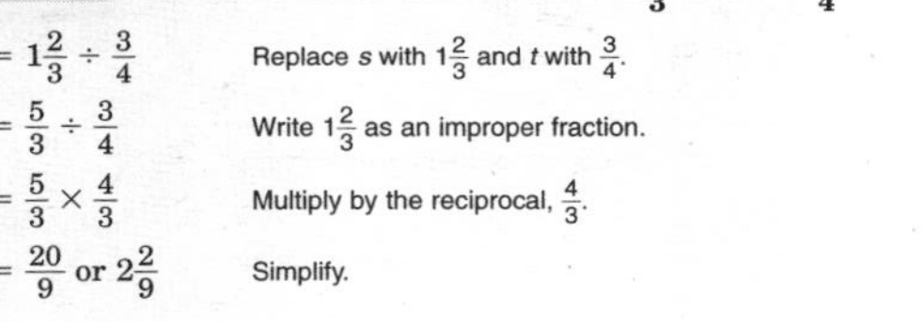

$s \div t = 1\frac{2}{3} \div \frac{3}{4}$ Replace s with $1\frac{2}{3}$ and t with $\frac{3}{4}$.

$= \frac{5}{3} \div \frac{3}{4}$ Write $1\frac{2}{3}$ as an improper fraction.

$= \frac{5}{3} \times \frac{4}{3}$ Multiply by the reciprocal, $\frac{4}{3}$.

$= \frac{20}{9}$ or $2\frac{2}{9}$ Simplify.

Exercises

Divide. Write in simplest form.

1. $2\frac{1}{2} \div \frac{4}{5}$ $\mathbf{3\frac{1}{8}}$
2. $1\frac{2}{3} \div 1\frac{1}{4}$ $\mathbf{1\frac{1}{3}}$
3. $5 \div 1\frac{3}{7}$ $\mathbf{3\frac{1}{2}}$
4. $2\frac{1}{3} \div \frac{7}{9}$ **3**
5. $5\frac{2}{5} \div \frac{9}{10}$ **6**
6. $7\frac{1}{2} \div 1\frac{2}{3}$ $\mathbf{4\frac{1}{2}}$
7. $3\frac{5}{6} \div 2$ $\mathbf{1\frac{11}{12}}$
8. $2\frac{1}{4} \div \frac{2}{7}$ $\mathbf{7\frac{7}{8}}$
9. $9 \div 1\frac{1}{9}$ $\mathbf{8\frac{1}{10}}$
10. $\frac{4}{5} \div 2\frac{6}{7}$ $\mathbf{\frac{7}{25}}$
11. $1\frac{8}{9} \div 5$ $\mathbf{\frac{17}{45}}$
12. $\frac{3}{8} \div 2\frac{1}{4}$ $\mathbf{\frac{1}{6}}$

13. ALGEBRA If $x = 1\frac{1}{4}$ and $y = 3$, what is $x \div y$? $\mathbf{\frac{5}{12}}$

14. ALGEBRA Evaluate $18 \div t$ if $t = \frac{9}{11}$. **22**

Lesson 5–10

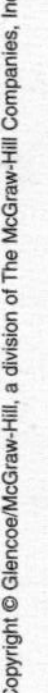

NAME ______________ DATE ________ PERIOD ____

5-10 Practice

Dividing Mixed Numbers

Divide. Write in simplest form.

1. $3\frac{2}{3} \div 2$ **$1\frac{5}{6}$**
2. $10 \div 1\frac{1}{4}$ **8**
3. $4\frac{3}{4} \div \frac{7}{8}$ **$5\frac{3}{7}$**
4. $1\frac{15}{16} \div \frac{7}{8}$ **$2\frac{3}{14}$**
5. $7\frac{1}{2} \div 1\frac{1}{4}$ **6**
6. $3\frac{3}{8} \div 2\frac{1}{4}$ **$1\frac{1}{2}$**
7. $2\frac{1}{10} \div 1\frac{1}{5}$ **$1\frac{3}{4}$**
8. $4\frac{1}{2} \div 2\frac{7}{10}$ **$1\frac{2}{3}$**

ALGEBRA Evaluate the expression if $r = 2\frac{4}{5}$, $s = 1\frac{3}{4}$, and $t = \frac{2}{3}$.

9. $t \div 10$ **$\frac{1}{15}$**
10. $s \div t$ **$2\frac{5}{8}$**
11. $r \div s$ **$1\frac{3}{5}$**
12. $r \div (st)$ **$2\frac{2}{5}$**

13. PIPES How many $\frac{3}{4}$-foot lengths of pipe can be cut from a $6\frac{1}{3}$-foot pipe? **8**

14. TRUCKING A truck driver drove 300 miles in $6\frac{3}{4}$ hours. How many miles per hour did the driver drive?
$44\frac{4}{9}$ mph

Copyright © Glencoe/McGraw-Hill, a division of The McGraw-Hill Companies, Inc.

NAME ______________ DATE ________ PERIOD ____

6-1 Study Guide and Intervention

Ratios and Rates

A **ratio** is a comparison of two numbers by division. A common way to express a ratio is as a fraction in simplest form. Ratios can also be written in other ways. For example, the ratio $\frac{2}{3}$ can be written as 2 to 3, 2 out of 3, or 2:3.

Examples **Refer to the diagram at the right.**

1 Write the ratio in simplest form that compares the number of circles to the number of triangles.

circles → $\frac{4}{5}$ ← triangles   The GCF of 4 and 5 is 1.

So, the ratio of circles to triangles is $\frac{4}{5}$, 4 to 5, or 4:5. For every 4 circles, there are 5 triangles.

2 Write the ratio in simplest form that compares the number of circles to the total number of figures.

circles → $\frac{4}{10} = \frac{2}{5}$ ← total figures (÷ 2)   The GCF of 4 and 10 is 2.

The ratio of circles to the total number of figures is $\frac{2}{5}$, 2 to 5, or 2:5. For every two circles, there are five total figures.

A **rate** is a ratio of two measurements having different kinds of units. When a rate is simplified so that it has a denominator of 1, it is called a **unit rate**.

Example 3 **Write the ratio *20 students to 5 computers* as a unit rate.**

$\frac{20 \text{ students}}{5 \text{ computers}} = \frac{4 \text{ students}}{1 \text{ computer}}$ (÷ 5)   Divide the numerator and the denominator by 5 to get a denominator of 1.

The ratio written as a unit rate is *4 students to 1 computer*.

Exercises

Write each ratio as a fraction in simplest form.

1. 2 guppies out of 6 fish **$\frac{1}{3}$**
2. 12 puppies to 15 kittens **$\frac{4}{5}$**
3. 5 boys out of 10 students **$\frac{1}{2}$**

Write each rate as a unit rate.

4. 6 eggs for 3 people **2 eggs per person**
5. $12 for 4 pounds **$3 per pound**
6. 40 pages in 8 days **5 pages per day**

NAME ______________ DATE ________ PERIOD ____

6-1 Practice
Ratios and Rates

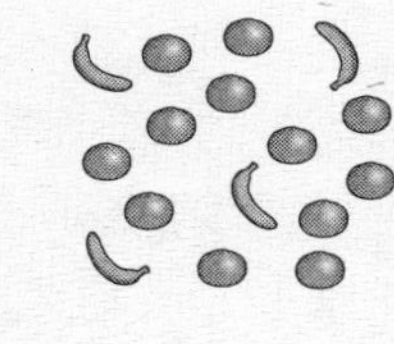

1. **FRUITS** Find the ratio of bananas to oranges in the graphic at the right. Write the ratio as a fraction in simplest form. Then explain its meaning.
   $\frac{1}{3}$; This means for every 1 banana, there are 3 oranges.

2. **MODEL TRAINS** Hiroshi has 4 engines and 18 box cars. Find the ratio of engines to box cars. Write the ratio as a fraction in simplest form. Then explain its meaning.
   $\frac{2}{9}$; This means for every 2 engines, there are 9 box cars.

3. **ZOOS** A petting zoo has 5 lambs, 11 rabbits, 4 goats, and 4 piglets. Find the ratio of goats to the total number of animals. Then explain its meaning.
   $\frac{1}{6}$, 1 to 6, or 1:6; This means 1 out of every 6 animals is a goat.

4. **FOOD** At the potluck, there were 6 pecan pies, 7 lemon pies, 13 cherry pies, and 8 apple pies. Find the ratio of apple pies to the total number of pies. Then explain its meaning.
   $\frac{4}{17}$, 4 to 17, or 4:17; This means 4 out of every 17 pies were apple pies.

Write each rate as a unit rate.

5. 3 inches of snow in 6 hours **$\frac{0.5 \text{ in.}}{1 \text{ h}}$**

6. \$46 for 5 toys **$\frac{\$9.20}{1 \text{ toy}}$**

7. **TRAINS** The Nozomi train in Japan can travel 558 miles in 3 hours. At this rate, how far can the train travel per hour? **186 mi**

ANALYZE TABLES For Exercises 8 and 9, refer to the table showing tide pool animals.

Animals Found in a Tide Pool	
Animal	**Number**
Anemones	11
Limpets	14
Snails	18
Starfish	9

8. Find the ratio of limpets to snails. Then explain its meaning.
   $\frac{7}{9}$, 7 to 9, or 7:9; This means there are 7 limpets for every 9 snails.

9. Find the ratio of snails to the total number of animals. Then explain its meaning.
   $\frac{9}{26}$, 9 to 26, or 9:26; This means that 9 out of 26 animals are snails.

NAME ______________ DATE ________ PERIOD ____

6-2 Study Guide and Intervention
Ratio Tables

A **ratio table** organizes data into columns that are filled with pairs of numbers that have the same ratio, or are equivalent. **Equivalent ratios** express the same relationship between two quantities.

Example 1 BAKING **You need 1 cup of rolled oats to make 24 oatmeal cookies. Use the ratio table at the right to find how many oatmeal cookies you can make with 5 cups of rolled oats.**

Cups of Oats	1				5
Oatmeal Cookies	24				■

Find a pattern and extend it.

Cups of Oats	1	2	3	4	5
Oatmeal Cookies	24	48	72	96	120

(+ 1 between each Cups of Oats entry; + 24 between each Oatmeal Cookies entry)

So, 120 oatmeal cookies can be made with 5 cups of rolled oats.

Multiplying or dividing two related quantities by the same number is called **scaling**. You may sometimes need to *scale back* and then *scale forward* or vice versa to find an equivalent ratio.

Example 2 SHOPPING **A department store has socks on sale for 4 pairs for \$10. Use the ratio table at the right to find the cost of 6 pairs of socks.**

Pairs of Socks		4	6
Cost in Dollars		10	■

There is no whole number by which you can multiply 4 to get 6. Instead, scale back to 2 and then forward to 6.

Pairs of Socks	2	4	6
Cost in Dollars	5	10	15

(÷ 2, × 3)

So, the cost of 6 pairs of socks would be \$15.

Exercises

1. **EXERCISE** Keewan bikes 6 miles in 30 minutes. At this rate, how long would it take him to bike 18 miles? **90 min**

Distance Biked (mi)	6		18
Time (min)	30		■

2. **HOBBIES** Christine is making fleece blankets. 6 yards of fleece will make 2 blankets. How many blankets can she make with 9 yards of fleece? **3 blankets**

Yards of Fleece		6	9
Number of Blankets		2	■

NAME ______________________ DATE ____________ PERIOD _____

6-2 Practice

Ratio Tables

For Exercises 1–3, use the ratio tables given to solve each problem.

1. **CAMPING** To disinfect 1 quart of stream water to make it drinkable, you need to add 2 tablets of iodine. How many tablets do you need to disinfect 4 quarts? **8 tablets**

Number of Tablets	2			■
Number of Quarts	1			4

2. **BOOKS** A book store bought 160 copies of a book from the publisher for $4,000. If the store gives away 2 books, how much money will it lose? **$50**

Number of Copies	160		2
Cost in Dollars	4,000		■

3. **BIRDS** An ostrich can run at a rate of 50 miles in 60 minutes. At this rate, how long would it take an ostrich to run 18 miles? **21.6 min**

Distance Run (mi)	50		18
Time (min)	60		■

4. **DISTANCE** If 10 miles is about 16 kilometers and the distance between two towns is 45 miles, use a ratio table to find the distance between the towns in kilometers. Explain your reasoning. **72 km; If 10 mi is about 16 km, 90 mi is about 144 km. Since 45 mi is half of 90 mi, or 90 ÷ 2, the distance in km must also be half, or 144 ÷ 2.**

5. **SALARY** Luz earns $400 for 40 hours of work. Use a ratio table to determine how much she earns for 6 hours of work. **$60**

Sample answer:

Salary	400	10	60
Hours	40	1	6

RECIPES For Exercises 6–8, use the following information.

A soup that serves 16 people calls for 2 cans of chopped clams, 4 cups of chicken broth, 6 cups of milk, and 4 cups of cubed potatoes.

6. Create a ratio table to represent this situation.

Sample answer:

People Served	16			
Chopped Clams (cans)	2			
Chicken Broth (cups)	4			
Milk (cups)	6			
Cubed Potatoes (cups)	4			

7. How much of each ingredient would you need to make an identical recipe that serves 8 people? 32 people? **1 can clams, 2 cups broth, 3 cups milk, 2 cups potatoes; 4 cans clams, 8 cups broth, 12 cups milk, 8 cups potatoes**

8. How much of each ingredient would you need to make an identical recipe that serves 24 people? Explain your reasoning. **3 cans clams, 6 cups broth, 9 cups milk, 6 cups potatoes; Since 24 is three times 8, multiply the ingredients for 8 servings by three.**

Copyright © Glencoe/McGraw-Hill, a division of The McGraw-Hill Companies, Inc.

NAME ______________________ DATE ____________ PERIOD _____

6-3 Study Guide and Intervention

Proportions

Two quantities are said to be **proportional** if they have a constant ratio. A **proportion** is an equation stating that two ratios are equivalent.

Example 1 **Determine if the quantities in each pair of rates are proportional. Explain your reasoning and express each proportional relationship as a proportion.**

$35 for 7 balls of yarn; $24 for 4 balls of yarn.

Write each ratio as a fraction. Then find its unit rate.

$$\frac{\$35}{7 \text{ balls of yarn}} \overset{\div 7}{=} \frac{\$5}{1 \text{ ball of yarn}} \qquad \frac{\$24}{4 \text{ balls of yarn}} \overset{\div 4}{=} \frac{\$6}{1 \text{ ball of yarn}}$$

Since the ratios do not share the same unit rate, the cost is not proportional to the number of balls of yarn purchased.

Example 2 **Determine if the quantities in each pair of rates are proportional. Explain your reasoning and express each proportional relationship as a proportion.**

8 boys out of 24 students; 4 boys out of 12 students

Write each ratio as a fraction.

$$\frac{8 \text{ boys}}{24 \text{ students}} \overset{\div 2}{=} \frac{4 \text{ boys}}{12 \text{ students}}$$ ← The numerator and the denominator are divided by the same number.

Since the fractions are equivalent, the number of boys is proportional to the number of students.

Exercises

Determine if the quantities in each pair of rates are proportional. Explain your reasoning and express each proportional relationship as a proportion.

1. $12 saved after 2 weeks; $36 saved after 6 weeks
   yes; $\frac{\$12}{2 \text{ weeks}} = \frac{\$36}{6 \text{ weeks}}$

2. $9 for 3 magazines; $20 for 5 magazines **no**

3. 135 miles driven in 3 hours; 225 miles driven in 5 hours
   yes; $\frac{135 \text{ mi}}{3 \text{ h}} = \frac{225 \text{ mi}}{5 \text{ h}}$

4. 24 computers for 30 students; 48 computers for 70 students **no**

NAME ______________________ DATE ____________ PERIOD _____

6-3 Practice
Proportions

Determine if the quantities in each pair of ratios are proportional. Explain your reasoning and express each proportional relationship as a proportion.

1. 18 vocabulary words learned in 2 hours; 27 vocabulary words learned in 3 hours **Yes; since the ratios share the same unit rate, the number of words learned is proportional to the number of hours. $\frac{\text{18 words}}{\text{2 hours}} = \frac{\text{27 words}}{\text{3 hours}}$**

2. \$15 for 5 pairs of socks; \$25 for 10 pairs of socks **No; since the ratios do not share the same unit rate, the price is not proportional to the number of pairs of socks.**

3. 20 out of 45 students attended the concert; 12 out of 25 students attended the concert **No; since the fractions are not equivalent, the number of students who attended the concert is not proportional to the total number of students.**

4. 78 correct answers out of 100 test questions; 39 correct answers out of 50 test questions **Yes; since the fractions are equivalent, the number of correct answers is proportional to the number of questions on the test. $\frac{\text{78 correct answers}}{\text{100 questions}} = \frac{\text{39 correct answers}}{\text{50 questions}}$**

5. 15 minutes to drive 21 miles; 25 minutes to drive 35 miles **Yes; since the fractions are equivalent, the number of miles driven is proportional to the number of minutes. $\frac{\text{21 miles}}{\text{15 minutes}} = \frac{\text{35 miles}}{\text{25 minutes}}$**

ANIMALS **For Exercises 6–8, refer to the table on lengths of some animals with long tails. Determine if each pair of animals has the same body length to tail length proportions. Explain your reasoning.**

Animal Lengths (mm)		
Animal	Head & Body	Tail
Brown Rat	240	180
Hamster	250	50
Lemming	125	25
Opossum	480	360
Prairie Dog	280	40

6. brown rat and opossum **Yes; the ratios for the animals form equivalent fractions.**

7. hamster and lemming **Yes; the ratio for both animals have the same unit rate, $\frac{\text{5 mm head \& body}}{\text{1 mm tail}}$.**

8. opossum and prairie dog **No; the ratio for the opossum is $\frac{4}{3}$, but the ratio for the prairie dog is $\frac{7}{1}$. These are not equivalent fractions.**

NAME ______________________ DATE ____________ PERIOD _____

6-4 Study Guide and Intervention
Algebra: Solving Proportions

To *solve a proportion* means to find the unknown value in the proportion. By examining how the numerators or denominators of the proportion are related, you can perform an operation on one fraction to create an equivalent fraction.

Example 1 **Solve $\frac{3}{4} = \frac{b}{12}$.**

Find a value for b that would make the fractions equivalent.

$\frac{3}{4} = \frac{b}{12}$ (×3) Since 4 × 3 = 12, multiply the numerator and denominator by 3.

$b = 3 \times 3$ or 9

Example 2 NUTRITION **Three servings of broccoli contain 150 calories. How many servings of broccoli contain 250 calories?**

Set up the proportion. Let a represent the number of servings that contain 250 calories.

$\frac{\text{150 calories}}{\text{3 servings}} = \frac{\text{250 calories}}{a\text{ servings}}$

Find the unit rate.

$\frac{\text{150 calories}}{\text{3 servings}} = \frac{\text{50 calories}}{\text{1 serving}}$ (÷3)

Rewrite the proportion using the unit rate and solve using equivalent fractions.

$\frac{\text{50 calories}}{\text{1 serving}} = \frac{\text{250 calories}}{\text{5 servings}}$ (×5)

So, 5 servings of broccoli contain 250 calories.

Exercises

Solve each proportion.

1. $\frac{2}{3} = \frac{8}{n}$ **12**
2. $\frac{2}{4} = \frac{y}{8}$ **4**
3. $\frac{3}{5} = \frac{b}{15}$ **9**
4. $\frac{4}{5} = \frac{16}{w}$ **20**
5. $\frac{d}{16} = \frac{3}{8}$ **6**
6. $\frac{2}{y} = \frac{6}{9}$ **3**
7. MUSIC Jeremy spent \$33 on 3 CDs. At this rate, how much would 5 CDs cost? **\$55**

Lesson 6–4

NAME ______________ DATE ________ PERIOD ____

6-4 Practice

Algebra: Solving Proportions

Solve each proportion.

1. $\frac{2}{3} = \frac{n}{21}$ **14**

2. $\frac{2}{x} = \frac{16}{40}$ **5**

3. $\frac{80}{100} = \frac{b}{5}$ **4**

4. $\frac{m}{2} = \frac{75}{50}$ **3**

5. $\frac{6}{5} = \frac{42}{a}$ **35**

6. $\frac{3}{d} = \frac{21}{56}$ **8**

7. $\frac{4}{3} = \frac{f}{45}$ **60**

8. $\frac{h}{12} = \frac{70}{120}$ **7**

9. $\frac{3}{5} = \frac{27}{p}$ **45**

10. $\frac{26}{21} = \frac{r}{63}$ **78**

11. $\frac{17}{y} = \frac{102}{222}$ **37**

12. $\frac{7}{10} = \frac{c}{25}$ **17.5**

13. MAMMALS A pronghorn antelope can travel 105 miles in 3 hours. If it continued traveling at the same speed, how far could a pronghorn travel in 11 hours? **385 mi**

14. BIKES Out of 32 students in a class, 5 said they ride their bikes to school. Based on these results, predict how many of the 800 students in the school ride their bikes to school. **125 students**

15. MEAT Hamburger sells for 3 pounds for $6. If Alicia buys 10 pounds of hamburger, how much will she pay? **$20**

16. FOOD If 24 extra large cans of soup will serve 96 people, how many cans should Ann buy to serve 28 people? **7 cans**

17. BIRDS The ruby throated hummingbird has a wing beat of about 200 beats per second. About how many wing beats would a hummingbird have in 3 minutes? **about 36,000 wing beats**

Copyright © Glencoe/McGraw-Hill, a division of The McGraw-Hill Companies, Inc.

NAME ______________ DATE ________ PERIOD ____

6-5 Study Guide and Intervention

Problem-Solving Investigation: Look for a Pattern

When solving problems, one strategy that is helpful is to *look for a pattern.* In some problem situations, you can extend and examine a pattern in order to solve the problem.

You can use the *look for a pattern* strategy, along with the following four-step problem solving plan to solve a problem.

1 Understand – Read and get a general understanding of the problem.

2 Plan – Make a plan to solve the problem and estimate the solution.

3 Solve – Use your plan to solve the problem.

4 Check – Check the reasonableness of your solution.

Example MEDICINE **Monisha has the flu. The doctor gave her medicine to take over the next 2 weeks. The first 3 days she is to take 2 pills a day. Then the remaining days she is to take 1 pill. How many pills will Monisha have taken at the end of the 2 weeks?**

Understand You know she is to take the medicine for 2 weeks. You also know she is to take 2 pills the first 3 days and then only 1 pill the remaining days. You need to find the total number of pills.

Plan Start with the first week and look for a pattern.

Solve

Day	1	2	3	4	5	6	7
Number of Pills	2	2	2	1	1	1	1
Total Pills	2	2 + 2 = 4	4 + 2 = 6	6 + 1 = 7	7 + 1 = 8	8 + 1 = 9	9 + 1 = 10

After the first few days the number of pills increases by 1. You can add 7 more pills to the total for the first week, 10 + 7 = 17. So, by the end of the 2 weeks, Monisha will have taken 17 pills to get over the flu.

Check You can extend the table for the next 7 days to check the answer.

Exercise

TIME Buses arrive every 30 minutes at the bus stop. The first bus arrives at 6:20 A.M. Hogan wants to get on the first bus after 8:00 A.M. What time will the bus that Hogan wants to take arrive at the bus stop? **8:20 A.M.**

NAME ______________ DATE ________ PERIOD ____

6-5 Practice

Problem-Solving Investigation: Look for a Pattern

Mixed Problem Solving

Use the look for a pattern strategy to solve Exercises 1 and 2.

1. **MONEY** In 2005, Trey had $7,200 in his saving-for-college account and Juan had $8,000. Each year, Trey will add $400 and Juan will add $200. In what year will they both have the same amount of money in their accounts, not counting interest earned? How much will it be?
   2009; $8,800

2. **BUTTONS** Draw the next two figures in the pattern below.

Use any strategy to solve Exercises 3–7. Some strategies are shown below.

Problem-Solving Strategies
• Guess and check.
• Look for a pattern.
• Act it out.

3. **MUSIC** Last week Jason practiced playing his bassoon for 95 minutes. This week he practiced 5 more minutes than 3 times the number of minutes he practiced last week. How many minutes did Jason practice this week? **290 min**

4. **NUMBER SENSE** Describe the pattern below. Then find the missing number.

   5,000, 2,500, ■, 625, . . .

   Each number is half the previous number; 1,250

5. **TRAVEL** An express bus left the station at 6:30 a.m. and arrived at its destination at 12:00 noon. It traveled a distance of 260 miles and made only one stop for a half hour to drop off and pick up passengers. What was the average speed of the bus?
   52 mph

6. **MONEY** Len bought a $24.99 pair of pants and paid a total of $27.05, including tax. How much was the tax?
   $2.06

7. **PHOTOGRAPHY** Ms. Julian gives photography workshops. She collected $540 in fees for a workshop attended by 12 participants. Ms. Julian spent $15 per person for supplies for them and herself and $6 per person for box lunches for them and herself. How much money did Ms. Julian have left as profit?
   $267

NAME ______________ DATE ________ PERIOD ____

6-6 Study Guide and Intervention

Sequences and Expressions

A **sequence** is a list of numbers in a specific order. Each number in the sequence is called a **term**. An **arithmetic sequence** is a sequence in which each term is found by adding the same number to the previous term.

Example **Use words and symbols to describe the value of each term as a function of its position. Then find the value of the tenth term in the sequence.**

Position	1	2	3	4	n
Value of Term	4	8	12	16	?

Study the relationship between each position and the value of its term.

Notice that the value of each term is 4 times its position number. So the value of the term in position n is $4n$.

To find the value of the tenth term, replace n with 10 in the algebraic expression $4n$. Since $4 \times 10 = 40$, the value of the tenth term in the sequence is 40.

Position		Value of term
1	$\times 4 =$	4
2	$\times 4 =$	8
3	$\times 4 =$	12
4	$\times 4 =$	16
n	$\times 4 =$	$4n$

Exercises

Use words and symbols to describe the value of each term as a function of its position. Then find the value of the tenth term in the sequence.

1.

Position	3	4	5	6	n
Value of Term	1	2	3	4	?

subtract 2; $n - 2$; 8

2.

Position	1	2	3	4	n
Value of Term	5	10	15	20	?

multiply by 5; $5n$; 50

3.

Position	4	5	6	7	n
Value of Term	11	12	13	14	?

add 7; $n + 7$; 17

Lesson 6–6

Copyright © Glencoe/McGraw-Hill, a division of The McGraw-Hill Companies, Inc.

NAME ______________ DATE ________ PERIOD ____

6-6 Practice

Sequences and Expressions

Use words and symbols to describe the value of each term as a function of its position. Then find the value of the sixteenth term in the sequence.

1.

Position	2	3	4	5	n
Value of Term	8	12	16	20	■

Multiply by 4; 4*n*; 64

2.

Position	8	9	10	11	n
Value of Term	14	15	16	17	■

Add 6; $n + 6$; 22

3.

Position	11	12	13	14	n
Value of Term	4	5	6	7	■

Subtract 7; $n - 7$; 9

4.

Position	21	22	23	24	n
Value of Term	12	13	14	15	■

Subtract 9; $n - 9$; 7

Determine how the next term in each sequence can be found. Then find the next two terms in the sequence.

5. 3, 16, 29, 42, … **Add 13; 55, 68**

6. 29, 25, 21, 17, … **Subtract 4; 13, 9**

7. 1.2, 3.5, 5.8, 8.1, … **Add 2.3; 10.4, 12.7**

Find the missing number in each sequence.

8. 5, ■, 10, $12\frac{1}{2}$, … $\mathbf{7\frac{1}{2}}$

9. 11.5, 9.4, ■, 5.2 **7.3**

10. 40, ■, $37\frac{1}{3}$, 36, … $\mathbf{38\frac{2}{3}}$

11. MEASUREMENT There are 52 weeks in 1 year. In the space at the right, make a table and write an algebraic expression relating the number of weeks to the number of years. Then find Hana's age in weeks if she is 11 years old. **572 weeks**

Weeks	Years
52	1
104	2
156	3
52*n*	*n*

12. COMPUTERS There are about 8 bits of digital information in 1 byte. In the space at the right, make a table and write an algebraic expression relating the number of bits to the number of bytes. Then find the number of bits there are in one kilobyte if there are 1,024 bytes in one kilobyte. **8,192 bits**

Bits	Bytes
8	1
16	2
24	3
8*n*	*n*

Copyright © Glencoe/McGraw-Hill, a division of The McGraw-Hill Companies, Inc.

NAME ______________ DATE ________ PERIOD ____

6-7 Study Guide and Intervention

Proportions and Equations

A *function table* displays *input* and *output* values that represent a function. The function displayed in a function table can be represented with an *equation*.

Example 1 **Write an equation to represent the function displayed in the table.**

Input, x	1	2	3	4	5
Output, y	5	10	15	20	25

Examine how the value of each input and output changes.

As each input increases by 1, the output increases by 5. That is, the constant rate of change is 5.

Input, x	1	2	3	4	5
Output, y	5	10	15	20	25

(+1 between inputs; +5 between outputs)

So, the equation that represents the function is $y = 5x$.

Example 2 **Theo earns $6 an hour mowing lawns for his neighbors. Make a table and write an equation for the total amount t Theo earns for mowing h hours. How much will Theo earn for mowing lawns for 11 hours?**

As the number of hours increases by 1, the total earned increases by 6.

Hours, h	Total earned, t
1	$6
2	$12
3	$18
4	$24

(+1 between hours; +6 between totals)

So, the equation is $t = 6h$.

Let $h = 11$ to find how much Theo will earn in 11 hours.

$t = 6h$

$t = 6 \times 11$ or $66

Exercises

Write an equation to represent the function displayed in each table.

1.

Input, x	1	2	3	4	5
Output, y	2	4	6	8	10

$\mathbf{y = 2x}$

2.

Input, x	0	1	2	3	4
Output, y	0	6	12	18	24

$\mathbf{y = 6x}$

MUSIC Use the following information for Exercises 3–5.

A music store sells each used CD for $4.

3. Make a table to show the relationship between the number of c used CDs purchased and the total cost t. **See students' work.**

4. Write an equation to find t, the total cost in dollars for buying c used CDs. $\mathbf{t = 4c}$

5. How much will it cost to buy 5 used CDs? **$20**

Lesson 6–7

NAME ______________ DATE ________ PERIOD ____

6-7 Practice

Proportions and Equations

Write an equation to represent the function displayed in each table.

1.

Input, x	1	2	3	4	5
Output, y	7	14	21	28	35

$y = 7x$

2.

Input, x	0	1	2	3	4
Output, y	0	9	18	27	36

$y = 9x$

3.

Input, x	1	2	3	4	5
Output, y	13	26	39	52	65

$y = 13x$

4.

Input, x	10	20	30	40	50
Output, y	1	2	3	4	5

$y = x \div 10$

5.

Input, x	0	1	2	3	4
Output, y	0	14	28	42	56

$y = 14x$

6.

Input, x	4	8	12	16	20
Output, y	1	2	3	4	5

$y = x \div 4$

7.

Input, x	12	24	36	48	60
Output, y	1	2	3	4	5

$y = x \div 12$

8.

Input, x	6	12	18	24	30
Output, y	1	2	3	4	5

$y = x \div 6$

BATS Use the following information for Exercises 9–11.

A Little Brown Myotis bat can eat 500 mosquitoes in an hour.

9. In the space at the right, make a table to show the the relationship between the number of hours h and the number of mosquitoes eaten m.

Number of Hours, h	Number of Mosquitoes Eaten, m
1	500
2	1,000
3	1,500
4	2,000

10. Write an equation to find m, the number of mosquitoes a bat eats in h hours. **$m = 500h$**

11. How many mosquitoes can a Little Brown Myotis bat eat in 7 hours? **3,500 mosquitoes**

12. RECREATION A community center charges the amount shown in the table for using specialized exercise equipment. Write a sentence and an equation to describe the data. How much will it cost to use the exercise equipment for 6 months?
It costs $20 per month to use the specialized exercise equipment; $c = \$20m$; $120

Number of Months, m	Cost, c
1	$20
2	$40
3	$60

NAME ______________ DATE ________ PERIOD ____

7-1 Study Guide and Intervention

Percents and Fractions

To write a percent as a fraction, write it as a fraction with a denominator of 100. Then simplify.

Example 1 **Write 15% as a fraction in simplest form.**

15% means *15 out of 100*.

$15\% = \frac{15}{100}$ Definition of percent.

$= \frac{\cancel{15}^{3}}{\cancel{100}_{20}}$ or $\frac{3}{20}$ Simplify. Divide the numerator and denominator by the GCF, 5.

Example 2 **Write 180% as a fraction in simplest form.**

180% means *180 out of 100*.

$180\% = \frac{180}{100}$ Definition of percent.

$= \frac{\cancel{180}^{9}}{\cancel{100}_{5}}$ or $1\frac{4}{5}$ Simplify.

You can also write fractions as percents. To write a fraction as a percent, write a proportion and solve.

Example 3 **Write $\frac{2}{5}$ as a percent.**

$\frac{2}{5} = \frac{n}{100}$ Set up a proportion.

$\frac{2}{5} = \frac{40}{100}$ (× 20) Since 5 × 20 = 100, multiply 2 by 20 to find n.

So, $\frac{2}{5} = \frac{40}{100}$ or 40%

Example 4 **Write $\frac{7}{4}$ as a percent.**

$\frac{7}{4} = \frac{n}{100}$ Set up a proportion.

$\frac{7}{4} = \frac{175}{100}$ (× 25) Since 4 × 25 = 100, multiply 7 by 25 to find n.

So, $\frac{7}{4} = \frac{175}{100}$ or 175%.

Exercises

Write each percent as a fraction in simplest form.

1. 20% **$\frac{1}{5}$**
2. 35% **$\frac{7}{20}$**
3. 70% **$\frac{7}{10}$**
4. 60% **$\frac{3}{5}$**
5. 150% **$1\frac{1}{2}$**
6. 225% **$2\frac{1}{4}$**

Write each fraction as a percent.

7. $\frac{3}{10}$ **30%**
8. $\frac{2}{100}$ **2%**
9. $\frac{8}{5}$ **160%**
10. $\frac{1}{5}$ **20%**
11. $\frac{12}{5}$ **240%**
12. $\frac{13}{100}$ **13%**

Copyright © Glencoe/McGraw-Hill, a division of The McGraw-Hill Companies, Inc.

NAME ______________________ DATE __________ PERIOD ____

7-1 Practice
Percents and Fractions

Write each percent as a fraction in simplest form.

1. 60% $\frac{3}{5}$
2. 18% $\frac{9}{50}$
3. 4% $\frac{1}{25}$
4. 35% $\frac{7}{20}$
5. 10% $\frac{1}{10}$
6. 1% $\frac{1}{100}$
7. 175% $1\frac{3}{4}$
8. 258% $2\frac{29}{50}$
9. 325% $3\frac{1}{4}$
10. ENERGY The United States uses 24% of the world's supply of energy. What fraction of the world's energy is this? $\frac{6}{25}$

Write each fraction as a percent.

11. $\frac{6}{10}$ **60%**
12. $\frac{2}{5}$ **40%**
13. $\frac{9}{5}$ **180%**
14. $\frac{6}{4}$ **150%**
15. $\frac{7}{100}$ **7%**
16. $\frac{4}{100}$ **4%**

Write a percent to represent the shaded portion of each model.

17. **25%**
18. **72%**
19. **60%**
20.
21. **275%**
22. **148%**

23. ANALYZE TABLES The table shows what fraction of a vegetable garden contains each kind of vegetable. What percent of the garden contains other kinds of vegetables? **5%**

Plant	Beans	Corn	Tomatoes	Other
Fraction	$\frac{1}{5}$	$\frac{1}{2}$	$\frac{1}{4}$	■

NAME ______________________ DATE __________ PERIOD ____

7-2 Study Guide and Intervention
Circle Graphs

A **circle graph** is used to compare data that are parts of a whole. The pie-shaped sections show the groups. The percents add up to 100%.

Example 1 **The table shows the time Mike spends studying each subject during homework time. Sketch a circle graph of the data.**

Mike's Homework	
Subject	**Percent**
math	50%
social studies	15%
reading	25%
science	10%

- Write each percent as a fraction.

$50\% = \frac{50}{100}$ or $\frac{1}{2}$ $15\% = \frac{15}{100}$ or $\frac{3}{20}$

$25\% = \frac{25}{100}$ or $\frac{1}{4}$ $10\% = \frac{10}{100}$ or $\frac{1}{10}$

- Use a compass to draw a circle.
- Since $50\% = \frac{1}{2}$, shade and label $\frac{1}{2}$ of the circle for math.

Since $25\% = \frac{1}{4}$, shade and label $\frac{1}{4}$ of the circle for reading.

Split the remaining section so that one section is slightly larger than the other. Label the slightly larger section social studies for 15%, and the smaller one science for 10%.

Mike's Homework

Science 10%
Social Studies 15%
Math 50%
Reading 25%

Example 2 **In the circle graph to the right, how does the amount of time Mike spends studying math compare to the amount of time he studies reading?**

The section representing math is twice the size of the section representing reading. So, Mike spends twice as much time studying math as reading.

Exercises

SURVEYS **Use the table that shows the results of a favorite colors survey.**

Favorite Color	
Color	**Percent**
blue	33%
red	25%
green	25%
purple	10%
yellow	7%

1. Sketch a circle graph of the data.

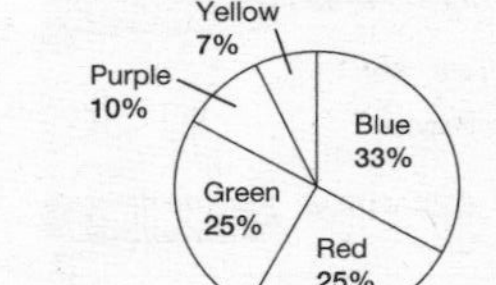

2. In your circle graph, which two sections represent the responses by the same amount of students? **red and green**
3. In your circle graph, how does the number of students that chose blue compare to the number of students that chose purple? **About three times as many students chose blue as purple.**

NAME ______________________ DATE ____________ PERIOD _____

7-2 Practice

Circle Graphs

1. **MUSIC** The table shows the percent of students in the school orchestra who played in each section. Sketch a circle graph to display the data.

Players in the Orchestra	
Section	**Percent of Players**
Brass	25%
Percussion	5%
Strings	45%
Woodwinds	25%

Players in the Orchestra

BLOOD For Exercises 2–5, use the graph that shows the percent of Americans having different blood types.

Blood Types in the U.S. Population

2. Which blood type is the least common among people of the United States? **Type AB**

3. About how much of the total U.S. population has Type O blood? **about half or 50%**

4. Which two sections of the graph represent about the same percent of people? Explain your reasoning. **Type O and Type A; Sample answer: The section for Type A looks to be about the same size as the section for Type O and 40% is close to 45%.**

5. How does Type A compare to Type AB in number of people having these two types? **Ten times as many people have Type A as have Type AB.**

6. **FOOD** A group of 100 students were asked about their favorite sandwiches. The chart shows their responses. In the space at the right, sketch a circle graph to compare the students' responses. What percent of the students chose luncheon meat or tuna as their favorite sandwich? **62%**

Favorite Sandwich	
Response	**Number of Students**
Egg Salad	12
Luncheon Meat	51
Nut Butter and Jelly	24
Tuna	11
Other	2

Favorite Sandwich

NAME ______________________ DATE ____________ PERIOD _____

7-3 Study Guide and Intervention

Percents and Decimals

To write a percent as a decimal, first rewrite the percent as a fraction with a denominator of 100. Then write the fraction as a decimal.

Example 1 **Write 23% as a decimal.**

$23\% = \frac{23}{100}$ Rewrite the percent as a fraction with a denominator of 100.

$= 0.23$ Write the fraction as a decimal.

Example 2 **Write 127% as a decimal.**

$127\% = \frac{127}{100}$ Rewrite the percent as a fraction with a denominator of 100.

$= 1.27$ Write the fraction as a decimal.

To write a decimal as a percent, first write the decimal as a fraction with a denominator of 100. Then write the fraction as a percent.

Example 3 **Write 0.44 as a percent.**

$0.44 = \frac{44}{100}$ Write the decimal as a fraction.

$= 44\%$ Write the fraction as a percent.

Example 4 **Write 2.65 as a percent.**

$2.65 = 2\frac{65}{100}$ Write *2 and 65 hundredths* as a mixed number.

$= \frac{265}{100}$ Write the mixed number as an improper fraction.

$= 265\%$ Write the fraction as a percent.

Exercises

Write each percent as a decimal.

1. 39% **0.39**
2. 57% **0.57**
3. 82% **0.82**
4. 135% **1.35**
5. 112% **1.12**
6. 0.4% **0.004**

Write each decimal as a percent.

7. 0.86 **86%**
8. 0.36 **36%**
9. 0.65 **65%**
10. 0.2 **20%**
11. 1.48 **148%**
12. 2.17 **217%**

Lesson 7–3

NAME ______________ DATE ________ PERIOD ____

7-3 Practice

Percents and Decimals

Express each percent as a decimal.

1. 29% **0.29**
2. 63% **0.63**
3. 4% **0.04**
4. 9% **0.09**
5. 148% **1.48**
6. 106% **1.06**
7. 10% **0.1**
8. 32% **0.32**
9. **ENERGY** The United States gets about 39% of its energy from petroleum. Write 39% as a decimal. **0.39**
10. **SCIENCE** About 8% of the earth's crust is made up of aluminum. Write 8% as a decimal. **0.08**

Express each decimal as a percent.

11. 0.45 **45%**
12. 0.12 **12%**
13. 1.68 **168%**
14. 2.73 **273%**
15. 0.2 **20%**
16. 0.7 **70%**
17. 0.95 **95%**
18. 0.46 **46%**
19. **POPULATION** In 2000, the number of people 65 years and older in Arizona was 0.13 of the total population. Write 0.13 as a percent. **13%**
20. **GEOGRAPHY** About 0.41 of Hawaii's total area is water. What percent is equivalent to 0.41? **41%**

Replace each ● with <, >, or = to make a true sentence.

21. 26% ● 0.3 **<**
22. 0.9 ● 9% **>**
23. 4.7 ● 47% **>**
24. **ANALYZE TABLES** A batting average is the ratio of hits to at bats. Batting averages are expressed as a decimal rounded to the nearest thousandth. Show two different ways of finding how much greater Derek Jeter's batting average was than Jason Giambi's batting average. Express as a percent.

New York Yankees, 2005 Batting Statistics	
Player	**Batting Average**
Jason Giambi	0.286
Derek Jeter	0.307
Hideki Matsui	0.297
Jorge Posada	0.257

Source: ESPN

Method 1: 0.307 − 0.286 = 0.021 or 2.1%. Method 2: Since 0.307 = 30.7% and 0.286 = 28.6%, then 30.7% − 28.6% = 2.1%.

NAME ______________ DATE ________ PERIOD ____

7-4 Study Guide and Intervention

Probability

When tossing a coin, there are two possible **outcomes**, heads and tails. Suppose you are looking for heads. If the coin lands on heads, this would be a favorable outcome or **simple event**. The chance that some event will happen (in this case, getting heads) is called **probability**. You can use a ratio to find probability. The probability of an event is a number from 0 to 1, including 0 and 1. The closer a probability is to 1, the more likely it is to happen.

impossible to occur — equally likely to occur — certain to occur

0 (0%), $\frac{1}{4}$ or 0.25 (25%), $\frac{1}{2}$ or 0.50 (50%), $\frac{3}{4}$ or 0.75 (75%), 1 (100%)

Example 1 **There are four equally likely outcomes on the spinner. Find the probability of spinning green or blue.**

red, blue, green, yellow

$$P(\text{green or blue}) = \frac{\text{number of favorable outcomes}}{\text{number of possible outcomes}} = \frac{2}{4} \text{ or } \frac{1}{2}$$

The probability of landing on green or blue is $\frac{1}{2}$, 0.50, or 50%.

Complementary events are two events in which either one or the other must happen, but both cannot happen at the same time. The sum of the probabilities of complementary events is 1.

Example 2 **There is a 25% chance that Sam will win a prize. What is the probability that Sam will not win a prize?**

$P(\text{win}) + P(\text{not win}) = 1$

$0.25 + P(\text{not win}) = 1$ Replace P(win) with 0.25.

$-0.25 \quad = -0.25$ Subtract 0.25 from each side.

$P(\text{not win}) = 0.75$

So, the probability that Sam won't win a prize is 0.75, 75%, or $\frac{3}{4}$.

Exercises

1. There is a 90% chance that it will rain. What is the probability that it will not rain?
$\frac{1}{10}$, 0.10, or 10%

One pen is chosen without looking from a bag that has 3 blue pens, 6 red, and 3 green. Find the probability of each event. Write each answer as a fraction, a decimal, and a percent.

2. P(green) **$\frac{1}{4}$, 0.25, or 25%**
3. P(blue or red) **$\frac{3}{4}$, 0.75, or 75%**
4. P(yellow) **0, 0.0, or 0%**

Lesson 7–4

NAME ________________ DATE ________ PERIOD ____

7-4 Practice
Probability

The spinner shown is spun once. Find each probability. Write each answer as a fraction, a decimal, and a percent.

1. P(C) **$\frac{1}{6}$, 0.1$\overline{6}$, 16%**
2. P(G) **0, 0.0, 0%**
3. P(M or P) **$\frac{1}{3}$, 0.$\overline{3}$, 33%**
4. P(B, E, or A) **$\frac{1}{2}$, 0.5, 50%**
5. P(not vowel) **$\frac{2}{3}$, 0.$\overline{6}$, 66%**
6. P(not M) **$\frac{5}{6}$, 0.8$\overline{3}$, 83%**

Eight cards are marked 3, 4, 5, 6, 7, 8, 9, and 10 such that each card has exactly one of these numbers. A card is picked without looking. Find each probability. Write each answer as a fraction, a decimal, and a percent.

7. P(9) **$\frac{1}{8}$, 0.125, 12.5%**
8. P(5 or 7) **$\frac{1}{4}$, 0.25, 25%**
9. P(greater than 5) **$\frac{5}{8}$, 0.625, 62.5%**
10. P(less than 3) **0, 0.0, 0%**
11. P(odd) **$\frac{1}{2}$, 0.5, 50%**
12. P(4, 7, or 8) **$\frac{3}{8}$, 0.375, 37.5%**
13. P(not 6) **$\frac{7}{8}$, 0.875, 87.5%**
14. P(not 5 and not 10) **$\frac{3}{4}$, 0.75, 75%**

The spinner is spun once. Write a sentence stating how likely it is for each event to happen. Justify your answer.

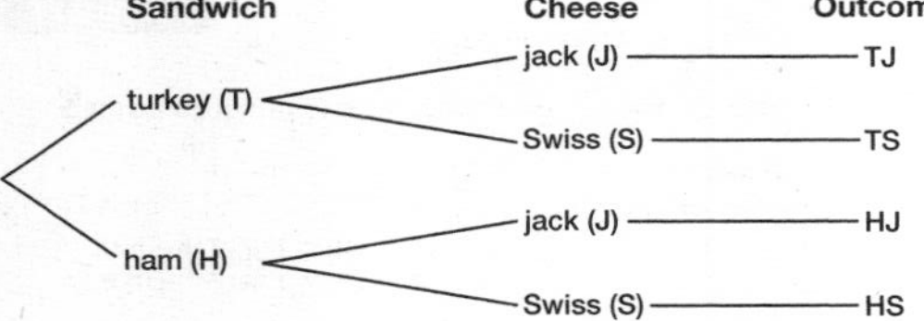

15. fish **Spinning a fish is not likely since the probability is $\frac{1}{10}$ or 10%.**
16. cat **The chances of spinning a cat or not spinning a cat are equally likely since the probability of spinning a cat is 50%.**
17. bird, cat, or fish **Spinning a bird, cat, or fish is very likely since the probability is 80%**
18. **PLANTS** Of the water lilies in the pond, 43% are yellow. The others are white. A frog randomly jumps onto a lily. Describe the complement of the frog landing on a yellow lily and find its probability.
The complement of the frog landing on a yellow lily is landing on a white lily. The probability of the complement is $\frac{57}{100}$, 0.57, or 57%.

Copyright © Glencoe/McGraw-Hill, a division of The McGraw-Hill Companies, Inc.

NAME ________________ DATE ________ PERIOD ____

7-5 Study Guide and Intervention
Constructing Sample Spaces

The **Fundamental Counting Principle** is another way to find the number of possible outcomes. This principle states that if there are m outcomes for a first choice and n outcomes for a second choice, then the total number of possible outcomes can be found by finding $m \times n$.

Example 1 **How many sandwiches are possible from a choice of turkey or ham with jack cheese or Swiss cheese?**

Draw a tree diagram.

Sandwich	Cheese	Outcome
turkey (T)	jack (J)	TJ
	Swiss (S)	TS
ham (H)	jack (J)	HJ
	Swiss (S)	HS

There are four possible sandwiches.

Example 2 **Using the Fundamental Counting Principle, how many sandwiches are possible from a choice of roast beef, turkey, or ham, with a choice of jack, cheddar, American, or Swiss cheese? Find the probability of chossing a ham with jack cheese sandwich.**

There are twelve possible sandwiches. To determine the number of possible outcomes, multiply the number of first choices, 3, by the number of second choices, 4, to determine that there are 12 possible outcomes. So, P(ham, jack) = $\frac{1}{12}$, or 0.083, or 8.3%.

Exercises

First use the Fundamental Counting Principle to determine the number of possible outcomes. Then, check your result and find the sample space by drawing a tree diagram. Finally, find the probability.

1. buy a can or a bottle of grape or orange soda
Find P(bottle, grape).
See students' work.
4 possible outcomes;
P(b, g) = $\frac{1}{4}$, 0.25, or 25%

2. toss a coin and roll a number cube
Find P(4, tails).
See students' work.
12 possible outcomes;
P(4, tails) = $\frac{1}{12}$, 0.08$\overline{3}$, or 8.$\overline{3}$%

3. wear jeans or shorts with a blue, white, black, or red T-shirt. Find P(jeans, white T-shirt).
See students' work. 8 possible outcomes; P(j, w) = $\frac{1}{8}$, 0.125, or 12.5%

Lesson 7–5

Copyright © Glencoe/McGraw-Hill, a division of The McGraw-Hill Companies, Inc.

NAME _______________ DATE _________ PERIOD ____

7-5 Practice

Constructing Sample Spaces

1. SCULPTURE Diego is lining up driftwood sculptures in front of his woodshop. He has a dolphin, gull, seal, and a whale. In how many different ways can he line up his sculptures? Make an organized list to show the sample space.
24 ways; Let D = dolphin, G = gull, S = seal, and W = whale.

DGSW	GDSW	SDGW	WDGS
DGWS	GDWS	SDWG	WDSG
DSGW	GSDW	SGDW	WGDS
DSWG	GSWD	SGWD	WGSD
DWGS	GWDS	SWDG	WSDG
DWSG	GWSD	SWGD	WSGD

2. CYCLES A cycle shop sells bicycles, tricycles, and unicycles in a single color of red, blue, green, or white. Draw a tree diagram to find how many different combinations of cycle types and colors are possible.
12 combinations

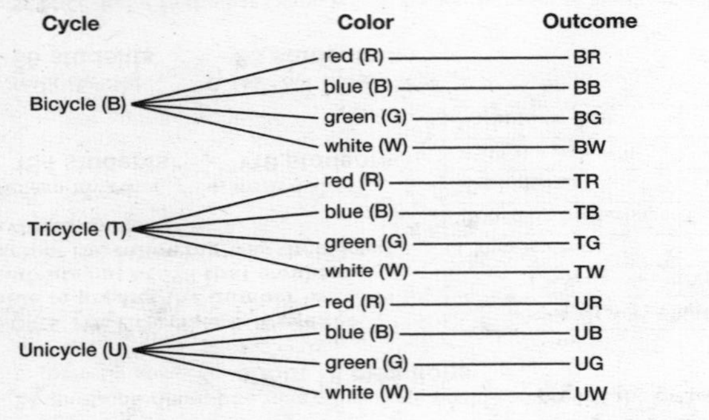

For Exercises 3–5, a coin is tossed, and the spinners shown are spun.

Spinner 1: B, C, D — Spinner 2: A, G, E

3. Using the Fundamental Counting Principle, how many outcomes are possible? **18**

4. What is P(heads, C, G)? **$\frac{1}{18}$, $0.0\overline{5}$, or 5.5%**

5. Find P(tails, D, a vowel). **$\frac{1}{9}$, $0.\overline{1}$, or 11.1%**

Copyright © Glencoe/McGraw-Hill, a division of The McGraw-Hill Companies, Inc.

NAME _______________ DATE _________ PERIOD ____

7-6 Study Guide and Intervention

Making Predictions

A **survey** is a method of collecting information. The group being surveyed is the **population**. To save time and money, part of the group, called a **sample**, is surveyed.

A good sample is:

- selected at **random**, or without preference,
- representative of the population, and
- large enough to provide accurate data.

Examples **Every sixth student who walked into the school was asked how he or she got to school.**

School Transportation	
Method	**Students**
walk	10
ride bike	10
ride bus	15
get ride	5

1 What is the probability that a student at the school rode a bike to school?

$P(\text{ride bike}) = \dfrac{\text{number of students that rode a bike}}{\text{number of students surveyed}}$

$= \dfrac{10}{40}$ or $\dfrac{1}{4}$

So, $P(\text{ride bike}) = \frac{1}{4}$, 0.25, or 25%.

2 There are 360 students at the school. Predict how many bike to school.

Write a proportion. Let s = number of students who will ride a bike.

$\dfrac{10}{40} = \dfrac{s}{360}$

You can solve the proportion to find that of the 360 students, 90 will ride a bike to school.

Exercises

SCHOOL Use the following information and the table shown. Every tenth student entering the school was asked which one of the four subjects was his or her favorite.

Favorite Subject	
Subject	**Students**
Language Arts	10
Math	10
Science	15
Social Studies	5

1. Find the probability that any student attending school prefers science.
$\frac{3}{8}$, 0.375, or 37.5%

2. There are 400 students at the school. Predict how many students would prefer science. **150 students**

Lesson 7–6

NAME ______________ DATE ________ PERIOD ____

7-6 Practice

Making Predictions

QUIZ SHOW For Exercises 1 and 2, use the following information.

On a quiz show, a contestant correctly answered 9 of the last 12 questions.

1. Find the probability of the contestant correctly answering the next question.
   $\frac{3}{4}$, 0.75, or 75%

2. Suppose the contestant continues on the show and tries to correctly answer 24 questions. About how many questions would you predict the contestant to correctly answer? **about 18 questions**

CHORES For Exercises 3–6, use the table to predict the number of students out of 528 that would say each of the following was their least favorite chore.

Least Favorite Chore	
Chore	**Number of Students**
Clean my room	7
Take out the garbage	4
Wash dishes	5
Walk the dog	3
Vacuum or dust	5

3. clean my room **154 students**
4. wash dishes **110 students**
5. walk the dog **66 students**
6. take out the garbage **88 students**

7. **SCIENCE** Refer to the bar graph below. A science museum manager asked some of the visitors at random during a typical day which exhibit they preferred. If there are 630 visitors on a typical day, predict the number of visitors who prefer the magnets exhibit. Compare this to the number of visitors who prefer the weather exhibit.

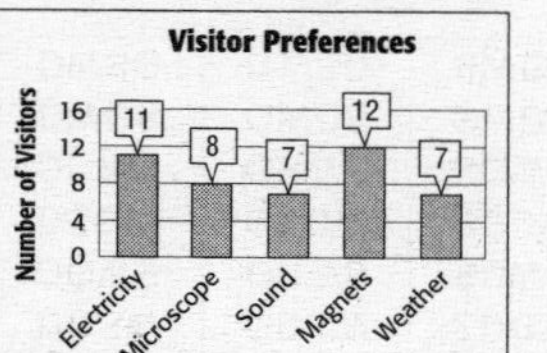

About 168 visitors prefer the magnet exhibit, and the number of visitors that prefer the weather exhibit is 98. So, there are about 70 more visitors that prefer the magnets exhibit to the weather exhibit.

NAME ______________ DATE ________ PERIOD ____

7-7 Study Guide and Intervention

Problem-Solving Investigation: Solve a Simpler Problem

When solving problems, one strategy that is helpful is to *solve a simpler problem.* Using some of the information presented in the problem, you may be able to set up and solve a simpler problem.

You can use the *solve a simpler problem* strategy, along with the following four-step problem solving plan to solve a problem.

1 Understand – Read and get a general understanding of the problem.

2 Plan – Make a plan to solve the problem and estimate the solution.

3 Solve – Use your plan to solve the problem.

4 Check – Check the reasonableness of your solution.

Example PUZZLES **Steven and Darshelle are putting together a 500 piece puzzle. So far they have 40% of the puzzle complete. How many pieces are left for them to fit into the puzzle?**

Understand We know the total number of pieces in the puzzle and that 40% of the pieces are already put together in the puzzle. We need to find the number of pieces left to fit in the puzzle.

Plan Solve a simpler problem by finding 100% − 40% or 60% of the 500 pieces. First find 10% of 500 and then use the result to find 60% of 500.

Solve Since 10%, or $\frac{1}{10}$ of 500 is 50.
So, 60%, or $\frac{6}{10}$ of 500 is 6×50 or 300.
Steven and Darshelle still have 300 pieces left to fit in the puzzle.

Check We know that 40% or 4 out of every 10 pieces of the puzzle are already put together in the puzzle. Since $500 \div 10 \times 4 = 200$ pieces and $200 + 300 = 500$, the answer is correct.

Exercise

SCHOLARSHIPS Crosswood Elementary School received $450 in donations for its scholarship fund. If 30% of the contributions were from local businesses, how much money did the local businesses contribute? **$135**

Copyright © Glencoe/McGraw-Hill, a division of The McGraw-Hill Companies, Inc.

NAME ________________ DATE ________ PERIOD ____

7-7 Practice

Problem-Solving Investigation: Solve a Simpler Problem

Mixed Problem Solving

Use the solve a simpler problem strategy to solve Exercises 1–3.

1. ART An artist plans to make 1 clay pot the first week and triple the number of clay pots each week for 5 weeks. How many clay pots will the artist make the fifth week? **81 clay pots**

2. GEOGRAPHY The total area of Wisconsin is 65,498 square miles. Of that, about 80% is land area. About how much of Wisconsin is not land area? **Sample answer: about 13,100 square miles**

3. SCIENCE Sound travels through sea water at a speed of about 1,500 meters per second. At this rate, how far will sound travel in 2 minutes? **Sample answer: 60 = 6 × 10, 6 × 1,500 = 9,000 and (9,000 × 10) × 2 = 180,000 m**

Use any strategy to solve Exercises 4–8. Some strategies are shown below.

Problem-Solving Strategies
• Guess and check.
• Solve a simpler problem.

4. MUSIC Tanya scored 50 out of 50 points in her latest piano playing evaluation. She scored 42, 48, and 45 on previous evaluations. What score does she need on the next evaluation to have an average score of 45? **a score of 40**

5. EXERCISE At the community center, 9 boys and 9 girls are playing singles table tennis. If each girl plays against each boy exactly once, how many games are played? **81 games**

6. CLOCK The clock in the bell tower rings every half hour. How many times will it ring in one week? **336 times**

7. VENN DIAGRAMS The Venn diagram shows information about the sixth graders in the school.

Sixth Graders

U

B 15 | 9 | 18 C

100

U = all sixth graders
B = sixth graders in the band
C = sixth graders in the chorus

How many more sixth graders in the school do not participate in band or chorus than do participate in band or chorus? **Add and subtract; 15 + 9 + 18 = 42, 100 − 42 = 58; so, 58 sixth graders do not participate; 58 − 42 = 16; 16 more do not participate than do participate.**

8. MONEY Kono wants to give $69 to charity. He will give each of 3 charities an equal amount of money. How much money will each charity receive? **Divide: $69 ÷ 3 = $23**

Copyright © Glencoe/McGraw-Hill, a division of The McGraw-Hill Companies, Inc.

NAME ________________ DATE ________ PERIOD ____

7-8 Study Guide and Intervention

Estimating with Percents

The table below shows some commonly used percents and their fraction equivalents.

Percent-Fraction Equivalents				
$20\% = \frac{1}{5}$	$50\% = \frac{1}{2}$	$80\% = \frac{4}{5}$	$25\% = \frac{1}{4}$	$33\frac{1}{3}\% = \frac{1}{3}$
$30\% = \frac{3}{10}$	$60\% = \frac{3}{5}$	$90\% = \frac{9}{10}$	$75\% = \frac{3}{4}$	$66\frac{2}{3}\% = \frac{2}{3}$
$40\% = \frac{2}{5}$	$70\% = \frac{7}{10}$	$100\% = 1$		

Examples **Estimate each percent.**

1 20% of 58

20% is $\frac{1}{5}$.

Round 58 to 60 since it is divisible by 5.

$\frac{1}{5}$ of 60 is 12.

So, 20% of 58 is about 12.

2 76% of 21.

76% is close to 75% or $\frac{3}{4}$.

Round 21 to 20 since it is divisible by 4.

$\frac{1}{4}$ of 24 is 5.

So $\frac{3}{4}$ of 20 is 3 × 5 or 15

So, 76% of 21 is about 15.

Example 3 **Isabel is reading a book that has 218 pages. She wants to complete 25% of the book by Friday. About how many pages should she read by Friday?**

25% os $\frac{1}{4}$. Round 218 to 200.

$\frac{1}{4}$ of 200 is 50.

So, Isabel should read about 50 pages by Friday.

Exercises

Estimate each percent. **1–6. Sample answers given.**

1. 49% of 8
$\frac{1}{2}$ of 8 is 4

2. 24% of 27
$\frac{1}{4}$ of 28 is 7

3. 19% of 46
$\frac{1}{5}$ of 45 is 9

4. 62% of 20
$\frac{3}{5}$ of 20 is 12

5. 40% of 51
$\frac{2}{5}$ of 50 is 20

6. 81% of 32
$\frac{4}{5}$ of 30 is 24

7. TIPS Jodha wants to tip the pizza delivery person about 20%. If the cost of the pizzas is $15.99, what would be a reasonable amount to tip?
Sample answer: $\frac{1}{5}$ of $15 is $3.

NAME ______________________ DATE ____________ PERIOD ____

7-8 Practice

Estimating with Percents

Estimate each percent. Sample answers are given.

1. 51% of 62
$\frac{1}{2}$ of 60 is 30

2. 39% of 42
$\frac{2}{5}$ of 40 is 16

3. 78% of 148
$\frac{4}{5}$ of 150 is 120

4. 34% of 99
$\frac{1}{3}$ of 99 is 33

5. 74% of 238
$\frac{3}{4}$ of 240 is 180

6. 70% of 103
$\frac{7}{10}$ of 100 is 70

7. 22% of 152
$\frac{1}{5}$ of 150 is 30

8. 91% of 102
$\frac{9}{10}$ of 100 is 90

9. 26% of 322
$\frac{1}{4}$ of 320 is 80

10. 65% of 181
$\frac{2}{3}$ of 180 is 120

11. 98% of 60
$\frac{1}{1}$ of 60 is 60

12. 11% of 10
$\frac{1}{10}$ of 10 is 1

13. Estimate twenty-nine percent of forty-eight.
Sample answer: $\frac{3}{10}$ of 50 is 15

14. Estimate sixty-two percent of one hundred twenty-four.
Sample answer: $\frac{3}{5}$ of 125 is 75

Estimate the percent that is shaded in each figure.

15. **about 75%**

16. **about 25%**

17. **about 80%**

18. **WORK** Karl made $365 last month doing odd jobs after school. If 75% of the money he made was from doing yard work, about how much did Karl make doing yard work?
Sample answer: $\frac{3}{4}$ of $360 is $270

19. **HOMEWORK** Jin spent 32 hours on math and language arts homework last month. She spent 11 hours on math. About what percent of her homework hours were spent on language arts? Explain.
Sample answer: 32 − 11 = 21 language arts hours and $\frac{21}{32}$ is about $\frac{20}{30}$ or $\frac{2}{3}$. Since $\frac{2}{3} = 66\frac{2}{3}\%$, about $66\frac{2}{3}\%$ of Jin's homework hours were spent on language arts.

NAME ______________________ DATE ____________ PERIOD ____

8-1 Study Guide and Intervention

Length in the Customary System

The most commonly used customary units of length are shown in the table.

Customary Units Of Length	
Unit	**Model**
1 inch (in.)	width of a quarter
1 foot (ft) = 12 in.	length of a large adult foot
1 yard (yd) = 3 ft	length from nose to fingertip
1 mile (mi) = 1,760 yd	10 city blocks

Most rulers are divided into eighths of an inch, so you can measure to the nearest eighth inch.

Example 1 **Draw a line segment measuring $1\frac{5}{8}$ inches.**

in. 1 2

Draw a line segment from 0 to $1\frac{5}{8}$.

Example 2 **Measure the length of the nail to the nearest half, fourth, or eighth inch.**

in. 1 2 3

The nail is between $2\frac{7}{8}$ inches and 3 inches.
It is closer to $2\frac{7}{8}$ inches.
The length of the nail is about $2\frac{7}{8}$ inches.

- To change from larger units of length to smaller units, multiply.
- To change from smaller units of length to larger units, divide.

Examples **Complete.**

3 **3 yd = __?__ ft**

Since 1 yard = 3 feet, multiply by 3.
3 × 3 = 9
So, 3 yards = 9 feet.

4 **24 in. = __?__ ft**

Since 1 foot = 12 inches, divide by 12.
24 ÷ 12 = 2
So, 24 inches = 2 feet.

Exercises

1. Draw a line segment that is $\frac{3}{4}$ in. long.

2. Measure the length of the object to the nearest half, fourth, or eighth inch. **$1\frac{5}{8}$ in.**

Complete.

3. 3 ft = __?__ in. **36**

4. 15 ft = __?__ yd **5**

5. 2 mi = __?__ yd **3,520**

NAME ______ DATE ______ PERIOD ____

8-1 Practice

Length in the Customary System

Draw a line segment of each length.

1. $\frac{5}{8}$ in.
2. $3\frac{3}{8}$ in.
3. $2\frac{1}{4}$ in.
4. $1\frac{1}{2}$ in.

Measure the length of each line segment or object to the nearest half, fourth, or eighth inch.

5. **$1\frac{1}{4}$ in.**
6. **1 in.**
7. **$1\frac{3}{8}$ in.**
8. **$1\frac{7}{8}$ in.**
9. **$\frac{1}{2}$ in.**
10. **$2\frac{1}{8}$ in.**

Complete.

11. 5 yd = ____ ft **15**
12. 3 yd = ____ in. **108**
13. 6 mi = ____ yd **10,560**
14. 4 mi = ____ ft **21,120**
15. 72 in. = ____ ft **6**
16. 8 ft = ____ yd **$2\frac{2}{3}$**
17. 48 in. = ____ yd **$1\frac{1}{3}$**
18. 9,680 yd = ____ mi **$5\frac{1}{2}$**
19. 15,840 ft = ____ mi **3**

Determine the greater measurement. Explain your reasoning.

20. $1\frac{2}{3}$ yards or 64 inches
64 in.; $1\frac{2}{3}$ yd is the same as 60 in., which is less than 64 in.

21. 58 inches or $5\frac{1}{2}$ feet
$5\frac{1}{2}$ ft; $5\frac{1}{2}$ is the same as 66 in., which is more than 58 in.

22. HUMAN BODY The small intestine is 20 feet long and the large intestine is 5 feet long. What is the total length of the intestines in yards?
$8\frac{1}{3}$ yd

23. BICYCLES Raj estimates that the length of his bicycle is 66 inches. Is this reasonable? Why or why not?
Yes, it is reasonable; Sample answer: 66 inches is the same as $5\frac{1}{2}$ feet, which would be about right for a bicycle

Copyright © Glencoe/McGraw-Hill, a division of The McGraw-Hill Companies, Inc.

NAME ______ DATE ______ PERIOD ____

8-2 Study Guide and Intervention

Capacity and Weight in the Customary System

The most commonly used customary units of capacity are shown below.

Customary Units Of Capacity	
Unit	**Model**
1 **fluid ounce** (fl oz)	2 tablespoons of water
1 **cup** (c) = 8 fl oz	coffee cup
1 **pint** (pt) = 2 c	small ice cream container
1 **quart** (qt) = 2 pt	large measuring cup
1 **gallon** (gal) = 4 qt	large plastic jug of milk

- To change from larger units of length to smaller units, multiply.
- To change from smaller units of length to larger units, divide.

Example 1 **Complete.**

2 gal = __?__ qt — THINK 1 gallon = 4 quarts

2 × 4 = 8 — Multiply to change a larger unit to a smaller unit.

So, 2 gallons = 8 quarts.

The most commonly used customary units of weight are shown below.

Customary Units Of Weight	
Unit	**Model**
1 **ounce** (oz)	pencil
1 **pound** (lb) = 16 oz	package of notebook paper
1 **ton** (T) = 2,000 lb	small passenger car

Example 2 FOOD **A box of cereal weighs 32 ounces. How many pounds is this?**

32 oz = __?__ lb — THINK 16 ounces = 1 pound

32 ÷ 16 = 2 — Divide to change ounces to pounds.

So, 32 ounces = 2 pounds.

Exercises

Complete.

1. 2 pt = __?__ c **4**
2. 32 fl oz = __?__ c **4**
3. 3 lb = __?__ oz **48**
4. 16 qt = __?__ gal **4**
5. 3 qt = __?__ pt **6**
6. 3 T = __?__ lb **6,000**
7. 16 c = __?__ qt **4**
8. 2 gal = __?__ pt **16**
9. 64 oz = __?__ lb **4**

NAME ______________ DATE ________ PERIOD _____

8-2 Practice

Capacity and Weight in the Customary System

Complete.

1. 6 gal = ____ qt **24**
2. 4 pt = ____ c **8**
3. 32 fl oz = ____ c **4**
4. 9 qt = ____ pt **18**
5. 15 qt = ____ gal $3\frac{3}{4}$
6. 7 gal = ____ pt **56**
7. 3,000 lb = ____ T $1\frac{1}{2}$
8. 68 oz = ____ lb $4\frac{1}{4}$
9. 7 T = ____ lb **14,000**

Write and solve a proportion to complete each conversion.

10. 9 qt = ____ pt $\frac{9\text{ qt}}{x\text{ pt}} = \frac{1\text{ qt}}{2\text{ pt}}$; 18
11. 5 lb = ____ oz $\frac{5\text{ lb}}{x\text{ oz}} = \frac{1\text{ lb}}{16\text{ oz}}$; 80
12. 56 fl oz = ____ c $\frac{56\text{ fl oz}}{x\text{ c}} = \frac{8\text{ fl oz}}{1\text{ c}}$; 7

Choose the better estimate for each measure.

13. fluid ounces or pints **pints**
14. ounces or pounds **ounces**
15. pints or gallons **gallons**

Find the greater quantity. Explain your reasoning.

16. 18 quarts or 4 gallons
18 qt; 4 gal = 16 qt, which is less than 18 qt.
17. 3 pints or 36 fluid ounces
3 pt; 3 pt = 48 fl oz, which is more than 36 fl oz.
18. FISH The average weight of the largest fish, the whale shark, is 50,000 pounds. How many tons is this? **25 T**
19. HONEY To gather enough nectar to make 1 pound of honey, a bee must visit 2 million flowers. How many flowers must a bee visit to make 64 ounces of honey? **8 million flowers**
20. PAINTING Mr. Krauss needs 8 gallons of paint to paint his fences. He has 9 quart cans and 22 pint cans of paint. Does he have enough paint? Explain.
No; Since 22 pt = 11 qt, he has 20 qt altogether, which is 5 gallons.

NAME ______________ DATE ________ PERIOD _____

8-3 Study Guide and Intervention

Length in the Metric System

The meter is the basic unit of length in the metric system. The most commonly used metric units of length are shown below.

Metric Units of Length		
Unit	**Model**	**Benchmark**
1 **millimeter** (mm)	thickness of a dime	25 mm ≈ 1 inch
1 **centimeter** (cm)	half the width of a penny	2.5 cm ≈ 1 inch
1 **meter** (m)	width of a doorway	1 m ≈ 1.1 yard
1 **kilometer** (km)	six city blocks	1.6 km ≈ 1 mile

Examples **Write the metric unit of length that you would use to measure each of the following.**

1 height of a box of popcorn

The height of a box of popcorn is more than the width of a penny, but less than the width of a doorway. So, the centimeter is an appropriate unit of measure.

2 length of a car

Since the length of a car is greater than the width of a doorway, but less than six city blocks, the meter is an appropriate unit of measure.

Example 3 **Measure the length of the line segment in centimeters.**

5 cm

cm 1 2 3 4 5

The line segment is 5 cm.

Exercises

Write the metric unit of length that you would use to measure each of the following.

1. height of a mountain **kilometer**
2. thickness of a dried bean **millimeter**
3. length of a pen **centimeter**
4. height of a table **meter**

Measure each line segment in centimeters and millimeters.

5. **2 cm; 20 mm**
6. **3.5 cm; 35 mm**
7. **4.3 cm; 43 mm**
8. **0.7 cm; 7 mm**

Lesson 8-3

NAME ______________ DATE ______ PERIOD ____

8-3 Practice

Length in the Metric System

Write the metric unit of length that you would use to measure each of the following.

1. length of a fly **millimeter**
2. thickness of a pen **millimeter**
3. length of a football field **meter**
4. width of a sheet of notebook paper **centimeter**
5. width of a drinking glass **centimeter**
6. height of a mountain **meter**
7. distance from New York City to Los Angeles, California **kilometer**
8. distance from one end of a school to the other end of the school **meter**

Estimate the length of each of the following. Then measure to find the actual length.

9. **Sample answer: 60 mm; 65 mm**

10. **Sample answer: 50 mm; 48 mm**

11. **Sample answer: 15 cm; 13 cm**

12. **Sample answer: 10 cm; 11 cm**

13. Which is greater: 6,200 meters or 5 kilometers? Explain your reasoning.
6,200 m; 6,200 m is the same as 6.2 km, which is greater than 5 km.
14. Which is less: 2 kilometers or 1 mile? Explain your reasoning.
1 mi; one km is the same as 0.6 mi, which is more than half a mile, so 2 km is more than one mi.
15. PICTURE FRAMES Yolanda is making a square picture frame from four pieces of wood. Should she be accurate to the nearest meter, to the nearest centimeter, or to the nearest millimeter? Explain your reasoning.
nearest millimeter; Sample answer: To fit together correctly, the pieces of wood must be exactly the same length.

Copyright © Glencoe/McGraw-Hill, a division of The McGraw-Hill Companies, Inc.

NAME ______________ DATE ______ PERIOD ____

8-4 Study Guide and Intervention

Mass and Capacity in the Metric System

In the metric system, the most commonly used units of mass are the milligram (mg), gram (g), and kilogram (kg). One milligram is 0.001 gram and 1 kilogram is 1,000 grams.

Metric Units of Mass		
Unit	**Model**	**Benchmark**
1 milligram (mg)	grain of salt	1 mg ≈ 0.00004 oz
1 gram (g)	small paper clip	1 g ≈ 0.04 oz
1 kilogram (kg)	six medium apples	1 kg ≈ 2 lb

Example 1 **Write the metric unit of mass that you would use to measure a portable radio. Then estimate the mass.**

A portable radio has a mass greater than six apples. So, the kilogram is the appropriate unit.

Estimate Since a portable radio is about three times heavier than six apples, the mass of a portable radio is about 3 kilograms.

The basic unit of capacity in the metric system is the liter (L). One milliliter (mL) is 0.001 liter.

Metric Units of Capacity		
Unit	**Model**	**Benchmark**
1 milliliter (mL)	eyedropper	1 mL ≈ 0.03 fl oz
1 liter (L)	small pitcher	1 L ≈ 1 qt

Example 2 **Write the metric unit of capacity that you would use to measure a mug of soup. Then estimate the capacity.**

A mug of soup is greater than an eyedropper and less than a small pitcher. So, the milliliter is the appropriate unit.

Estimate There are 1,000 milliliters in a liter. A small pitcher can fill about 4 mugs. So, a mug of soup is about 1,000 ÷ 4 or about 250 milliliters.

Exercises

Write the metric unit of mass or capacity that you would use to measure each of the following. Then estimate the mass or capacity.

1. peanut **gram; 2 g**
2. serving of salad dressing **milliliter; 6 mL**
3. eyelash **milligram; 1 mg**
4. large soda bottle **liter; 2 L**
5. bottle of milk **liter; 1 L**
6. house cat **kilogram; 4 kg**
7. screw **gram; 5 g**
8. pencil **gram; 10 g**

NAME ______________ DATE ________ PERIOD ____

8-4 Practice

Mass and Capacity in the Metric System

Write the metric unit of mass or capacity that you would use to measure each of the following. Then estimate the mass or capacity.

1. ballpoint pen
   gram; Sample answer: 15 g
2. grain of sand
   milligram; Sample answer: 10 mg
3. bear
   kilogram; Sample answer: 90 kg
4. egg
   gram; Sample answer: 40 g
5. nickel
   gram; Sample answer: 5 g
6. bowling ball
   kilogram; Sample answer: 7 kg
7. small feather
   milligram; Sample answer: 800 mg
8. liquid in a thermometer
   milliliter; Sample answer: 8 mL
9. shampoo bottle
   milliliter; Sample answer: 400 mL
10. plastic wading pool
    liter; Sample answer: 800 L
11. hummingbird feeder
    milliliter; Sample answer: 600 mL
12. banana
    gram; Sample answer: 400 g

ANALYZE TABLES **For Exercises 13 and 14, use the table at the right that shows the mass of squirrels.**

Squirrel Masses	
Squirrel	**Average Mass (g)**
African Pygmy	10
Eastern Gray	553
Red	285
Thirteen-Lined Ground	543

Sources: *Animal Fact File* and *National Audubon Society First Field Guide*

13. Is the combined mass of the African Pygmy squirrel, the Eastern Gray squirrel, and the Red squirrel more or less than one kilogram?
    less
14. Which squirrels from the table will have a combined mass closest to one kilogram? Explain your reasoning.
    Eastern Gray and Thirteen-Lined; Their combined mass is 1,096 grams, which is close to 1,000 grams or 1 kilogram.
15. COOKING Cooking oil comes in 1.42 liter bottles and 710 milliliter bottles. Which bottle is larger? Explain.
    1.42 L; A 1.42-liter bottle holds about $1\frac{1}{2}$ small pitchers of liquid. A 710-milliliter bottle holds about 710 times the amount an eyedropper holds. So, the 1.41-liter bottle is larger.
16. BEVERAGES A kiloliter is equal to 1,000 liters and is about the amount needed to fill 5 bathtubs. Each year, about 198 liters of soda is consumed per person in the United States. About how many bathtubs could be filled with the amount of soda drunk by 15 persons in a year?
    about 15 bathtubs
17. MEDICINE A multivitamin tablet contains 162 milligrams of calcium. If you take one vitamin tablet each day, how many milligrams of calcium will you consume in a week? **1,134 mg**

NAME ______________ DATE ________ PERIOD ____

8-5 Study Guide and Intervention

Problem-Solving Investigation: Use Benchmarks

When solving problems, one strategy that is helpful is to *use benchmarks*. A benchmark is a measurement by which other items can be measured. Sometimes you might not have the exact measuring tool to solve a problem. When this happens, you can use a benchmark to solve the problem.

You can use the *benchmark* strategy, along with the following four-step problem solving plan to solve a problem.

1 Understand – Read and get a general understanding of the problem.
2 Plan – Make a plan to solve the problem and estimate the solution.
3 Solve – Use your plan to solve the problem.
4 Check – Check the reasonableness of your solution.

Example CRAFTS **Aaliyah is buying fabric to make curtains for her bedroom. She needs 20 feet of fabric to make the curtains. Aaliyah knows that the distance from her nose to her finger when her arm is stretched out is about 1 yard. How can Aaliyah make sure she buys enough fabric without a measuring device?**

Understand Aaliyah needs to measure enough fabric for 20 feet.

Plan She can use the estimated measure from her nose to her finger to measure out enough yards of fabric to be at least 20 feet.

Solve Find how many yards of fabric she needs.

20 ft = __?__ yd

20 ft ÷ 3 = $6\frac{2}{3}$ yd

Aaliyah should count and measure the distance from her nose to her finger 7 times so that she has enough fabric.

Check Since 7 yards is equal to 21 feet, Aaliyah should have enough fabric using her estimated measurement.

Exercise

PETS At a dog show, Brandon was asked the length of his dog. He did not have a measuring device handy, but knew that the width of his hand was about 1 decimeter. Describe a way Brandon could estimate the length of his dog in centimeters.

Sample answer: Brandon could place each hand side-by-side along the length of his dog. Once he finds out how many hands long his dog is, he can multiply this by 10 to find the length in centimeters.

Copyright © Glencoe/McGraw-Hill, a division of The McGraw-Hill Companies, Inc.

NAME ______________________ DATE ____________ PERIOD _____

8-5 Practice

Problem-Solving Investigation: Use Benchmarks

Mixed Problem Solving

Use the benchmark strategy to solve Exercises 1 and 2.

1. FENCES Mr. Badilla is building a rectangular fence around his back yard. He needs to buy enough fencing material to cover two lengths and one width. Mr. Badilla knows that his walking stride is about one half meter long. Describe a way Mr. Badilla could estimate the amount of fencing material he will need.
Sample answer: Walk the length distance and count the number of strides, and divide by two. Walk the width distance and count the number of strides, and divide by two. Compute the total distance for two lengths and one width.

2. BEDROOM Mindy and her sister share a bedroom. They want to divide the room into a separate space for each of them by putting up a curtain of bed sheets. Sheets are 2 meters wide. Mindy has string and knows that the width of the bedroom door is 1 meter. Describe a way Mindy can estimate the number of sheets to buy.
Sample answer: Cut the string so that the length is the same as the width of the door. Determine how many string lengths are needed to divide the room. Divide the number of string lengths by 2 to find the number of sheets.

Use any strategy to solve Exercises 3–5. Some strategies are shown below.

Problem-Solving Strategies
• Guess and check.
• Look for a pattern.
• Use benchmarks.

3. MUSEUM The table shows attendance at a museum during the past months. Which is greater, the mean or the median attendance during this time?

Museum Attendance
840 900 725 600 700 985 625
960 825 800 841 900 725

the median

4. PICTURES Jon is putting a ribbon border around some picture frames. He knows that the length of his smallest finger is 6 centimeters. Describe a way that Jon can determine how much ribbon he will need.
Sample answer: Measure the distance around a picture frame with his finger. Multiply the number of finger lengths by 6 cm to estimate the length of ribbon for one picture frame and then multiply by the number of frames.

5. MONEY Theo bought a coat that sold for \$108.59. He paid a total of \$115.11, which included tax. How much did he pay in tax?
Subtract; \$115.11 − \$108.59 = \$6.52

Copyright © Glencoe/McGraw-Hill, a division of The McGraw-Hill Companies, Inc.

NAME ______________________ DATE ____________ PERIOD _____

8-6 Study Guide and Intervention

Changing Metric Units

To change from one unit to another within the metric system, you can either multiply or divide by powers of ten.

1,000	100	10	1	0.1	0.01	0.001
thousands	hundreds	tens	ones	tenths	hundredths	thousandths
kilo	hecto	deka	basic unit	deci	centi	milli

Each place value is 10 times the place value to its right.

- To change from larger units to smaller units, multiply.
- To change from smaller units to larger units, divide.

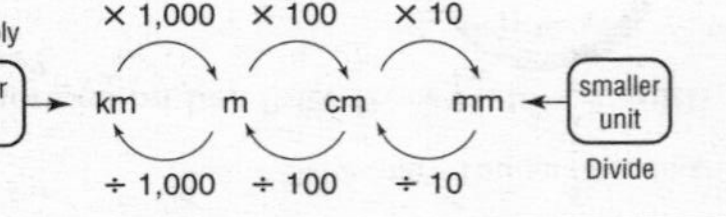

Examples **Complete.**

1 **650 cm = _?_ m**

Since 1 meter = 100 centimeters, divide by 100. 650 ÷ 100 = 6.5
So, 650 cm = 6.5 m.

2 **_?_ mL = 3 L**

Since 1 liter = 1,000 milliliters, multiply by 1,000. 3 × 1,000 = 3,000
So, 3,000 mL = 3 L.

3 **9,100 g = _?_ kg**

Since 1 kilogram = 1,000 grams, divide by 1,000. 9,100 ÷ 1,000 = 9.1
So, 9,100 g = 9.1 kg.

CHECK Since a kilogram is a larger unit than a gram, the number of kilograms should be less than the of grams. The answer seems reasonable.

Exercises

Complete.

1. 2 L = _?_ mL **2,000**
2. 400 mm = _?_ cm **40**
3. 8 g = _?_ mg **8,000**
4. 25 cm = _?_ mm **250**
5. 4,100 cm = _?_ m **41**
6. 3 m = _?_ mm **3,000**
7. _?_ m = 5 km **5,000**
8. 1,900 g = _?_ kg **1.9**
9. 6 kg = _?_ g **6,000**
10. 62 L = _?_ mL **62,000**
11. 900 mg = _?_ g **0.9**
12. _?_ km = 500 m **0.5**

NAME ________________ DATE ________ PERIOD ____

8-6 Practice
Changing Metric Units

Complete.

1. 91 mm = ____ cm **9.1**
2. 2 m = ____ mm **2,000**
3. ____ L = 12 mL **0.012**
4. ____ mg = 8 g **8,000**
5. ____ g = 2,500 mg **2.5**
6. ____ mL = 572 L **572,000**
7. 21 L = ____ mL **21,000**
8. 432 cm = ____ m **4.32**
9. ____ L = 821 mL **0.821**
10. 2,900 g = ____ kg **2.9**
11. 670 m = ____ km **0.67**
12. ____ g = 3 mg **0.003**
13. 300 mg = ____ kg **0.0003**
14. 500,000 mL = ____ kL **0.5**
15. 9 km = ____ cm **900,000**

Order each set of measurements from least to greatest.

16. 6.4 kg, 640 g, 600,000 mg **600,000 mg, 640 g, 6.4 kg**
17. 3.4 km, 33 cm, 340 mm **33 cm, 340 mm, 3.4 km**

18. **ANIMALS** An ostrich, the world's largest flightless bird, has a mass of 136 kilograms. A bee hummingbird, the world's smallest bird, has a mass of 2 grams. How much more mass does the ostrich have than the hummingbird? **135,998 g or 135.998 kg**

19. **TRAIL** Hal is hiking a trail to a waterfall viewing platform. It is 8,000 meters to the river, then 10,000 meters from the river to the base of the waterfall, and 600 meters further to the viewing platform. How many kilometers will Hal hike to reach the viewing platform? **18.6 km**

NAME ________________ DATE ________ PERIOD ____

8-7 Study Guide and Intervention
Measures of Time

Units of Time	
Unit	**Model**
1 **second** (s)	time needed to say 1,001
1 **minute** (min) = 60 seconds	time for 2 average TV commercials
1 **hour** (h) = 60 minutes	time for 2 weekly TV sitcoms

To add or subtract measures of time, first add or subtract the seconds, next add or subtract the minutes, and then add or subtract the hours. Rename if necessary in each step.

Example 1 **Find the sum of 3 h 14 min 12 s and 4 h 48 min 3 s.**

Estimate 3 h 14 min 12 s is about 3 h, and 4 h 48 min 3 s is about 5 h. 3 h + 5 h = 8 h.

```
  3 h 14 min 12 s
+ 4 h 48 min  3 s
  7 h 62 min 15 s
```

Add seconds first, then minutes, and finally hours. 62 minutes equals 1 hour 2 minutes.

So, the sum is 8 h 2 min 15 s. Compare the answer to the estimate.

Example 2 **Find the difference of 5 h 7 min 20 s and 2 h 25 min 12 s.**

Estimate 5 h 7 min 20 s is about 5 h, and 2 h 25 min 12 s is about 2 h. 5 h − 2 h = 3 h.

```
  5 h  7 min 20 s
− 2 h 25 min 12 s
```

Since you cannot subtract 25 minutes from 7 minutes, you must rename 5 hours 7 minutes as 4 hours 67 minutes.

```
  5 h  7 min 20 s         4 h 67 min 20 s
− 2 h 25 min 12 s   →   − 2 h 25 min 12 s
                          2 h 42 min  8 s
```

Compare the answer to the estimate.

Example 3 **Gloria practiced on her flute from 11:40 A.M. until 1:52 P.M. How long did she practice?**

You need to find how much time has elapsed. Gloria's practice time is 20 minutes + 1 hour 52 minutes or 1 hour 72 minutes. Now rename 72 minutes as 1 hour 12 minutes. 1 h + 1 h 12 min = 2 h 12 min. Gloria practiced for 2 hours 12 minutes.

11:40 A.M. to 12:00 noon is 20 minutes.

12:00 noon to 1:52 P.M. is 1 hour 52 minutes.

Exercises

Add or subtract.

1. 4 h 18 min 11 s − 3 h 15 min 4 s **1 h 3 min 7 s**
2. 6 h 7 min 42 s + 2 h 12 min 38 s **8 h 20 min 20 s**
3. 5 h 18 min 12 s − 2 h 6 min 41 s **3 h 11 min 31 s**

Find the elapsed time.

4. 4:25 P.M. to 11:55 P.M. **7 h 30 min**
5. 9:20 A.M. to 5:05 P.M. **7 h 45 min**
6. 10:30 A.M. to 1:43 P.M. **3 h 13 min**

Lesson 8–7

NAME ______________________ DATE ____________ PERIOD ____

8-7 Practice

Measures of Time

Add or subtract.

1. 23 h 52 min + 15 h 30 min = **39 h 22 min**
2. 17 min 14 s + 32 min 50 s = **50 min 4 s**
3. 8 h 39 min 43 s − 3 h 57 min 22 s = **4 h 42 min 21 s**
4. 4 h 49 min 28 s − 2 h 12 min 53 s = **2 h 36 min 35 s**
5. 28 h 13 min 26 s + 3 h 58 min 36 s = **32 h 12 min 2 s**
6. 9 h 37 s + 2 h 6 min 50 s = **11 h 7 min 27 s**
7. 4 h 39 s + 5 h 21 min 8 s + 49 min 11 s = **10 h 10 min 58 s**
8. 5 h 47 s + 52 s = **5 h 1 min 39 s**
9. 6 h − 2 h 35 min 41 s = **3 h 24 min 19 s**

Find the elapsed time.

10. 8:30 A.M. to 11:43 A.M. **3 h 13 min**
11. 4:32 P.M. to 8:12 P.M. **3 h 40 min**
12. 5:45 A.M. to 3:32 P.M. **9 h 47 min**
13. 8:30 P.M. to 10:53 A.M. **14 h 23 min**
14. ACTIVITIES On Saturday, Miguel spent 2 hours 30 minutes at basketball practice and 90 minutes at his pastry chef class. How much total time did Miguel spend doing these two activities? **4 h**
15. FURNITURE Una is painting a chair. She finished painting the first coat at 10:42 A.M. The paint needs to dry for at least 1 hour 45 minutes before another coat of paint can be put on. At what time will Una be able to paint a second coat? **12:27 P.M.**

Copyright © Glencoe/McGraw-Hill, a division of The McGraw-Hill Companies, Inc.

NAME ______________________ DATE ____________ PERIOD ____

8-8 Study Guide and Intervention

Measures of Temperature

Temperature is the measure of hotness or coldness of an object or environment. Temperature is measured in **degrees**.

Temperature in the metric system is measured in degrees **Celsius (°C)**. Temperature in the customary system is measured in degrees **Fahrenheit (°F)**.

Example 1 **Which is a more reasonable temperature for a glass of orange juice, 10°C or −20°C?**

Water freezes at 0°C, so −20°C is below freezing. A more reasonable temperature of a glass of orange juice is 10°C.

Example 2 **What is a reasonable estimate of the temperature in degrees Celsius and degrees Fahrenheit on a fall day?**

A fall day would have a temperature between a warm summer temperature of 90°F and a cold winter temperature of 30°F.

So, a reasonable fall temperature would be 60°F or 15°C.

Exercises

Choose the more reasonable temperature for each.

1. a newborn baby's temperature: 99°F or 129°F **99°F**
2. pie in oven: 75°C or 175°C **175°C**
3. ice cream sandwich: −15°F or 15°F **15°F**
4. cup of hot chocolate: 140°F or 240°F **140°F**

Give a reasonable estimate of the temperature in degrees Celsius and degrees Fahrenheit for each activity. **Sample answers are given.**

5. inside a basement **65°F and 20°C**
6. planting a garden outside **70°F and 25°C**
7. water skiing **90°F and 32°C**
8. temperature in a freezer **20°F and −5°C**

Lesson 8–8

NAME ______________________ DATE ____________ PERIOD _____

8-8 Practice

Measures of Temperature

Choose the more reasonable temperature for each.

1. inside your bedroom: 68°F or 120°F **68°F**
2. chocolate chips starting to melt in your hand: 60°F or 100°F **100°F**
3. snowflake: −15°C or 10°C **−15°C**
4. lava flowing from a volcano: 70°C or 100°C **100°C**
5. rain in a tropical forest: 10°C or 40°C **40°C**
6. water in a goldfish bowl: 68°F or 100°F **68°F**

Give a reasonable estimate of the temperature in degrees Celsius and degrees Fahrenheit for each activity. Sample answers are given.

7. surfing the Internet with a computer **20°C or 68°F**
8. water skiing **30°C or 85°F**
9. sitting in front of a fire burning in a fireplace **35°C or 90°F**
10. playing table tennis **20°C or 68°F**
11. sledding down a snow bank **−10°C or 20°F**
12. playing football **15°C or 60°F**
13. AIR CONDITIONER The Johnsons purchased an air conditioner. Should they set the thermostat at 18°C or 50°C? Explain your reasoning. **18°C; Body temperature is around 37°C, so 50°C would be too high a temperature to cool off people.**
14. AUTUMN It is a cool, crisp autumn day. If the temperature reads 15 degrees, is this 15°C or 15°F? **15°C**
15. PAINTING A paint can says not to paint if the air temperature is above 80°F. Your thermometer says the air temperature is 35°C. Should you paint today? Explain your reasoning. **No; 35°C is about the same temperature as 95°F, which is higher than 80°F.**
16. CHEMISTRY Iron is heated in the process of making steel. Iron starts to turn from a solid into a liquid at about 5,182°F. About how much hotter must iron be to start melting than frozen water needs to be to start melting? **about 5,150 degrees**

NAME ______________________ DATE ____________ PERIOD _____

9-1 Study Guide and Intervention

Measuring Angles

Angles have two **sides** that share a common endpoint called the **vertex**. Angles are measured in **degrees**. One degree is equal to $\frac{1}{360}$th of a circle. Angles can be classified according to their measure.

vertex → sides

Obtuse angles measure between 90° and 180°.
right angle symbol
Right angles measure 90°.
Acute angles measure between 0° and 90°.
Straight angles measure 180°.

Example 1 **Use a protractor to find the measure of the angle.**

To measure an angle, place the center of a protractor on the vertex of the angle. Place the zero mark of the scale along one side of the angle. Then read the angle measure where the other side of the angle crosses the scale.

The angle measures 30°.

30° 0°

Align the center of the protractor. This angle measures 30°.

Example 2 **Classify the angle at the right as *acute, obtuse, right,* or *straight*.**

The angle smaller than a right angle, so it is less than 90°

The angle is an acute angle.

Exercises

Use a protractor to find the measure of each angle. Then classify each angle as *acute, obtuse, right,* or *straight*.

1. **90°; right**
2. **60°; acute**
3. **140°; obtuse**
4. **180°; straight**
5. **140°; obtuse**
6. **30°; acute**

Lesson 9–1

Copyright © Glencoe/McGraw-Hill, a division of The McGraw-Hill Companies, Inc.

NAME ______________ DATE ________ PERIOD ____

9-1 Practice

Measuring Angles

Use a protractor to find the measure of each angle. Then classify each angle as *acute, obtuse, right,* or *straight*.

1. 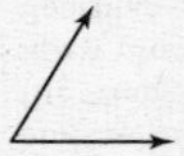 **60°; acute**
2.  **45°; acute**
3.  **145°; obtuse**
4.  **20°; acute**
5.  **180°; straight**
6.  **98°; obtuse**

7. SIGNS Measure the angles in the road sign. Then classify the angles. **90°; right angles**

DETOUR AHEAD

Find the measure of the indicated angle in each figure.

8. 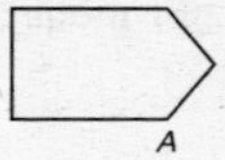 A **130°**
9.  R **70°**
10. 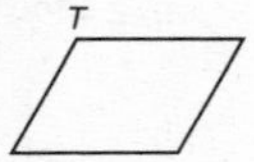 T **118°**

FLAGS **For Exercises 11–13, refer to the flag of Nepal shown at the right.**

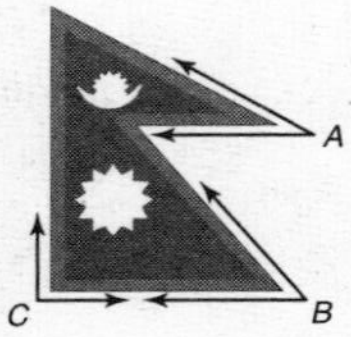

11. What is the measure of ∠A? **32°**
12. What is the measure of ∠B? **45°**
13. Classify ∠A, ∠B, and ∠C. **acute, acute, right**

A B C

NAME ______________ DATE ________ PERIOD ____

9-2 Study Guide and Intervention

Estimating and Drawing Angles

To estimate the measure of an angle, compare it to an angle whose measure you know.

You can use the measures of these angles to estimate measures of other angles.

A protractor and a straightedge can be used to draw angles.

45° 90° 135°

Example 1 **Estimate the measure of the angle shown.**

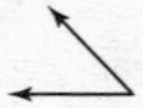

Compare the given angle to the angles shown above.

The angle is a little greater than 45°, so a reasonable estimate is about 45°.

Example 2 **Draw a 140° angle.**

Step 1
Draw one side. Mark the vertex and draw an arrow.

Step 2
Place the center point of the protractor on the vertex. Align the mark labeled 0 on the protractor with the line. Find 140° and make a dot.

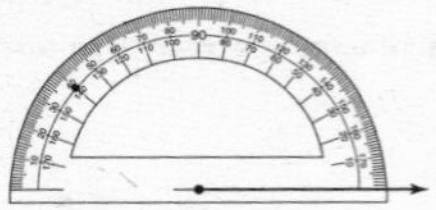

Step 3
Remove the protractor and use the straightedge to draw the side that connects the vertex and the dot.

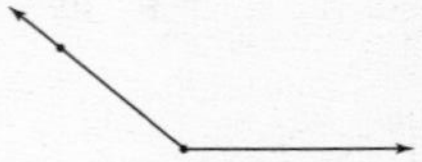

Exercises

Estimate the measure of each angle.

1.  **about 30°**
2.  **about 120°**
3.  **about 20°**

Use a protractor and a straightedge to draw angles having the following measurements.

4. 35° 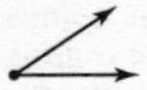
5. 110° 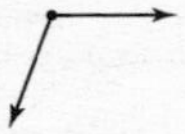
6. 15°

Lesson 9–2

NAME ______________ DATE ________ PERIOD ____

9-2 Practice

Estimating and Drawing Angles

Estimate the measure of each angle.

1. about 20°
2. about 45°
3. about 80°
4. about 135°
5. about 220°
6. about 270°

Use a protractor and a straightedge to draw angles having the following measurements.

7. 55°
8. 10°
9. 78°
10. 162°
11. 98°
12. 147°

13. **CASTLES** Caerlaverock Castle in Scotland is built in the shape of a triangle. Each angle of the triangle is 60°. In the space at the right, use a protractor and a straightedge to draw a floorplan of Caerlaverock Castle. Label each angle with its measure.

60° 60° 60°

NAME ______________ DATE ________ PERIOD ____

9-3 Study Guide and Intervention

Angle Relationships

Lesson 9–3

Vertical angles are the opposite angles formed by intersecting lines. Vertical angles are **congruent angles**, or angles with the same measure.

Example 1 **Find the value of x in the figure at the right.**

The angle labeled $x°$ and the angle labeled 40° are vertical angles. Therefore, they are congruent.

So, the value of x is 40.

Two angles are **complementary** if the sum of their measures is 90°.
Two angles are **supplementary** if the sum of their measures is 180°

Example 2 **Classify the pair of angles at the right as *complementary, supplementary,* or *neither.***

$130° + 50° = 180°$
The angles are supplementary.

Example 3 **Find the value of x in the figure at the right.**

Since the angles form a right angle, they are complementary.

$x° + 25° = 90°$ Definition of complementary angles
$65° + 25° = 90°$ THINK What measure added to 25° equals 90°?

So, the value of x is 65.

Exercises

Classify each pair of angles as *complementary, supplementary,* or *neither.*

1. 40°, 120° — neither
2. 60°, 30° — complementary
3. 110°, 80° — neither

Find the value of x in each figure.

4. $x°$, 150° — 30°
5. 110°, $x°$ — 110°
6. $x°$, 10° — 80°

NAME ______________ DATE ________ PERIOD ____

9-3 Practice

Angle Relationships

Classify each pair of angles as *complementary, supplementary,* or *neither.*

1. 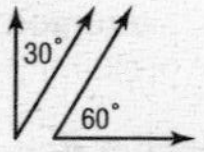 30°, 60° **complementary**
2. 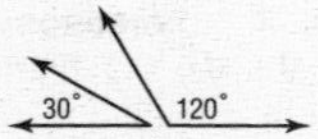 30°, 120° **neither**
3. 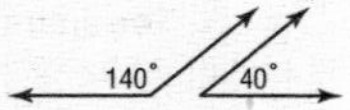 140°, 40° **supplementary**
4. 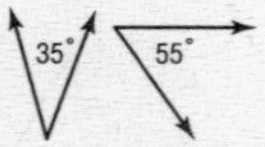 35°, 55° **complementary**
5. 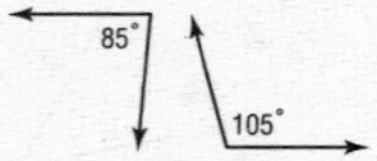 85°, 105° **supplementary**
6. 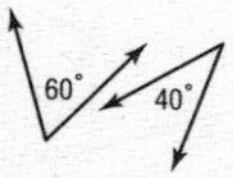 60°, 40° **neither**

Find the value of x in each figure.

7. 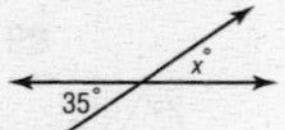 35°, x° **35°**
8. 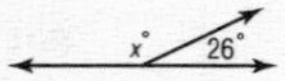 x°, 26° **154°**
9. 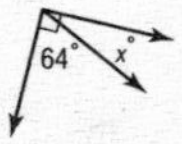 64°, x° **26°**

10. Angles A and B are complementary. Find $m\angle B$ if $m\angle A = 71°$. **19°**

11. Angles C and D are supplementary. Find $m\angle C$ if $m\angle D = 88°$. **92°**

GARDENS A semicircular garden is divided into four sections as show.

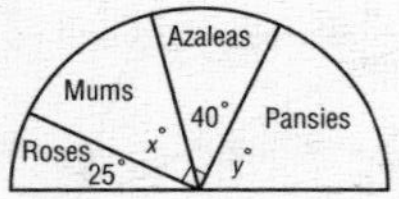

Azaleas, Mums, Roses 25°, x°, 40°, Pansies y°

12. What is the value of x? **50**

13. What is the value of y? **65**

NAME ______________ DATE ________ PERIOD ____

9-4 Study Guide and Intervention

Triangles

Acute triangles have all acute angles. **Right triangles** have one right angle. **Obtuse triangles** have one obtuse angle. The sum of the angle measures in a triangle is 180°.

Example 1 **Classify the triangle at the right as *acute, right,* or *obtuse.***

60°, 30°

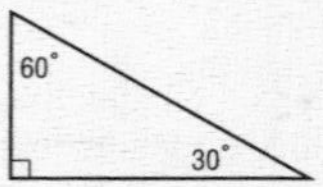

The triangle has one right angle.

So, the triangle is a right triangle.

Example 2 **Find the value of x in the triangle at the right.**

55°, x°, 45°

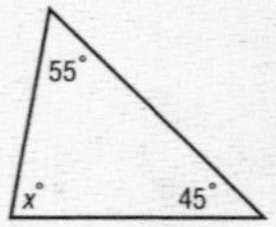

$x° + 55° + 45° = 180°$ The sum of the measures of the angles in a traingle is 180°.

$x° + 100° = 180°$ Add 55° and 45°.

$80° + 100° = 180°$ THINK What measure added to 100° equals 180°?

$x° = 80°$ The solution is 80°.

So, the value of x is 80.

Scalene triangles have no congruent sides. **Isosceles triangles** have at least 2 congruent sides. **Equilateral triangles** have 3 congruent sides.

Example 3 **Classify the triangle at the right as *scalene, isosceles,* or *equilateral.***

8 cm, 8 cm, 5 cm

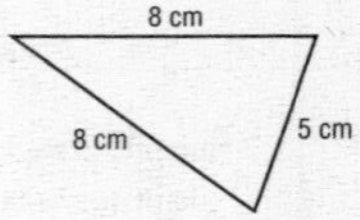

Two of the sides measure 8 centimeters, and are congruent.

So, the triangle is an isosceles triangle.

Exercises

Classify each triangle as *acute, right,* or *obtuse.*

1. 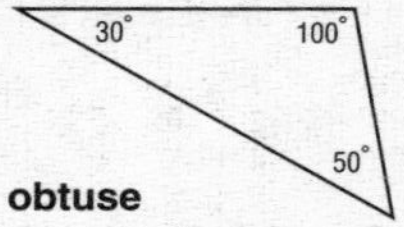 30°, 100°, 50° **obtuse**
2. 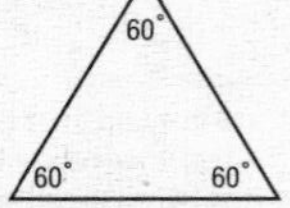 60°, 60°, 60° **acute**
3. 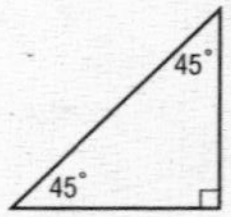 45°, 45° **right**

4. Find the value of x in the triangle at the right. **110°**

x°, 35°, 35°

5. Classify the triangle at the right as *scalene, isosceles,* or *equilateral.* **scalene**

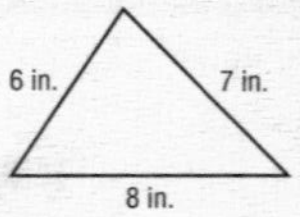

6 in., 7 in., 8 in.

Lesson 9–4

NAME ______________________ DATE __________ PERIOD ____

9-4 Practice
Triangles

Classify each triangle drawn or having the given angle measures as *acute, right,* or *obtuse*.

1. 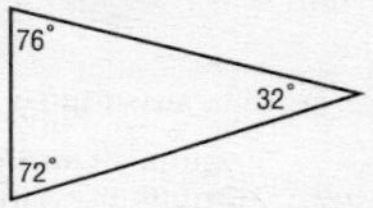 $76°$, $32°$, $72°$ **acute**
2. 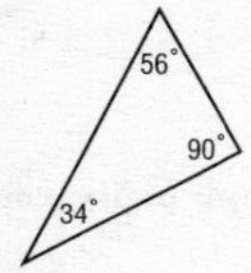 $56°$, $90°$, $34°$ **right**
3. 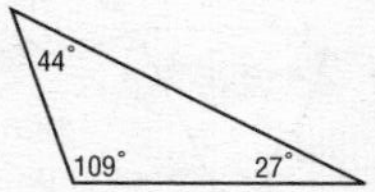 $44°$, $109°$, $27°$ **obtuse**
4. 81°, 76°, 23° **acute**
5. 118°, 34°, 28° **obtuse**
6. 90°, 60°, 30° **right**

Find the value of x in each triangle drawn or having the given angle measures.

7. 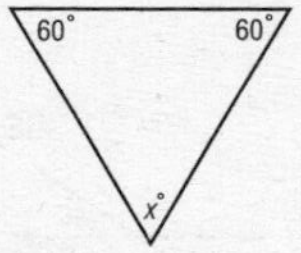 $60°$, $60°$, $x°$ **60**
8. 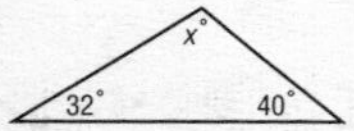 $32°$, $40°$, $x°$ **108**
9. 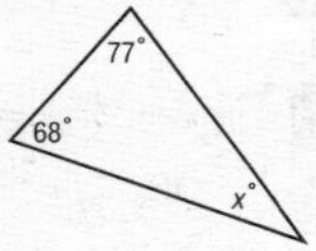 $77°$, $68°$, $x°$ **35**
10. 81°, 56°, $x°$ **43**
11. $x°$, 65°, 21° **94**
12. $x°$, 42°, 15° **123**

Classify each triangle drawn or described as *scalene, isosceles,* or *equilateral*.

13. 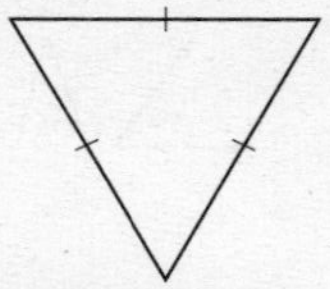 **equilateral; also isosceles**
14. 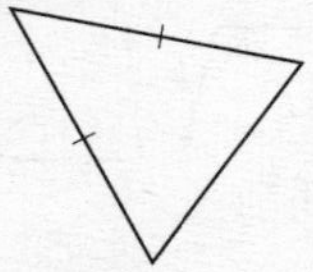 **isosceles**
15. 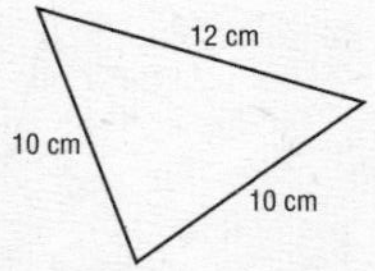 12 cm, 10 cm, 10 cm **isosceles**
16. sides: 20 in., 8 in., 14 in. **scalene**
17. sides: 7 ft, 6 ft, 7 ft **isosceles**
18. sides: 4 m, 10 m, 7 m **scalene**
19. What is the measure of the third angle of a triangle if one angle measures 39° and the other angle measures 78°? **63°**
20. What is the measure of the third angle of a right triangle if one of the angles measures 44°? **46°**

NAME ______________________ DATE __________ PERIOD ____

9-5 Study Guide and Intervention
Quadrilaterals

Quadrilaterals have four sides and four angles. The sum of the measures of the angles is 360°.

Example 1 **Find the value of x in the quadrilateral at the right.**

105°, 80°, 95°, $x°$

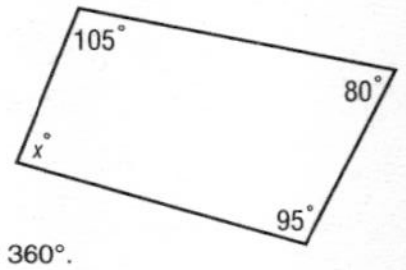

$x° + 105° + 80° + 95° = 360°$ The sum of the measures of the angles of a quadrilateral is 360°.

$x° + 280° = 360°$ Add 105°, 80°, and 95°.

$80° + 280° = 360°$ THINK What measure added to 280° equals 360°.

$x° = 80°$

So, the value of x is 80.

A **rectangle** has opposite sides congruent and parallel, and all right angles.
A **square** has all sides congruent, opposite sides parallel, and all right angles.
A **parallelogram** has opposite sides congruent and parallel, and opposite angles congruent.
A **rhombus** has all sides congruent, opposite sides parallel, and opposite angles congruent.
A **trapezoid** has exactly one pair of opposite sides parallel.

Example 2 **Classify the quadrilateral at the right.**

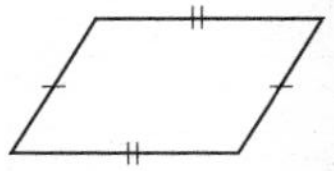

The figure has opposite sides congruent and parallel.
So, the figure is a parallelogram.

Exercises

Find the value of x in each quadrilateral.

1. 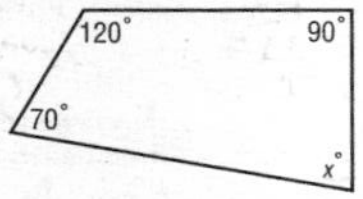 $120°$, $90°$, $70°$, $x°$ **80**
2. 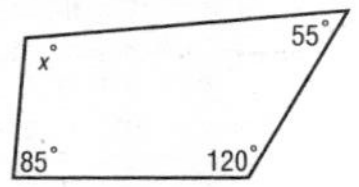 $55°$, $x°$, $85°$, $120°$ **100**
3. 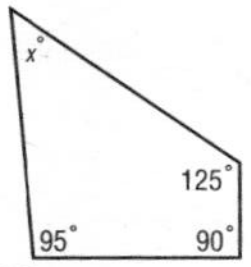 $x°$, $125°$, $95°$, $90°$ **50**

Classify each quadrilateral.

4. **square**
5. 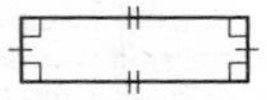 **rectangle**
6.  **trapezoid**

Copyright © Glencoe/McGraw-Hill, a division of The McGraw-Hill Companies, Inc.

NAME ______________ DATE ________ PERIOD ____

9-5 Practice

Quadrilaterals

Find the value of x in each quadrilateral.

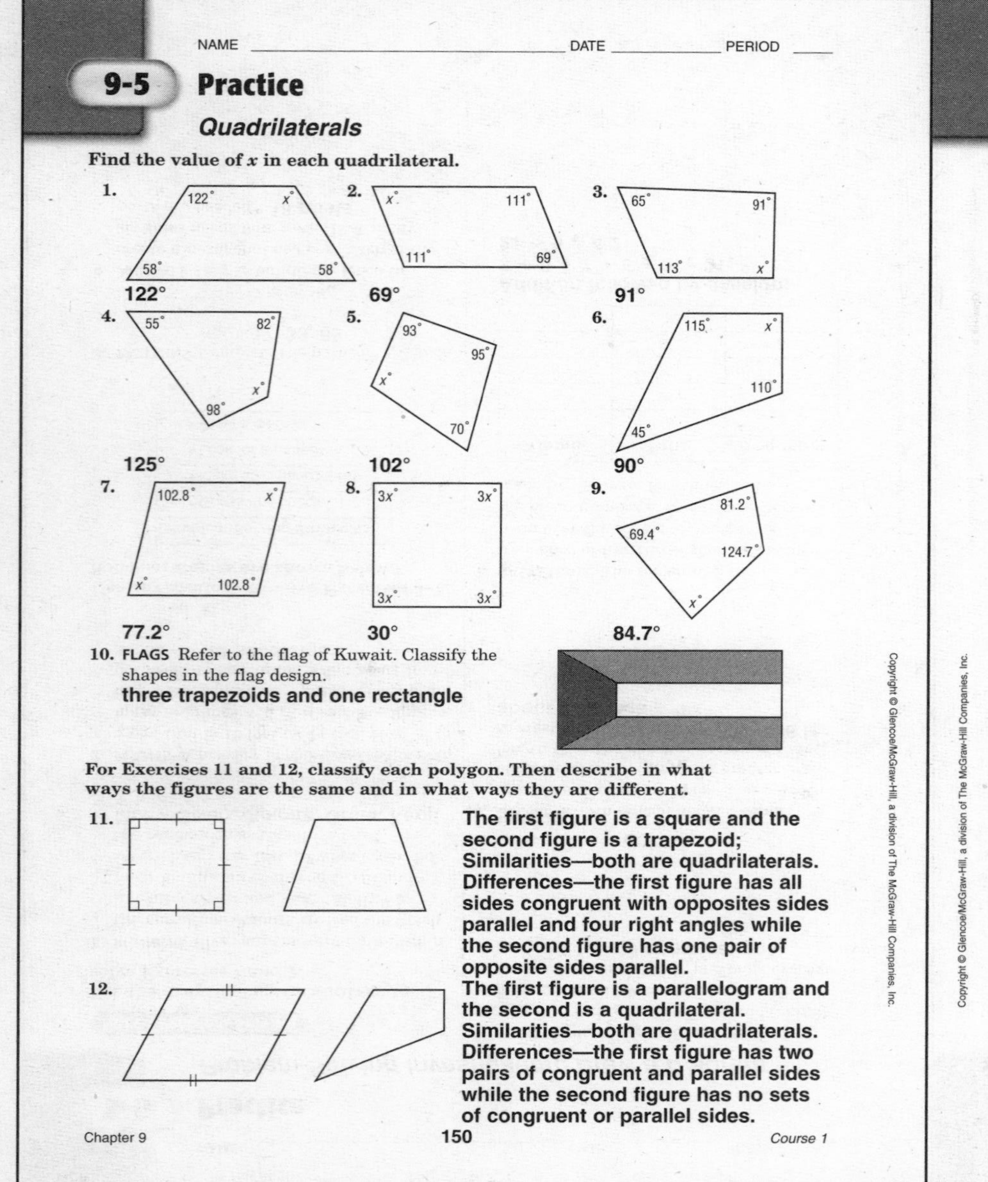

10. FLAGS Refer to the flag of Kuwait. Classify the shapes in the flag design.
three trapezoids and one rectangle

For Exercises 11 and 12, classify each polygon. Then describe in what ways the figures are the same and in what ways they are different.

11. **The first figure is a square and the second figure is a trapezoid; Similarities—both are quadrilaterals. Differences—the first figure has all sides congruent with opposites sides parallel and four right angles while the second figure has one pair of opposite sides parallel.**

12. **The first figure is a parallelogram and the second is a quadrilateral. Similarities—both are quadrilaterals. Differences—the first figure has two pairs of congruent and parallel sides while the second figure has no sets of congruent or parallel sides.**

NAME ______________ DATE ________ PERIOD ____

9-6 Study Guide and Intervention

Problem-Solving Investigation: Draw a Diagram

When solving problems, one strategy that is helpful is to *draw a diagram*. A problem may often describe a situation that is easier to solve visually. You can draw a diagram of the situation, and then use the diagram to solve the problem.

You can draw a diagram, along with the following four-step problem solving plan to solve a problem.

1 Understand – Read and get a general understanding of the problem.

2 Plan – Make a plan to solve the problem and estimate the solution.

3 Solve – Use your plan to solve the problem.

4 Check – Check the reasonableness of your solution.

Example LIBRARY **The school library is putting tables in an open area that is 28 feet by 50 feet. Each table is a square with sides measuring 5 feet, and the tables must be 6 feet apart from each other and the wall. How many tables can fit in this area?**

Understand You know all the dimensions. You need to find how many tables will fit in this area.

Plan Draw a diagram to see how many tables will fit.

Solve

5 ft, 6 ft, 6 ft distance from wall, 6 ft distance between tables, 6 ft distance from wall

The diagram shows that 8 tables will fit in this area in the library.

Check Make sure the dimensions meet the requirements. The distance across is 50 feet and the distance down is 28 feet. So, the answer is correct.

Exercise

PICTURE FRAME La Tasha is decorating a picture frame by gluing gem stones around the frame. The picture frame is 7 inches by $5\frac{1}{2}$ inches. Each gem stone is $\frac{1}{2}$-inch wide and La Tasha glues them 1 inch apart and 1 inch from the edge. How many gem stones can La Tasha fit on the frame?
10 gem stones

Lesson 9–6

NAME ______ DATE ______ PERIOD ______

9-6 Practice

Problem-Solving Investigation: Draw a Diagram

Mixed Problem Solving

Use the draw a diagram strategy to solve Exercises 1 and 2.

1. RUNNING Five runners were far ahead in the marathon. Juanita crossed the finish line after Owen and Molly. Molly was first. Juanita was between Greta and Owen. Kenji was last. In what order did the runners cross the finish line? **Molly, Owen, Juanita, Greta, Kenji**

2. PLANTS A nursery is planting seedlings in a plot that is 10 feet by 14 feet. How many seedlings will fit if each seedling is in a 1-foot square peat pot and each peat pot needs to be planted 3 feet apart from another? **12 seedlings**

Use any strategy to solve Exercises 3–7. Some strategies are shown below.

Problem-Solving Strategies
• Guess and check.
• Make an organized list.
• Look for a pattern.
• Draw a diagram.

3. PATTERNS Complete the pattern: 2, 3, 5, 9, ?, ?, ?. **17, 33, 65**

4. ANIMALS Jacy is building a fence to create a hexagonal dog pen. Each of the six sides needs four posts. How many posts are needed? **18 posts**

5. FOOD A lunch shop offers 2 kinds of soups, 3 kinds of sandwiches, and 3 kinds of beverages. How many combinations of one soup, one sandwich, and one beverage are possible? **18 combinations**

6. GEOMETRY An official doubles tennis court has a length of 78 feet and a width of 36 feet. How many times greater is the length than the width of the court to the nearest tenth? **Division; 78 ÷ 36 is about 2.2 times**

7. BASKETBALL The table gives the frequency of free throw shots made by a team over the course of five games. Find the mean number of free throw shots made by the team for games 1–5.

Game	Tally	Frequency
1	III	3
2	~~IIII~~	5
3	~~IIII~~ II	7
4	~~IIII~~	5
5	I	1

Addition followed by division; $3 + 5 + 7 + 5 + 1 = 21$; $21 \div 5 = 4.2$

NAME ______ DATE ______ PERIOD ______

9-7 Study Guide and Intervention

Similar and Congruent Figures

Figures that have the same size and shape are **congruent figures**.
Figures that have the same shape but not necessarily the same size are **similar figures**.

Examples **Tell whether each pair of figures is *similar*, *congruent*, or *neither*.**

1. The parallelograms have the same shape but not the same size, so they are similar.

2. The triangles have the same shape and size, so they are congruent.

3. The rectangles are neither the same size nor the same shape, so they are neither congruent nor similar.

Example 4 **The rectangles at the right are similar. What side of rectangle *ABCD* corresponds to side *ZY*?**

Corresponding sides represent the same side of similar figures. So, side DC corresponds to side ZY.

Exercises

Tell whether each pair of figures is *congruent*, *similar*, or *neither*.

1. **congruent**

2. **neither**

3. **similar**

For Exercises 4 and 5, refer to the similar parallelograms at the right.

4. What side of parallelogram $HIJK$ corresponds to side QR? **IJ**

5. What side or parallelogram $PQRS$ corresponds to side HK? **PS**

Copyright © Glencoe/McGraw-Hill, a division of The McGraw-Hill Companies, Inc.

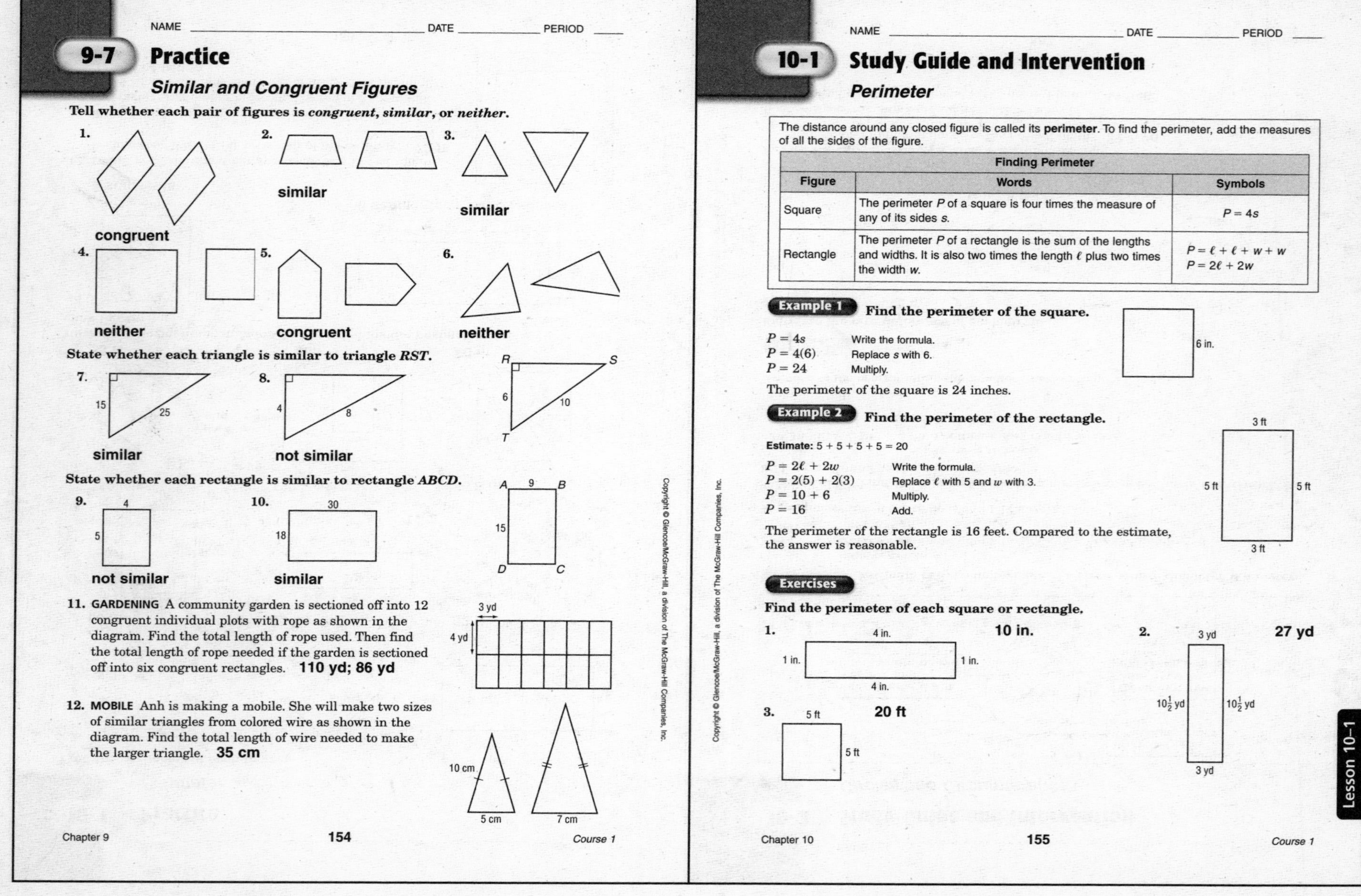

NAME ______________ DATE ________ PERIOD ____

9-7 Practice

Similar and Congruent Figures

Tell whether each pair of figures is *congruent, similar,* or *neither*.

1. congruent
2. similar
3. similar
4. neither
5. congruent
6. neither

State whether each triangle is similar to triangle *RST*.

7. similar

8. not similar

State whether each rectangle is similar to rectangle *ABCD*.

9. not similar

10. similar

11. **GARDENING** A community garden is sectioned off into 12 congruent individual plots with rope as shown in the diagram. Find the total length of rope used. Then find the total length of rope needed if the garden is sectioned off into six congruent rectangles. **110 yd; 86 yd**

12. **MOBILE** Anh is making a mobile. She will make two sizes of similar triangles from colored wire as shown in the diagram. Find the total length of wire needed to make the larger triangle. **35 cm**

NAME ______________ DATE ________ PERIOD ____

10-1 Study Guide and Intervention

Perimeter

The distance around any closed figure is called its **perimeter**. To find the perimeter, add the measures of all the sides of the figure.

Finding Perimeter		
Figure	**Words**	**Symbols**
Square	The perimeter P of a square is four times the measure of any of its sides s.	$P = 4s$
Rectangle	The perimeter P of a rectangle is the sum of the lengths and widths. It is also two times the length ℓ plus two times the width w.	$P = \ell + \ell + w + w$ $P = 2\ell + 2w$

Example 1 **Find the perimeter of the square.**

$P = 4s$ Write the formula.
$P = 4(6)$ Replace s with 6.
$P = 24$ Multiply.

The perimeter of the square is 24 inches.

Example 2 **Find the perimeter of the rectangle.**

Estimate: 5 + 5 + 5 + 5 = 20

$P = 2\ell + 2w$ Write the formula.
$P = 2(5) + 2(3)$ Replace ℓ with 5 and w with 3.
$P = 10 + 6$ Multiply.
$P = 16$ Add.

The perimeter of the rectangle is 16 feet. Compared to the estimate, the answer is reasonable.

Exercises

Find the perimeter of each square or rectangle.

1. **10 in.**

2. **27 yd**

3. **20 ft**

Lesson 10–1

NAME ______________ DATE ________ PERIOD ____

10-1 Practice
Perimeter

Find the perimeter of each figure.

1. 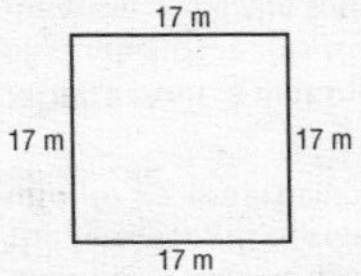 17 m, 17 m, 17 m, 17 m
68 mm

2. 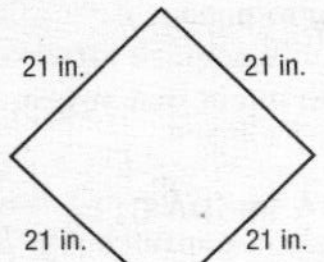 21 in., 21 in., 21 in., 21 in.
84 in.

3. 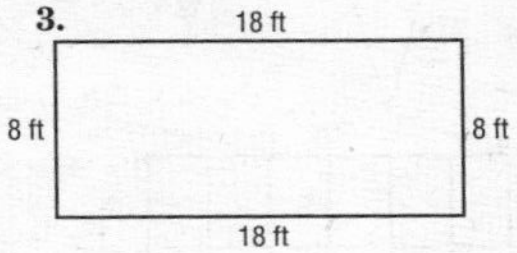 18 ft, 8 ft, 8 ft, 18 ft
52 ft

4. 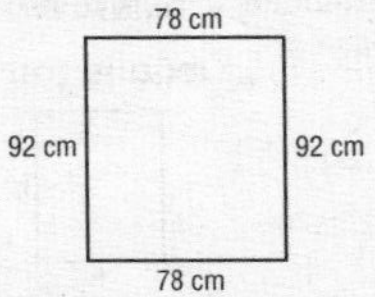 78 cm, 92 cm, 92 cm, 78 cm
340 cm

5. 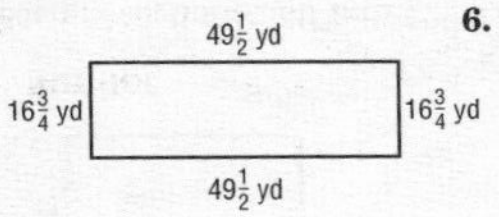 $49\frac{1}{2}$ yd, $16\frac{3}{4}$ yd, $16\frac{3}{4}$ yd, $49\frac{1}{2}$ yd
$132\frac{1}{2}$ yd

6. 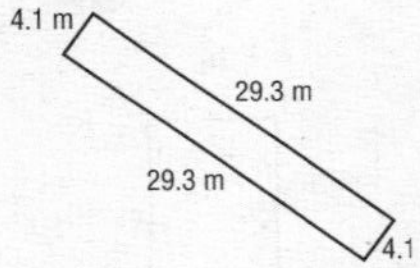 4.1 m, 29.3 m, 29.3 m, 4.1
66.8 m

7. 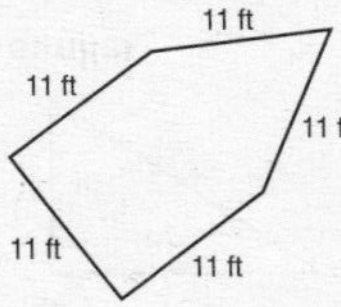 11 ft, 11 ft, 11 ft, 11 ft, 11 ft
55 ft

8. 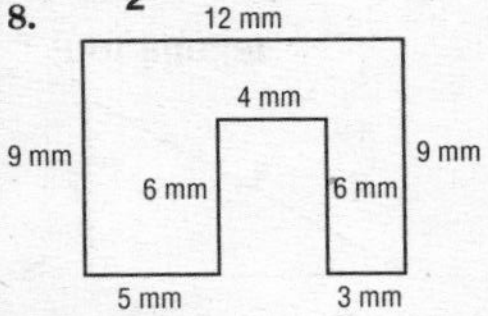 12 mm, 4 mm, 9 mm, 9 mm, 6 mm, 6 mm, 5 mm, 3 mm
54 mm

9. 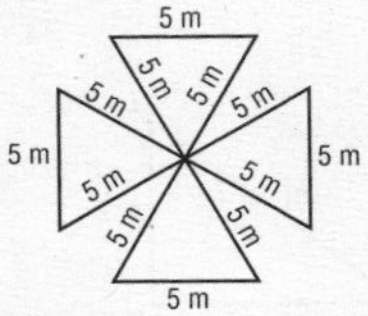 5 m (each side)
60 m

How many segments x units long are needed for the perimeter of each figure?

10. 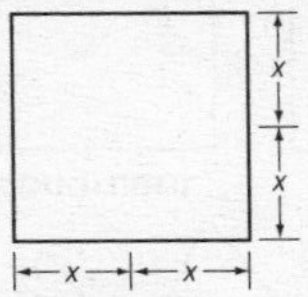 **8 segments**

11. 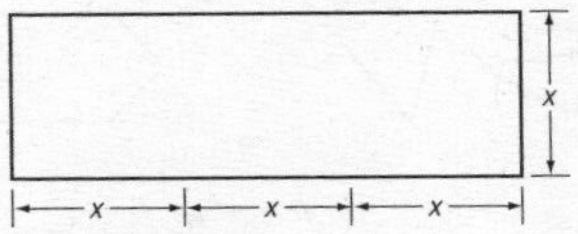 **8 segments**

12. **POOLS** A 4-foot wide walkway surrounds a 10-foot square wading pool. What is the perimeter of the walkway? **72 ft**

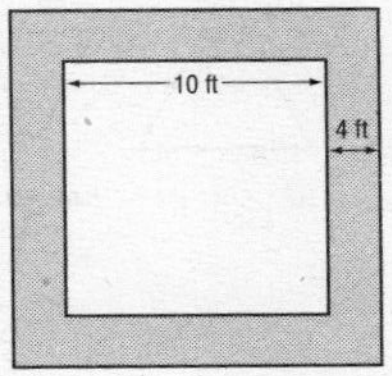

13. **RUGS** Jan wants to sew a fringe border on all sides of a rectangular rug for her bedroom. The rug is 3.4 feet wide and 5.5 feet long. How many feet of fringe does she need?
17.8 ft of fringe

NAME ______________ DATE ________ PERIOD ____

10-2 Study Guide and Intervention
Circles and Circumference

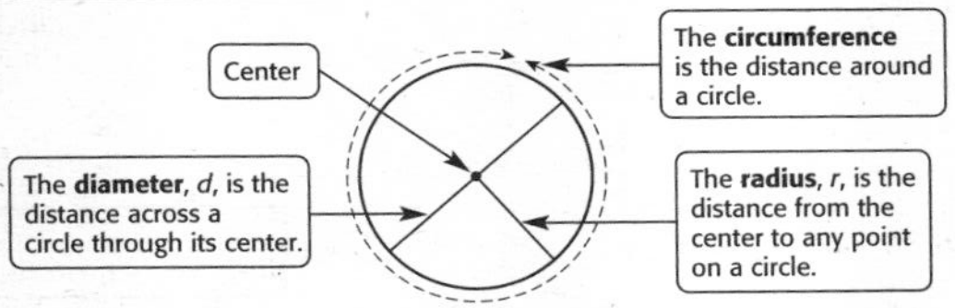

Lesson 10–2

Center

The **circumference** is the distance around a circle.

The **diameter**, d, is the distance across a circle through its center.

The **radius**, r, is the distance from the center to any point on a circle.

The circumference of a circle is equal to π times its diameter or π times twice its radius. $C = \pi d$ or $C = 2\pi r$

Example 1 **Estimate the circumference of a circle whose diameter is 4 meters.**

$C = \pi d$ Write the formula.
$\approx 3 \times 4$ Replace π with 3 and d with 4.
≈ 12 Multiply.

The circumference of the circle is about 12 meters.

Example 2 **Find the circumference of a circle whose radius is 13 inches. Use 3.14 for π. Round to the nearest tenth.**

$C = 2\pi r$ Write the formula.
$= 2 \times 3.14 \times 13$ Replace r with 13 and π with 3.14.
$= 81.64$ Multiply.

Rounded to the nearest tenth, the circumference is about 81.6 inches.

Exercises

Estimate the circumference of each circle.

1. 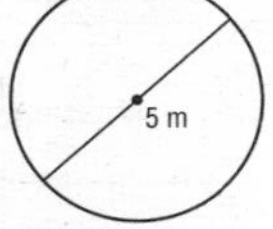 5 m **16 m**

2. 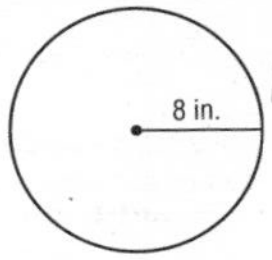 8 in. **50 in.** 48 in

3. 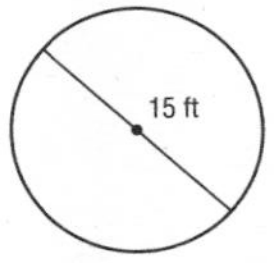 15 ft **47 ft**

4. The radius of a circle measures 16 miles. Find the measure of its circumference to the nearest tenth. Use 3.14 for π. **100.5 mi**

5. Find the circumference of a circle whose diameter is 12 yards. Use 3.14 for π. Round to the nearest tenth. **37.7 yd**

6. Find the circumference of a circle with a radius of 7 inches. Use 3.14 for π. Round to the nearest tenth. **44.0 in.**

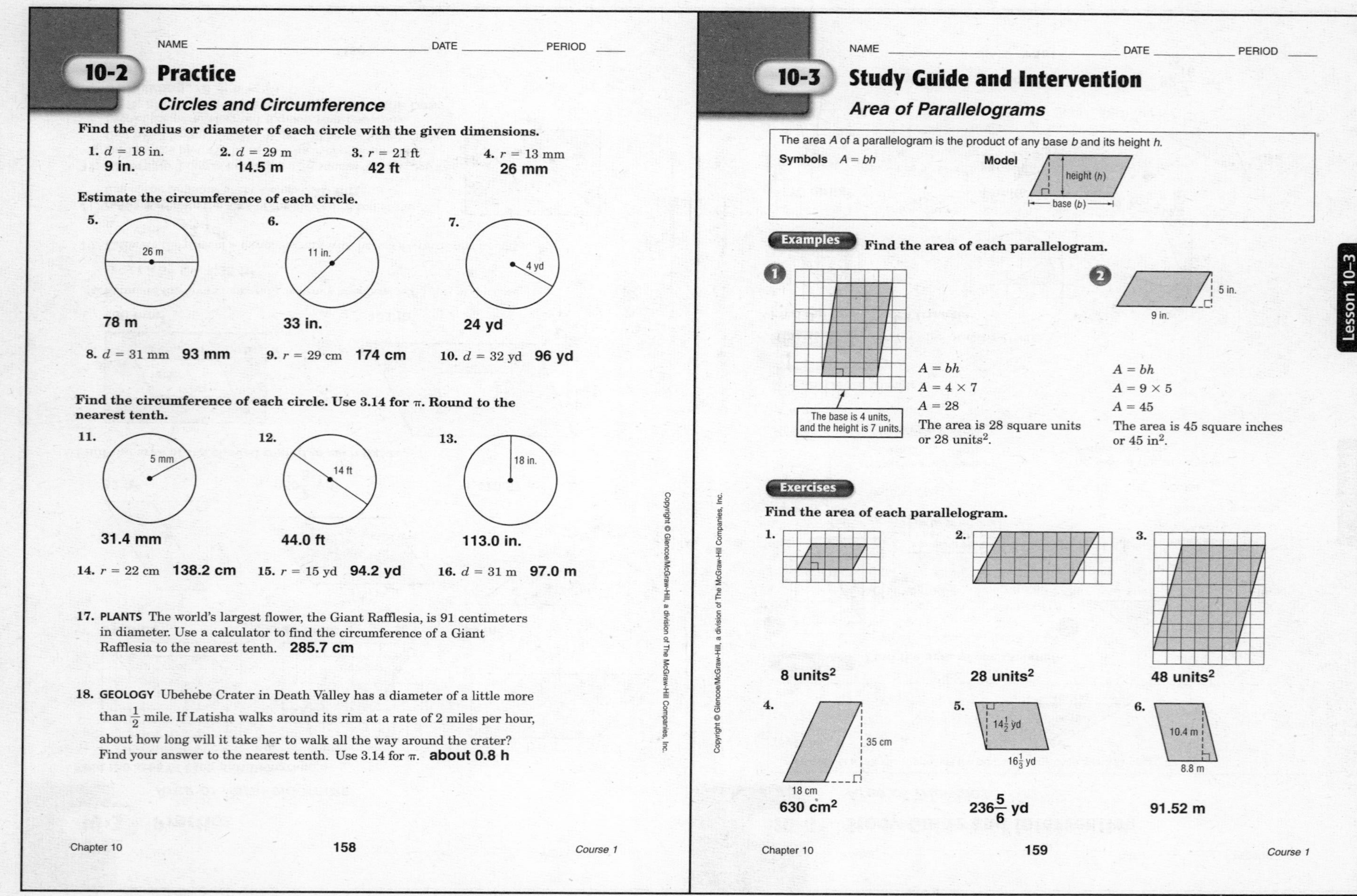

NAME ______________ DATE ________ PERIOD ____

10-2 Practice

Circles and Circumference

Find the radius or diameter of each circle with the given dimensions.

1. $d = 18$ in. **9 in.**
2. $d = 29$ m **14.5 m**
3. $r = 21$ ft **42 ft**
4. $r = 13$ mm **26 mm**

Estimate the circumference of each circle.

5. (26 m) **78 m**
6. (11 in.) **33 in.**
7. (4 yd) **24 yd**
8. $d = 31$ mm **93 mm**
9. $r = 29$ cm **174 cm**
10. $d = 32$ yd **96 yd**

Find the circumference of each circle. Use 3.14 for π. Round to the nearest tenth.

11. (5 mm) **31.4 mm**
12. (14 ft) **44.0 ft**
13. (18 in.) **113.0 in.**
14. $r = 22$ cm **138.2 cm**
15. $r = 15$ yd **94.2 yd**
16. $d = 31$ m **97.0 m**

17. **PLANTS** The world's largest flower, the Giant Rafflesia, is 91 centimeters in diameter. Use a calculator to find the circumference of a Giant Rafflesia to the nearest tenth. **285.7 cm**

18. **GEOLOGY** Ubehebe Crater in Death Valley has a diameter of a little more than $\frac{1}{2}$ mile. If Latisha walks around its rim at a rate of 2 miles per hour, about how long will it take her to walk all the way around the crater? Find your answer to the nearest tenth. Use 3.14 for π. **about 0.8 h**

NAME ______________ DATE ________ PERIOD ____

10-3 Study Guide and Intervention

Area of Parallelograms

The area A of a parallelogram is the product of any base b and its height h.

Symbols $A = bh$ **Model** height (h), base (b)

Examples **Find the area of each parallelogram.**

1. The base is 4 units, and the height is 7 units.

$A = bh$
$A = 4 \times 7$
$A = 28$
The area is 28 square units or 28 units^2.

2. (9 in., 5 in.)

$A = bh$
$A = 9 \times 5$
$A = 45$
The area is 45 square inches or 45 in^2.

Exercises

Find the area of each parallelogram.

1. **8 units^2**
2. **28 units^2**
3. **48 units^2**
4. (18 cm, 35 cm) **630 cm^2**
5. ($14\frac{1}{2}$ yd, $16\frac{1}{3}$ yd) **$236\frac{5}{6}$ yd**
6. (10.4 m, 8.8 m) **91.52 m**

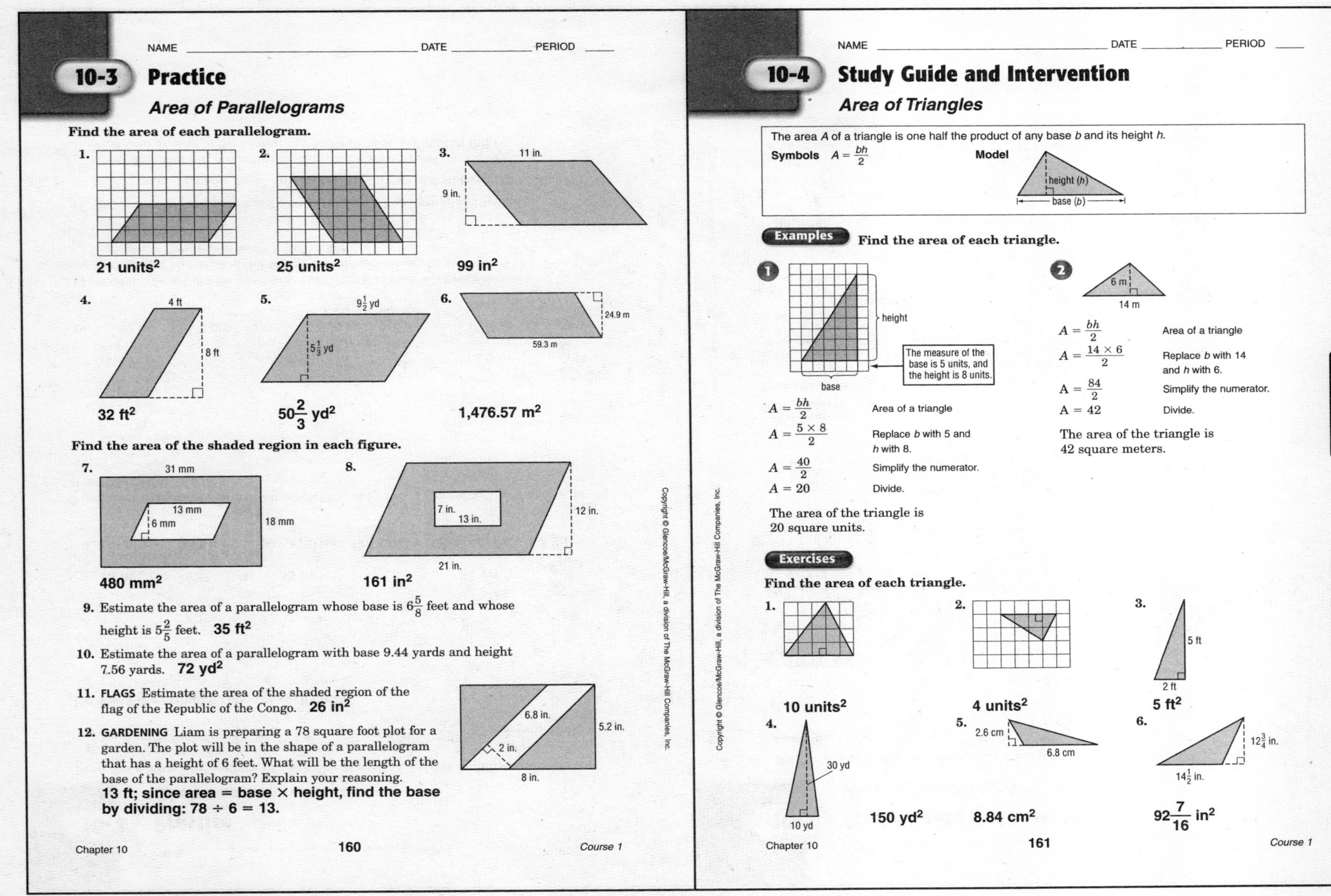

NAME ______________________ DATE __________ PERIOD _____

10-3 Practice

Area of Parallelograms

Find the area of each parallelogram.

1. **21 units²**

2. **25 units²**

3. 11 in., 9 in. **99 in²**

4. 4 ft, 8 ft **32 ft²**

5. $9\frac{1}{2}$ yd, $5\frac{1}{3}$ yd **$50\frac{2}{3}$ yd²**

6. 59.3 m, 24.9 m **1,476.57 m²**

Find the area of the shaded region in each figure.

7. 31 mm, 18 mm, 13 mm, 6 mm **480 mm²**

8. 21 in., 12 in., 7 in., 13 in. **161 in²**

9. Estimate the area of a parallelogram whose base is $6\frac{5}{8}$ feet and whose height is $5\frac{2}{5}$ feet. **35 ft²**

10. Estimate the area of a parallelogram with base 9.44 yards and height 7.56 yards. **72 yd²**

11. **FLAGS** Estimate the area of the shaded region of the flag of the Republic of the Congo. **26 in²**

12. **GARDENING** Liam is preparing a 78 square foot plot for a garden. The plot will be in the shape of a parallelogram that has a height of 6 feet. What will be the length of the base of the parallelogram? Explain your reasoning. **13 ft; since area = base × height, find the base by dividing: 78 ÷ 6 = 13.**

NAME ______________________ DATE __________ PERIOD _____

10-4 Study Guide and Intervention

Area of Triangles

The area A of a triangle is one half the product of any base b and its height h.

Symbols $A = \frac{bh}{2}$

Model

Examples Find the area of each triangle.

1

$A = \frac{bh}{2}$ Area of a triangle

$A = \frac{5 \times 8}{2}$ Replace b with 5 and h with 8.

$A = \frac{40}{2}$ Simplify the numerator.

$A = 20$ Divide.

The area of the triangle is 20 square units.

2

$A = \frac{bh}{2}$ Area of a triangle

$A = \frac{14 \times 6}{2}$ Replace b with 14 and h with 6.

$A = \frac{84}{2}$ Simplify the numerator.

$A = 42$ Divide.

The area of the triangle is 42 square meters.

Exercises

Find the area of each triangle.

1. **10 units²**

2. **4 units²**

3. 5 ft, 2 ft **5 ft²**

4. 30 yd, 10 yd **150 yd²**

5. 2.6 cm, 6.8 cm **8.84 cm²**

6. $12\frac{3}{4}$ in., $14\frac{1}{2}$ in. **$92\frac{7}{16}$ in²**

NAME ______________________ DATE ____________ PERIOD _____

10-4 Practice

Area of Triangles

Find the area of each triangle.

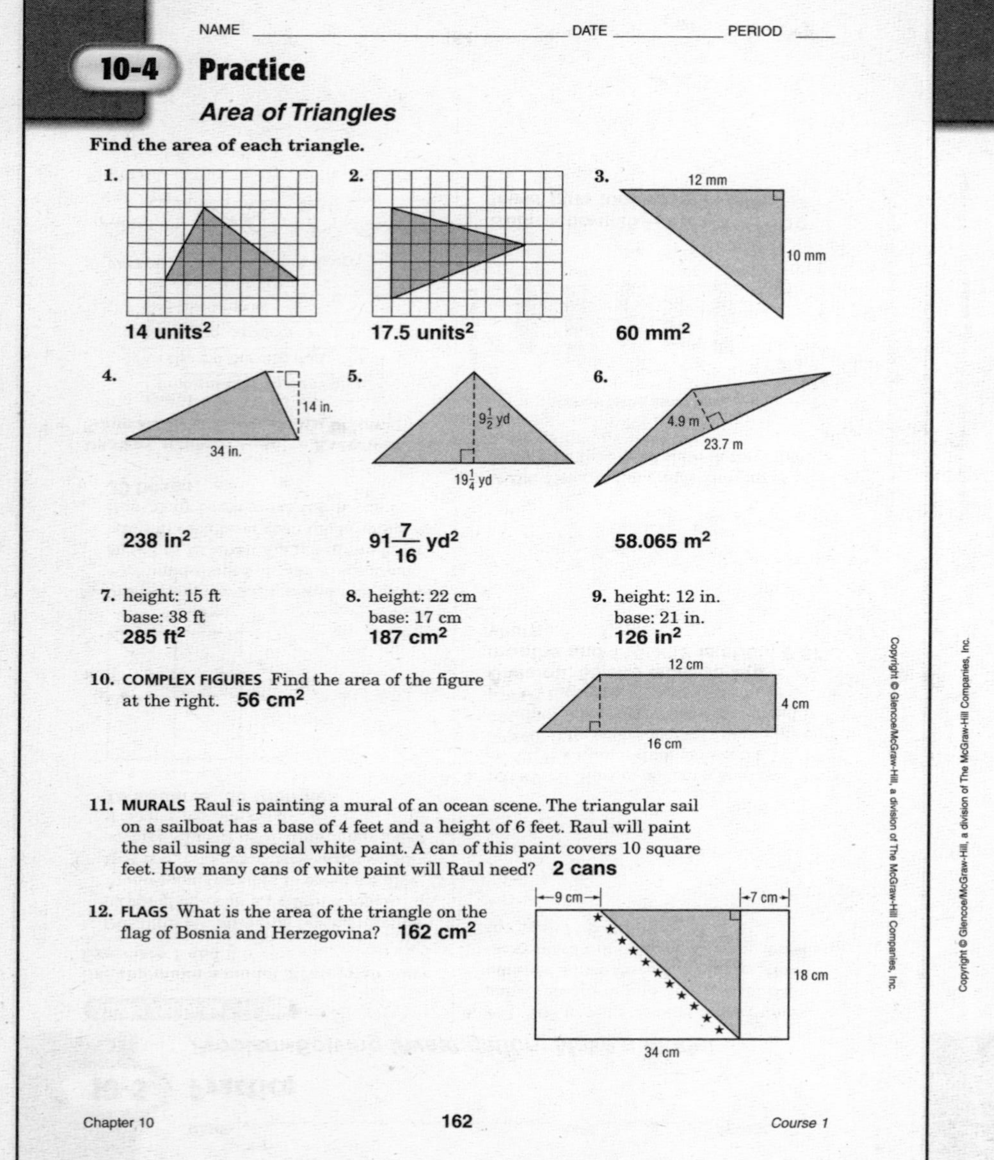

1. **14 units^2**

2. **17.5 units^2**

3. **60 mm^2**

4. **238 in^2**

5. **$91\frac{7}{16}$ yd^2**

6. **58.065 m^2**

7. height: 15 ft
base: 38 ft
285 ft^2

8. height: 22 cm
base: 17 cm
187 cm^2

9. height: 12 in.
base: 21 in.
126 in^2

10. COMPLEX FIGURES Find the area of the figure at the right. **56 cm^2**

11. MURALS Raul is painting a mural of an ocean scene. The triangular sail on a sailboat has a base of 4 feet and a height of 6 feet. Raul will paint the sail using a special white paint. A can of this paint covers 10 square feet. How many cans of white paint will Raul need? **2 cans**

12. FLAGS What is the area of the triangle on the flag of Bosnia and Herzegovina? **162 cm^2**

Copyright © Glencoe/McGraw-Hill, a division of The McGraw-Hill Companies, Inc.

NAME ______________________ DATE ____________ PERIOD _____

10-5 Study Guide and Intervention

Problem-Solving Investigation: Make a Model

When solving problems, one strategy that is helpful is to *make a model.* If a problem gives data that can be displayed visually, it may be useful to make a model of the situation. The model can then be used in order to solve the problem.

You can use the *make a model* strategy, along with the following four-step problem solving plan to solve a problem.

1 Understand – Read and get a general understanding of the problem.

2 Plan – Make a plan to solve the problem and estimate the solution.

3 Solve – Use your plan to solve the problem.

4 Check – Check the reasonableness of your solution.

Example DISPLAYS **A grocery store employee is making a pyramid display of boxes of a new cereal. If he doesn't want to have more than 4 rows in his display, what is the least number of cereal boxes he can use?**

Understand The cereal boxes need to be stacked in the shape of a pyramid. There should only be 4 rows in the pyramid. We need to know the minimum number of boxes of cereal needed to make a pyramid.

Plan Make a model to find the number of cereal boxes needed.

Solve Use a rectangle to represent each cereal box.

The least number of boxes needed is 4 + 3 + 2 + 1, or 10 boxes.

Check Count the number of boxes in the model. There are 10 boxes.

Exercise

TILING Michael has 18 decorative square tiles to make a design on a kitchen backsplash. He wants to arrange them in a rectangular shape with the least perimeter possible. How many tiles will be in each row? **3 tiles or 6 tiles**

NAME ______________________ DATE ____________ PERIOD _____

10-5 Practice

Problem-Solving Investigation: Make a Model

Mixed Problem Solving

Use the make a model strategy to solve Exercises 1 and 2.

1. QUILTING Ms. Mosely is sewing together blocks of fabric in a pattern of small squares and triangles to make a quilt that is 3 feet square. How many small squares will she need? How many small triangles will she need?
18 squares; 36 triangles

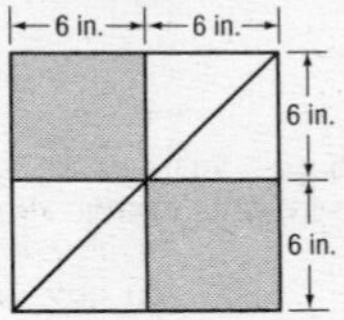

6 in. 6 in. 6 in. 6 in.

2. DISPLAY Anaba is stacking cereal boxes in a pyramid-shaped display. The bottom layer has 10 boxes. There are two fewer boxes in each layer than the layer below. How many boxes are in the display?
30 boxes

Use any strategy to solve Exercises 3–6. Some strategies are shown below.

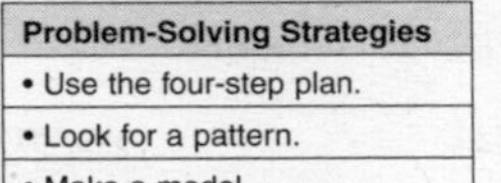

Problem-Solving Strategies
• Use the four-step plan.
• Look for a pattern.
• Make a model.

3. PATTERNS Draw the next figure.

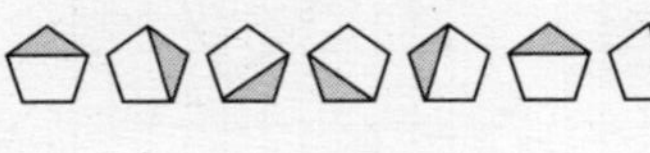

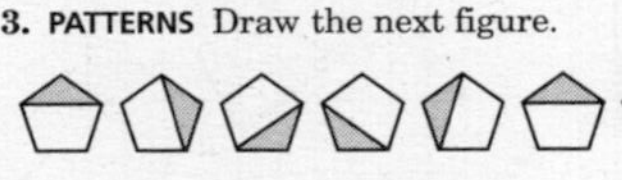
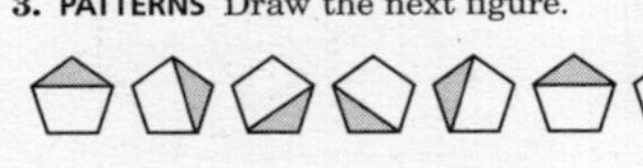
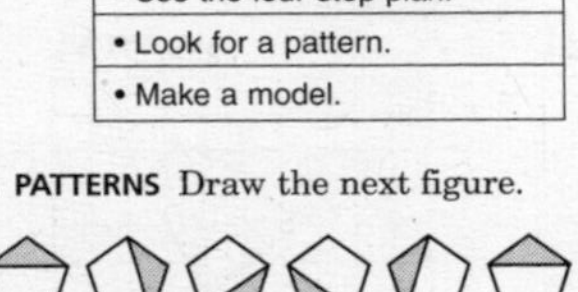
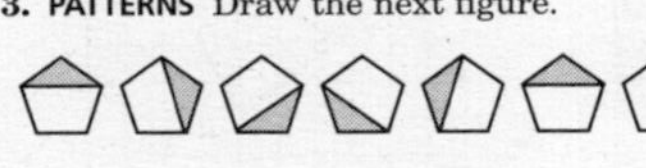
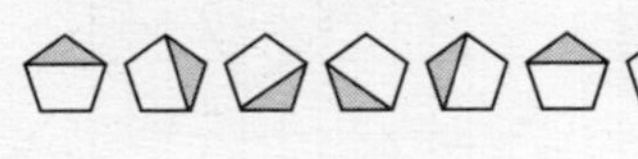

4. ART Kris folded a piece of construction paper into thirds and then in half. He punched a hole through all layers. How many holes will there be when he unfolds the paper? **6 holes**

5. LOANS Mr. Kartini bought a boat on credit. His loan, including interest, is $9,860. If he makes monthly payments of $85, how many years will it take him to pay off the loan?
Division; $9,860 ÷ $85 is 116 months and 116 ÷ 12 is about 9.67 years.

6. MUSIC Refer to the graph. How many fewer girls took band class in 2005 than in 2004?

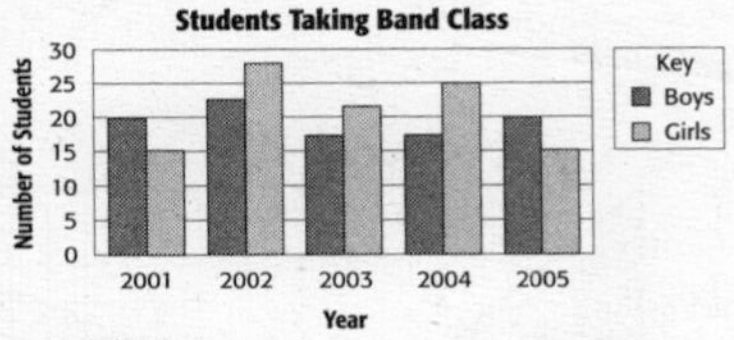

Students Taking Band Class

Number of Students: 0, 5, 10, 15, 20, 25, 30

Year: 2001, 2002, 2003, 2004, 2005

Key: Boys, Girls

Subtraction; 25 − 15 = 10, so 10 fewer girls took band in 2005.

NAME ______________________ DATE ____________ PERIOD _____

10-6 Study Guide and Intervention

Volume of Rectangular Prisms

The amount of space inside a three-dimensional figure is the **volume** of the figure. Volume is measured in **cubic units**. This tells you the number of cubes of a given size it will take to fill the prism.

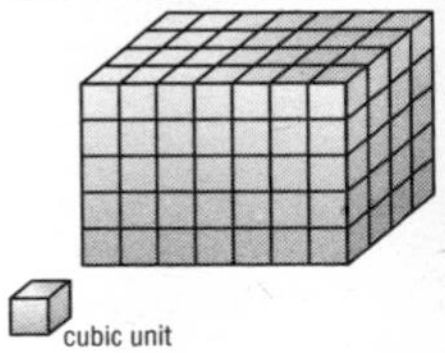

cubic unit

The volume V of a rectangular prism is the product of its length ℓ, width w, and height h.
Symbols $V = \ell wh$

Model (ℓ, w, h)

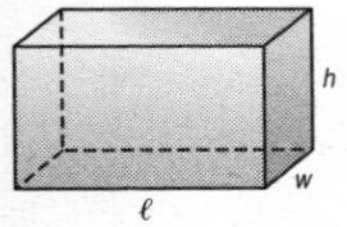

You can also multiply the area of the base B by the height h to find the volume V.
Symbols $V = Bh$

Model (B, h)

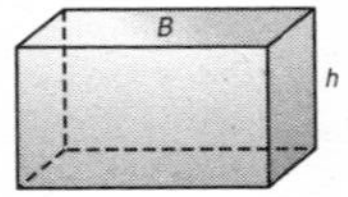

Example **Find the volume of the rectangular prism.** (10 ft, 5 ft, 2 ft)

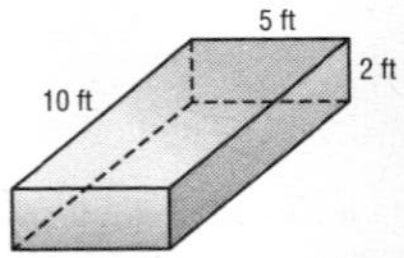

Method 1 Use $V = \ell wh$.
$V = \ell wh$
$V = 10 \times 5 \times 2$
$V = 100$
The volume is 100 ft³.

Method 2 Use $V = Bh$.
$V = Bh$ — B, the area of the base, is 10 × 5 or 50.
$V = 50 \times 2$
$V = 100$
The volume is 100 ft³.

Exercises

Find the volume of each prism.

1. 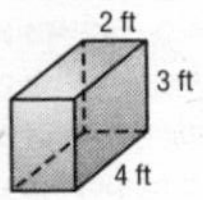 (2 ft, 3 ft, 4 ft) **24 ft³**

2. 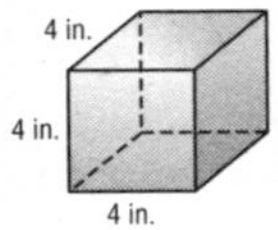 (4 in., 4 in., 4 in.) **64 in³**

3. 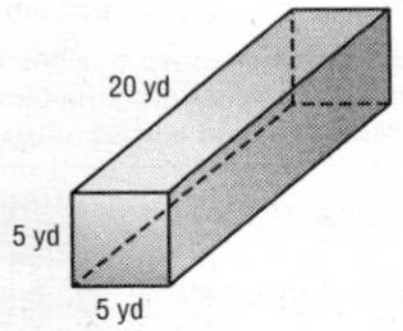 (20 yd, 5 yd, 5 yd) **500 yd³**

4. 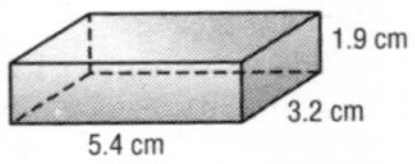 (1.9 cm, 3.2 cm, 5.4 cm) **32.832 cm³**

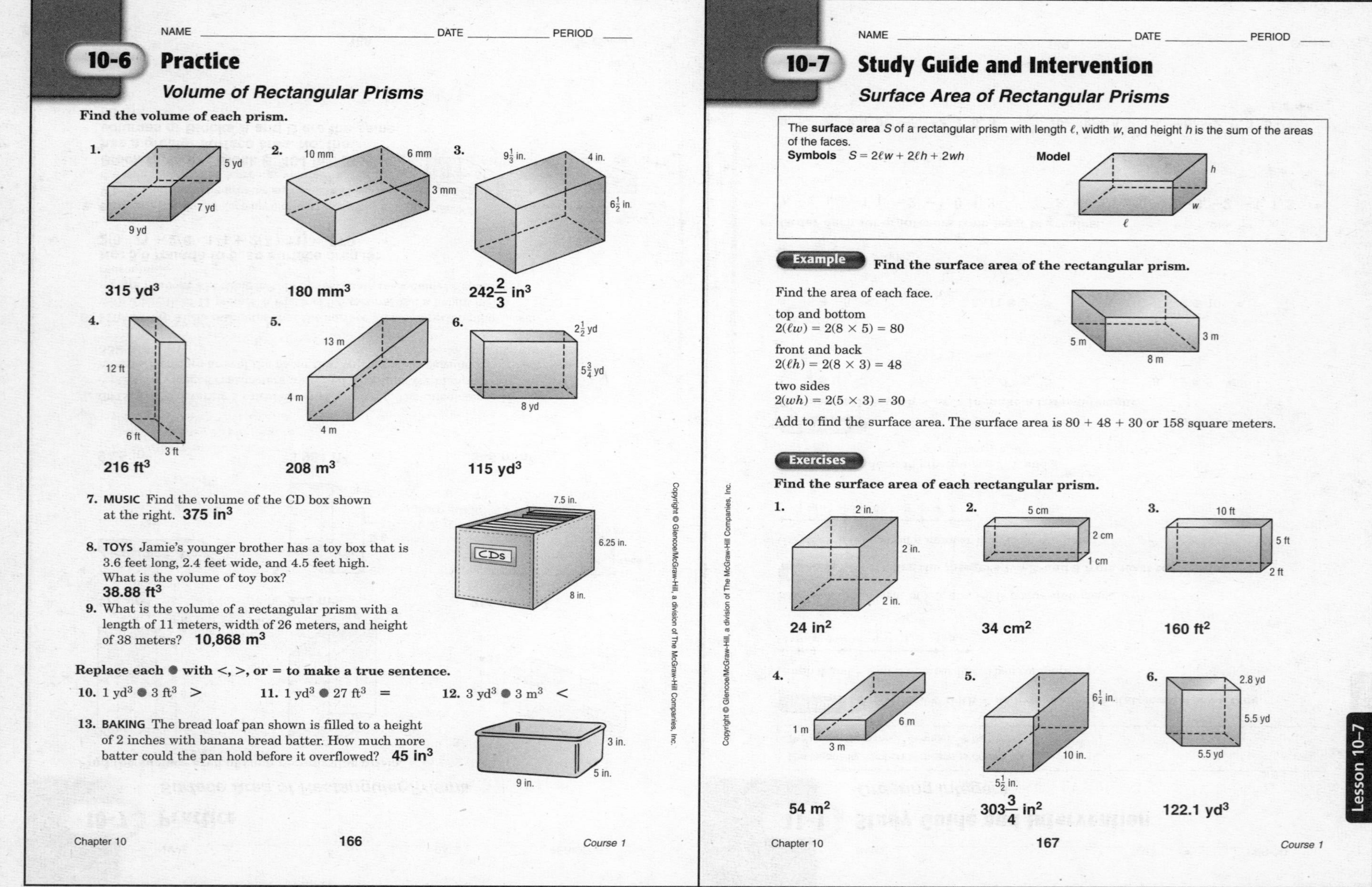

NAME ________ DATE ______ PERIOD ____

10-6 Practice

Volume of Rectangular Prisms

Find the volume of each prism.

1. 5 yd, 7 yd, 9 yd — **315 yd³**
2. 10 mm, 6 mm, 3 mm — **180 mm³**
3. $9\frac{1}{3}$ in., 4 in., $6\frac{1}{2}$ in. — **$242\frac{2}{3}$ in³**
4. 12 ft, 6 ft, 3 ft — **216 ft³**
5. 13 m, 4 m, 4 m — **208 m³**
6. $2\frac{1}{2}$ yd, $5\frac{3}{4}$ yd, 8 yd — **115 yd³**

7. MUSIC Find the volume of the CD box shown at the right. **375 in³**

8. TOYS Jamie's younger brother has a toy box that is 3.6 feet long, 2.4 feet wide, and 4.5 feet high. What is the volume of toy box? **38.88 ft³**
9. What is the volume of a rectangular prism with a length of 11 meters, width of 26 meters, and height of 38 meters? **10,868 m³**

Replace each ● with <, >, or = to make a true sentence.

10. 1 yd³ ● 3 ft³ **>**
11. 1 yd³ ● 27 ft³ **=**
12. 3 yd³ ● 3 m³ **<**

13. BAKING The bread loaf pan shown is filled to a height of 2 inches with banana bread batter. How much more batter could the pan hold before it overflowed? **45 in³**

NAME ________ DATE ______ PERIOD ____

10-7 Study Guide and Intervention

Surface Area of Rectangular Prisms

The **surface area** S of a rectangular prism with length ℓ, width w, and height h is the sum of the areas of the faces.

Symbols $S = 2\ell w + 2\ell h + 2wh$

Model

Example **Find the surface area of the rectangular prism.**

Find the area of each face.

top and bottom
$2(\ell w) = 2(8 \times 5) = 80$

front and back
$2(\ell h) = 2(8 \times 3) = 48$

two sides
$2(wh) = 2(5 \times 3) = 30$

Add to find the surface area. The surface area is 80 + 48 + 30 or 158 square meters.

Exercises

Find the surface area of each rectangular prism.

1. 2 in., 2 in., 2 in. — **24 in²**
2. 5 cm, 2 cm, 1 cm — **34 cm²**
3. 10 ft, 5 ft, 2 ft — **160 ft²**
4. 1 m, 3 m, 6 m — **54 m²**
5. $6\frac{1}{4}$ in., 10 in., $5\frac{1}{2}$ in. — **$303\frac{3}{4}$ in²**
6. 2.8 yd, 5.5 yd, 5.5 yd — **122.1 yd³**

NAME ______________ DATE ________ PERIOD ____

10-7 Practice

Surface Area of Rectangular Prisms

Find the surface area of each rectangular prism.

1. 5 yd, 3 yd, 9 yd
174 yd²

2. 7 m, 4 m, 8 m
232 m²

3. 3.8 cm, 3.8 cm, 12 cm
211.28 cm²

4. $9\frac{1}{2}$ in., 3 in., $1\frac{1}{2}$ in.
94.5 in²

5. 20 ft, 26 ft, 32 ft
3,984 ft²

6. 17 mm, 5 mm, 4 mm
346 mm²

7. GIFTS Eric is covering a calculator with gift wrap. The calculator is 15 centimeters long, 8 centimeters wide, and 2 centimeters high. What is the minimum surface area of the paper that will cover the calculator?
332 cm²

8. ESTIMATION Alicia estimates that the surface area of a rectangular prism with a length of 11 meters, a width of 5.6 meters, and a height of 7.2 meters is about 334 cubic feet. Is her estimate reasonable? Explain your reasoning.
No; 5.6 rounds to 6, so surface area is: $2(6 \cdot 7) + 2(6 \cdot 11) + 2(7 \cdot 11) = 370$

9. BLOCKS Find the surface area of each play block. Which block has the greater surface area? Does the same block have a greater volume? Explain.
Block A: 94 in²; Block B: 104 in²; Block B has a greater surface area. No, the volumes of Blocks A and B are the same, 60 in³.

Block A: 3 in., 4 in., 5 in.
Block B: 2 in., 5 in., 6 in.

NAME ______________ DATE ________ PERIOD ____

11-1 Study Guide and Intervention

Ordering Integers

The inequality symbol '>' means *is greater than*.
The inequality symbol '<' means *is less than*.

Example 1 **Replace ● with < or > to make the statement 4 ● −5 true.**

Graph 4 and −5 on a number line. Then compare.

−5 −4 −3 −2 −1 0 1 2 3 4 5

Since 4 is to the right of −5, 4 > −5 is a true statement.

Example 2 **Order the integers 1, −2, and 3 from least to greatest.**

Graph each integer on a number line. Then compare.

−5 −4 −3 −2 −1 0 1 2 3 4 5

The order from least to greatest is −2, 1, and 3.

Exercises

Replace each ● with < or > to make a true statement.

1. −2 ● 0 **<**
2. 3 ● −3 **>**
3. −9 ● 8 **<**
4. −8 ● −3 **<**
5. 11 ● 3 **>**
6. −2 ● 10 **<**

Order each set of integers from least to greatest.

7. −2, 3, 0, −1, 1 **−2, −1, 0, 1, 3**
8. 3, −3, −2, 1, −1 **−3, −2, −1, 1, 3**
9. 5, −7, −2, 1, 9 **−7, −2, 1, 5, 9**
10. −2, 1, 5, −5, 0 **−5, −2, 0, 1, 5**

NAME ______________________ DATE __________ PERIOD ____

11-1 Practice

Ordering Integers

Replace each ● with < or > to make a true sentence.

1. 18 ● 23 **<**
2. −9 ● −1 **<**
3. −3 ● −5 **>**
4. 8 ● −2 **>**
5. 6 ● −3 **>**
6. 0 ● 8 **<**
7. 6 ● −7 **>**
8. −23 ● −16 **<**

Order each set of integers from least to greatest.

9. 10, −5, 3 16, −1, 0, and 1
−5, −1, 0, 1, 3, 10, 16
10. −2.5, 4, 23, −1, 5, −3, and 0.66
−3, −2.5, −1, 0.66, 4, 5, 23
11. 1, −2.5, 0.75, 3, and −0.75
−2.5, −0.75, 0.75, 1, 3
12. 63, −34, 36, −27, −13, and 12
−34, −27, −13, 12, 36, 63

Order each set of integers from greatest to least.

13. 8, 43, −25, 12, −14, and 3
43, 12, 8, 3, −14, −25
14. −8, 32, 55, −32, −19, and −3
55, 32, −3, −8, −19, −32
15. −100, −89, −124, −69, and −52
−52, −69, −89, −100, −124
16. 6, 17, −20, 15, −19, and 26
26, 17, 15, 6, −19, −20

ROLLER COASTERS The table shows how several roller coasters compare to the Mantis. Refer to the table to answer Exercises 17–20.

Roller Coaster	Lift Heights (ft)	Vertical Drop (ft)
Gemini	−20	−19
Magnum XL-200	60	58
Top Thrill Dragster	275	263
Mantis	0	0
Millenium Force	165	163
Mean Streak	16	18
Raptor	−8	−18

Source: Cedar Point

17. Which roller coaster has the greatest lift height?
Top Thrill Dragster
18. What is the median lift height for the roller coasters listed? Round to the nearest tenth.
161 feet
19. Arrange the given roller coasters from least to greatest lift height.
Gemini, Raptor, Mantis, Mean Streak, Magnum XL-200, Millenium Force, Top Thrill Dragster
20. What is the median of the data for vertical drop? **155 feet**

NAME ______________________ DATE __________ PERIOD ____

11-2 Study Guide and Intervention

Adding Integers

- The sum of two positive integers is always positive.
- The sum of two negative integers is always negative.
- The sum of a positive integer and a negative integer is sometimes positive, sometimes negative, and sometimes zero.

Example 1 **Find −3 + (−2).**

Method 1 Use counters.

Place 3 negative counters on the mat to show −3.

Place 2 negative counters on the mat to show −2.

So, −3 + (−2) = −5.

Method 2 Use a number line.

Start at 0. Move 3 units to the left to show −3. From there, move 2 units to the left to show −2.

−2 −3

−6 −5 −4 −3 −2 −1 0 1 2 3 4 5 6

Example 2 **Find 4 + (−1).**

Method 1 Use counters.

Place 4 positive counters on the mat to show +4. Place 1 negative counter on the mat to show −1.

So, 4 + (−1) = 3.

Method 2 Use a number line.

Start at 0. Move 4 units to the right to show +4. From there, move 1 unit to the left to show −1.

+4 −1

−6 −5 −4 −3 −2 −1 0 1 2 3 4 5 6

Exercises

Add. Use counters or a number line if necessary.

1. 3 + (−6) **−3**
2. −9 + 8 **−1**
3. −4 + 7 **+3 or 3**
4. 6 + (−6) **0**
5. −8 + (−2) **−10**
6. 2 + (−5) **−3**
7. 6 + (−12) **−6**
8. −6 + (−5) **−11**
9. 4 + (−3) **+1 or 1**
10. −12 + 5 **−7**
11. −4 + 10 **+6 or 6**
12. −3 + (−5) **−8**

NAME ______________________ DATE __________ PERIOD ____

11-2 Practice
Adding Integers

Add. Use counters or a number line if necessary.

1. +8 + (+4) **+12 or 12**
2. −10 + (+7) **−3**
3. −2 + (−10) **−12**
4. +9 + (−1) **+8 or 8**
5. −6 + (−5) **−11**
6. +8 + (+9) **+17 or 17**
7. +5 + (−3) **+2 or 2**
8. −4 + (−9) **−13**
9. −2 + (+14) **+12 or 12**
10. −15 + (+13) **−2**
11. +10 + (+4) **+14 or 14**
12. +8 + (−12) **−4**
13. +16 + (−5) **+11 or 11**
14. +9 + (−3) **+6 or 6**
15. −3 + (−8) **−11**
16. −1 + (+1) **0**

Add.

17. 2 + (−9) + 3 + 6 **2**
18. 3 + (−8) + 7 + (−1) + (−11) **−10**
19. 11 + 7 + (−3) + 5 + (−4) **16**
20. −2 + (−14) + 9 + 0 + 6 **−1**

21. **RAPPELLING** The Moaning Caverns in California are 410 feet deep. A rappeller descends by rope 165 feet into the main cavern. How much deeper can the rappeller go into the cavern?
245 feet

22. **SEWING** Keisha discovered a mistake in her cross-stitch project after she had completed a row. To remove the mistake she had to pull out 72 stitches. She then sewed 39 stitches before having to change to a new thread color. If her starting point is zero, at what point is she in the row now?
−33

23. Which expression is represented by the number line below?
−7 + 12 = 5

+12
−7
−11 −10 −9 −8 −7 −6 −5 −4 −3 −2 −1 0 1 2 3 4 5 6 7 8 9 10 11

NAME ______________________ DATE __________ PERIOD ____

11-3 Study Guide and Intervention
Subtracting Integers

To subtract an integer, add its opposite.

Example 1 **Find −4 − (−3).**

Method 1 Use counters.

Place 4 negative counters on the mat to show −4. Remove 3 negative counters to show subtracting −3.

So, −4 − (−3) = −1.

Method 2 Use the rule.

−4 − (−3) = −4 + 3 To subtract −3, add 3.
= −1 Simplify.

Example 2 **Find −3 − 1.**

Method 1 Use counters.

Place 3 negative counters on the mat to show −3. To subtract +1, you must remove 1 positive counter. But there are no positive counters on the mat. You must add 1 zero pair to the mat. The value of the mat does not change. Then you can remove 1 positive counter.

The difference of −3 and 1 is −4.

So, −3 − 1 = −4.

Method 2 Use the rule.

−3 − 1 = −3 + (−1) To subtract 1, add −1.
= −4 Simplify.

Exercises

Subtract. Use counters if necessary.

1. +8 − 5 **3**
2. −4 − 2 **−6**
3. 7 − (−5) **12**
4. −3 − (−5) **2**
5. 6 − (−10) **16**
6. −8 − (−4) **−4**
7. −1 − 4 **−5**
8. 2 − (−2) **4**
9. −5 − (−1) **−4**
10. 7 − 2 **5**
11. −9 − (−9) **0**
12. 6 − (−2) **8**
13. −8 − (−14) **6**
14. −2 − 9 **−11**
15. 5 − 15 **−10**

Lesson 11–3

Copyright © Glencoe/McGraw-Hill, a division of The McGraw-Hill Companies, Inc.

NAME ______________ DATE ________ PERIOD ____

11-3 Practice

Subtracting Integers

Subtract. Use counters if necessary.

1. 12 − 9 **3**
2. 11 − 13 **−2**
3. −6 − 15 **−21**
4. 8 − 4 **4**
5. −8 − (−15) **7**
6. −8 − (−5) **−3**
7. 10 − (−12) **22**
8. −1 − 6 **−7**
9. 5 − (−5) **10**
10. −7 − (−13) **6**
11. −17 − (−19) **2**
12. 3 − (−13) **16**
13. −3 − 9 **−12**
14. 14 − (−4) **18**
15. 0 − (−8) **8**
16. −13 − (−12) **−1**

17. The table at the right shows the results of two consecutive Biology tests for James, Mazen, Mia, and Shameeka. What is the test differential for each student?
James: 12; Mazen: −9; Mia: 16; Shameeka: −2

Biology Test Results		
Student	**Test 1**	**Test 2**
James	84	96
Mazen	98	89
Mia	70	86
Shameeka	100	98

18. ALGEBRA Evaluate $c - d$ if $c = 4$ and $d = 9$. **−5**

19. The blue whale can dive as deep as 1,640 feet. A blue whale is at 600 feet below sea level and rises 370 feet to feed. It then dives 90 feet. Where is it?
−320 feet

20. SWIMMING Sara swims at the community center every day. One week she swam a total of 13.5 hours. Complete the table.

Day	Number of Hours
Monday	1.5
Tuesday	2.0
Wednesday	1.5
Thursday	1.5
Friday	2.0
Saturday	**3.0**
Sunday	2.0

NAME ______________ DATE ________ PERIOD ____

11-4 Study Guide and Intervention

Multiplying Integers

- The product of two integers with different signs is negative.
- The product of two integers with the same sign is positive.

Examples **Multiply.**

1 **2 × (−1)**

2 × (−1) = −2 The integers have different signs. The product is negative.

2 **−4 × 3**

−4 × 3 = −12 The integers have different signs. The product is negative.

3 **3 × 5**

3 × 5 = 15 The integers have the same sign. The product is positive.

4 **−2 × (−4)**

−2 × (−4) = 8 The integers have the same sign. The product is positive.

Exercises

Multiply.

1. 3 × (−3) **−9**
2. −5 × (−2) **10**
3. −8 × (−1) **8**
4. −2 × 8 **−16**
5. 4 × −3 **−12**
6. −3 × (−2) **6**
7. 5 × (−4) **−20**
8. −10 × (−4) **40**
9. −3 × 6 **−18**
10. −3 × (−10) **30**
11. 6 × (−4) **−24**
12. −7 × (−7) **49**

NAME ______________________ DATE __________ PERIOD _____

11-4 Practice

Multiplying Integers

Multiply.

1. -2×15 **−30**	2. $-4 \times (-11)$ **44**	3. $-3 \times (-3)$ **9**	4. $7(2)$ **14**
5. $6(-8)$ **−48**	6. 13×8 **104**	7. $15(-6)$ **−90**	8. -12×3 **−36**
9. $-10(-4)$ **40**	10. $-1(-7)$ **7**	11. 8×3 **24**	12. $-6 \times (-4)$ **24**
13. 13×7 **91**	14. $2 \times (-6)$ **−12**	15. -9×9 **−81**	16. $-3(-14)$ **42**
17. $9(-3 - 8)$ **−99**	18. $-7(4)(-5)$ **140**	19. $-2(6 + (-7))$ **2**	20. $7(-3 + 3)$ **0**
21. $-2(8 + (-6))$ **−4**	22. $3(-5)(2)$ **−30**	23. $4(-2 + 9)$ **28**	24. $-3(-4 - 4)$ **24**

25. **PATTERNS** Find the next two numbers in the pattern. Then describe the pattern.

$$8, -24, 72, -216, \ldots$$

648, −1,944; Each previous term is multiplied by −3.

26. **ALGEBRA** Find the value of mn if $m = -7$ and $n = -12$. **84**

27. **CONSTRUCTION** The arm and torch of the Statue of Liberty were completed for the International Centennial Exhibition in Philadelphia in 1876. It took 20 men working 10 hours a day, 7 days a week, to complete it for the exhibition. What was the total number of hours worked in a week?
1,400 hours

28. **EXERCISE** After finishing her workout, Felicia's heart rate decreased by 2 beats per minute for each of the next 5 minutes. Write an integer to represent the change in her heart rate at the end of 5 minutes. **−10**

NAME ______________________ DATE __________ PERIOD _____

11-5 Study Guide and Intervention

Problem-Solving Investigation: Work Backward

When solving problems, one strategy that is helpful is to *work backward.* Sometimes you can use information in the problem to work backwards to find what you are looking for, or the answer to the problem.

You can use the *work backward* strategy, along with the following four-step problem solving plan to solve a problem.

1 Understand – Read and get a general understanding of the problem.

2 Plan – Make a plan to solve the problem and estimate the solution.

3 Solve – Use your plan to solve the problem.

4 Check – Check the reasonableness of your solution.

Example **TIME Meagan is meeting her friends at the library at 6:30 P.M. Before her mom takes her to the library, they are going to stop by her grandma's house to drop something off. It takes 15 minutes to get from her house to her grandma's house and they will stay and visit for 30 minutes. If it takes 5 minutes to get from her grandma's house to the library, what time should Meagan and her mom leave their house?**

Understand We know the time Meagan is meeting her friends at the library. We need to find what time Meagan and her mom should leave their house.

Plan To find the time they should leave, start with the 6:30 P.M. and first subtract 5 minutes for the time it takes to get from her grandma's house to the library.

Solve

Time from grandma's to library:	6:30 P.M. − 5 minutes = 6:25 P.M.
Time visiting with grandma:	6:25 P.M. − 30 minutes = 5:55 P.M.
Time from home to grandma's:	5:55 P.M. − 15 minutes = 5:40 P.M.

Meagan and her mom should leave their house at 5:40 P.M.

Check Add up all the times, 15 min + 30 min + 5 min = 50 min. When you subtract 50 minutes from 6:30, the result is 5:40, so the answer is correct.

Exercise

NUMBER SENSE A number is divided by 3. Next, 7 is added to the quotient. Then, 10 is subtracted from the sum. If the result is 5, what is the number? **24**

Lesson 11–5

Copyright © Glencoe/McGraw-Hill, a division of The McGraw-Hill Companies, Inc.

NAME ______________________ DATE ____________ PERIOD _____

11-5 Practice

Problem-Solving Investigation: Work Backward

Mixed Problem Solving

Work backward to solve Exercises 1 and 2.

1. NUMBER SENSE A number is multiplied by 4. Next, 3 is added to the product, and then 11 is subtracted. If the result is 24, what is the number? **8**

2. Ichiko has guitar practice at 5:00 P.M. on Wednesday. It takes 20 minute for him to get to his lesson from school. He spends an hour in the science lab before leaving. If it takes 10 minutes to get ready for the lab, what time does his last class end? **3:30 p.m.**

Use any strategy to solve Exercises 3–6. Some strategies are shown below.

Problem-Solving Strategies
• Act it out.
• Make a table.
• Choose the method of computation.

3. GEOGRAPHY North America has an area of 21,393,762 square kilometers. South America has an area of 17,522,371 square kilometers. What is the combined area of these two continents? **38,916,133 km^2**

4. FLIGHT SCHOOL The list shows how many times each of 20 students practiced with a piloting simulator at a flight training school one day.

9 11 12 9 6 12 10 8 13 14
8 9 13 11 10 8 12 9 10 8

Make a frequency table to find how many more students practiced with the simulator 9–11 times than 12–14 times. **3 more students**

Practicing with Simulator		
No. of Times	Tally	Frequency
6–8	𝍸	5
9–11	𝍸 IIII	9
12–14	𝍸 I	6

5. FOOD The total cost for a take-out lunch was $20. If four friends share the cost equally, how much will each friend pay? **You can divide mentally; $20 ÷ 4 = $5**

6. MONEY Mai had $210 in her checking account at the beginning of the month. She wrote checks for $32 and $9.59. At the end of the month, the bank credited her account with $0.84 interest. How much money did Mai have in the account then? **Sample answer: You can use addition to find the total amount to be subtracted, and then use addition to find the balance; $210 − ($32 + $9.59) + $0.84 = $169.25**

Copyright © Glencoe/McGraw-Hill, a division of The McGraw-Hill Companies, Inc.

NAME ______________________ DATE ____________ PERIOD _____

11-6 Study Guide and Intervention

Dividing Integers

- The quotient of two integers with different signs is negative.
- The quotient of two integers with the same sign is positive.

Example 1 **Use counters to find $-6 \div 2$.**

There are 2 groups of 3 negative counters each.

So, $-6 \div 2 = -3$.

Examples **Divide.**

2 $10 \div (-5)$

Since $-5 \times (-2) = 10$, it follows that $10 \div (-5) = -2$.

3 $-12 \div (-3)$

Since $-3 \times 4 = -12$, it follows that $-12 \div (-3) = 4$.

Exercises

Divide.

1. $4 \div (-2)$ **−2**
2. $-9 \div (-3)$ **3**
3. $-8 \div 2$ **−4**
4. $-21 \div 7$ **−3**
5. $30 \div (-5)$ **−6**
6. $-24 \div 4$ **−6**
7. $-36 \div 6$ **−6**
8. $-45 \div (-5)$ **9**
9. $-81 \div 9$ **−9**
10. $-3 \div (-3)$ **1**
11. $70 \div (-7)$ **−10**
12. $-64 \div (-8)$ **8**

13. ALGEBRA Find the value of $a \div b$ if $a = -18$ and $b = 6$. **−3**

14. ALGEBRA For what value of p is $p \div 5 = -7$ true? **−35**

NAME ______________________ DATE ____________ PERIOD _____

11-6 Practice
Dividing Integers

Divide.

1. $33 \div (-3)$ **−11**
2. $-84 \div (-6)$ **14**
3. $-26 \div 13$ **−2**
4. $92 \div (-23)$ **−4**
5. $-96 \div 4$ **−24**
6. $36 \div (-6)$ **−6**
7. $76 \div 4$ **19**
8. $-12 \div (-6)$ **2**
9. $-30 \div (-5)$ **6**
10. $-42 \div 7$ **−6**
11. $18 \div (-2)$ **−9**
12. $-27 \div 9$ **−3**
13. $69 \div 23$ **3**
14. $52 \div 13$ **4**
15. $-40 \div (-10)$ **4**
16. $28 \div (-4)$ **−7**
17. $\frac{-8-7}{-5}$ **3**
18. $\frac{5-(-4)+(-9+6)}{-6}$ **−1**
19. $\frac{(21 \div 3) \times 8}{-4}$ **−14**
20. $\frac{(-3+(-2)) \times (-6+1)}{5}$ **5**

21. **MILKING** It takes 20 minutes for a cow to be milked by a milking machine. How many cows can be milked in 6 hours?
18 cows

22. **ALGEBRA** What is the value of $s \div t$ if $s = -18$ and $t = -6$?
3

23. **TESTING** Thi wants to find the average of her last four math tests. She scored 96 on her first test. Use the table to find her average score for the four tests.
92.25

Thi's Tests	
Test 1	0
Test 2	−13
Test 3	−5
Test 4	3

24. **GASOLINE** The price of a gallon of gasoline increased by 5 cents one week, decreased by 3 cents each of the next two weeks, and increased by 7 cents the fourth week. Find the average change in the price of gasoline for the 4 weeks.
1.5 cents per week

NAME ______________________ DATE ____________ PERIOD _____

11-7 Study Guide and Intervention
The Coordinate Plane

The *x*-axis and *y*-axis separate the coordinate system into four regions called **quadrants**.

Example 1 **Identify the ordered pair that names point *A*.**

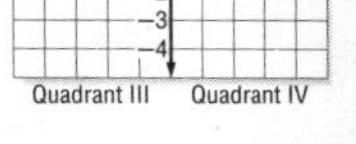

Step 1 Move left on the *x*-axis to find the *x*-coordinate of point *A*, which is −3.

Step 2 Move up the *y*-axis to find the *y*-coordinate, which is 4.

Point *A* is named by (−3, 4).

Example 2 **Graph point *B* at (5, 4).**

Use the coordinate plane shown above. Start at 0. The *x*-coordinate is 5, so move 5 units to the right.

Since the *y*-coordinate is 4, move 4 units up.

Draw a dot. Label the dot *B*.
See grid at the top of the page.

Exercises

Use the coordinate plane at the right. Write the ordered pair that names each point.

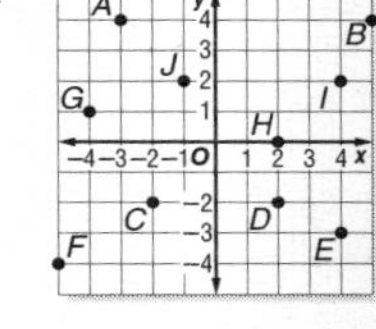

1. *C* **(−2, −2)**
2. *D* **(2, −2)**
3. *E* **(4, −3)**
4. *F* **(−5, −4)**
5. *G* **(−4, 1)**
6. *H* **(2, 0)**
7. *I* **(4, 2)**
8. *J* **(−1, 2)**

Graph and label each point using the coordinate plane at the right.

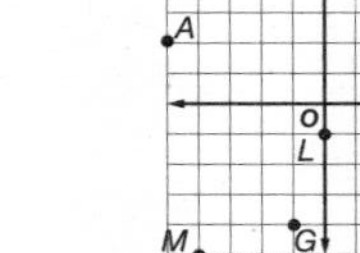

9. *A*(−5, 2)
10. *M*(−4, −5)
11. *G*(−1, −4)
12. *L*(0, −1)
13. *N*(1, 5)
14. *I*(2, 1)

Copyright © Glencoe/McGraw-Hill, a division of The McGraw-Hill Companies, Inc.

NAME ______________ DATE ________ PERIOD ____

11-7 Practice

The Coordinate Plane

Use the coordinate plane at the right for Exercises 1–6. Identify the point for each ordered pair.

1. (−3, 4) **K**
2. (−4, −3) **F**
3. (−2, −2) **B**
4. (3, −1) **E**
5. (0, 1) **H**
6. (−1, −4) **J**

For exercises 7–12, use the coordinate plane above. Write the ordered pair that names each point. Then identify the quadrant where each point is located.

7. *C* **(−4, 1); II**
8. *L* **(3, 2); I**
9. *D* **(1, 5); I**
10. *A* **(1, −5); IV**
11. *G* **(−2, 2); II**
12. *I* **(0, −2); none**

Graph and label each point on the coordinate plane at the right.

13. *L*(−2, 0)
14. *M*(5, 2)
15. *N*(−4, −3)
16. *P*(1, −1)
17. *Q*(0, −4)
18. *R*(3, −3)

Use the map of the Alger Underwater Preserve in Lake Superior to answer the following questions.

19. In which quadrant is the Stephen M. Selvick located?
none
20. What is the ordered pair that represents the location of the Bermuda? the Superior?
Bermuda: (−2, −1)
Superior: (4, 1)
21. Which quadrant contains Williams Island?
II
22. Which shipwreck is closest to the origin?
Herman H. Hetler

Copyright © Glencoe/McGraw-Hill, a division of The McGraw-Hill Companies, Inc.

NAME ______________ DATE ________ PERIOD ____

11-8 Study Guide and Intervention

Translations

- A transformation is a movement of a geometric figure.
- The resulting figure is called the image.
- A translation is the sliding of a figure without turning it.
- A translation does not change the size or shape of a figure.

Example 1 **Translate triangle *ABC* 5 units to the right.**

Step 1 Move each vertex of the triangle 5 units right. Label the new vertices A', B', C'.

Step 2 Connect the new vertices to draw the triangle. The coordinates of the vertices of the new triangle are $A'(2, 4)$, $B'(2, 2)$, and $C'(5, 0)$.

Example 2 A placemat on a table has vertices at (0, 0), (3, 0), (3, 4), and (0, 4). Find the vertices of the placemat after a translation of 4 units right and 2 units up.

Vertex	$(x + 4, y + 2)$	New vertex
(0, 0)	(0 + 4, 0 + 2)	(4, 2)
(3, 0)	(3 + 4, 0 + 2)	(7, 2)
(3, 4)	(3 + 4, 4 + 2)	(7, 6)
(0, 4)	(0 + 4, 4 + 2)	(4, 6)

Exercises

Find the coordinates of the image of (2, 4), (1, 5), (1, −3), and (3, −4) under each transformation.

1. 2 units right
(4, 4), (3, 5), (3, −3), (5, −4)
2. 4 units down
(2, 0), (1, 1), (1, −7), (3, −8)

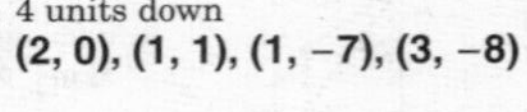

3. 3 units left and 4 units down
(−1, 0), (−2, 1), (−2, −7), (3, −8)
4. 5 units right and 3 units up
(7, 7), (6, 8), (6, 0), (8, −1)

Lesson 11–8

NAME ______________________ DATE ____________ PERIOD _____

11-8 Practice

Translations

1. Translate LMN 5 units down. Graph triangle $L'M'N'$.

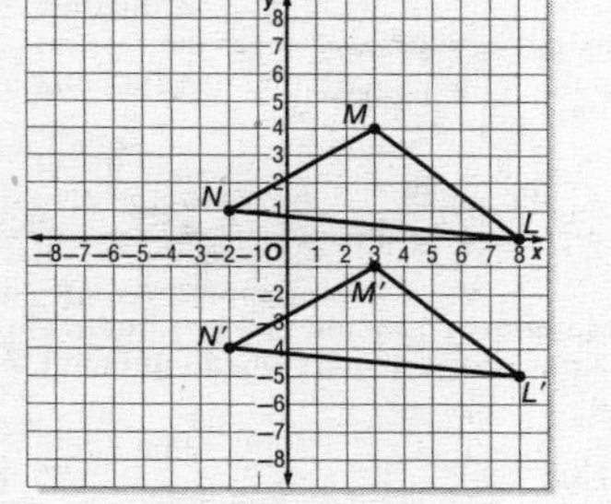

2. Translate TRI 2 units left and 3 units up. Graph $T'R'I'$.

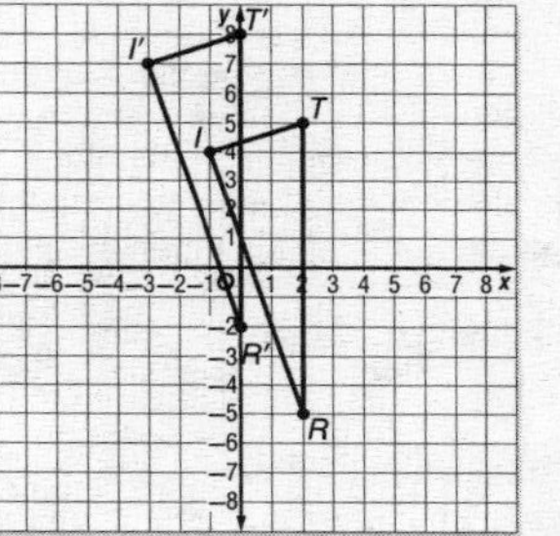

A table has vertices of (0, 3), (6, 2), (0, 8), and (−2, 5) on a floor. Find the vertices of the table after each translation.

3. 4 units right
(4, 3), (10, 2), (4, 8), (2, 5)

4. 2 units left
(−2, 3), (4, 2), (−2, 8), (−4, 5)

5. 6 units up
(0, 9), (6, 8), (0, 14), (−2, 11)

6. 9 units down
(0, −6), (6, −7), (0, −1), (−2, −4)

7. 1 unit left and 5 units up
(−1, 8), (5, 7), (−1, 13), (−3, 10)

8. 7 units right and 8 units up
(7, 11), (13, 10), (7, 16), (5, 13)

9. 4 units left and 6 units down
(−4, −3), (2, −4), (−4, 2), (−6, −1)

10. 9 units right and 3 units down
(9, 0), (15, −1), (9, 5), (7, 2)

11. 1 unit left and 9 units up
(−1, 12), (5, 11), (−1, 17), (−3, 14)

12. 5 units right and 7 units down
(5, −4), (11, −5), (5, 1), (3, −2)

13. One of the vertices of a square is (3, 5). What is the ordered pair of the image after a translation of 3 units up, 5 units left and then 4 units down? What translation will give the same result? **(2, 0); 1 unit down 5 units left**

NAME ______________________ DATE ____________ PERIOD _____

11-9 Study Guide and Intervention

Reflections

- A reflection is the mirror image that is created when a figure is flipped over a line.
- A reflection is a type of geometric transformation.
- When reflecting over the x-axis, the y-coordinate changes to its opposite.
- When reflecting over the y-axis, the x-coordinate changes to its opposite.

Example 1 **Reflect triangle ABC over the x-axis.**

Step 1 Graph triangle ABC on a coordinate plane. Then count the number of units between each vertex and the x-axis.

A is 4 units from the axis.
B is 2 units from the axis.
C is 0 units from the axis.

Step 2 Make a point for each vertex the same distance away from the x-axis on the opposite side of the x-axis and connect the new points to form the image of the triangle. The new points are $A'(-3, -4)$, $B'(-2, -2)$, and $C'(0, 0)$.

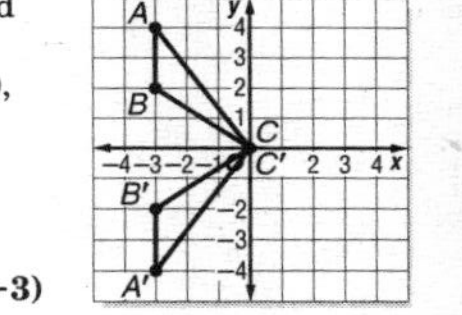

Exercises

Find the coordinates of the image of (2, 4), (1, 5), (1, −3) and (3, −4) under each transformation.

1. a reflection over the x-axis
(2, −4), (1, −5), (1, 3), (3, 4)

2. a reflection over the y-axis.
(−2, 4), (−1, 5), (−1, −3), (−3, −4)

Find the coordinates of the image of (−1, 1), (3, −2) and (0, 5) under each transformation.

3. a reflection over the x-axis
(−1, −1), (3, 2), (0, −5)

4. a reflection over the y-axis
(1, 1), (−3, −2), (0, 5)

Lesson 11–9

Copyright © Glencoe/McGraw-Hill, a division of The McGraw-Hill Companies, Inc.

NAME ______________ DATE ________ PERIOD ____

11-9 Practice
Reflections

1. Reflect PQR over the x-axis. Graph $P'Q'R'$.

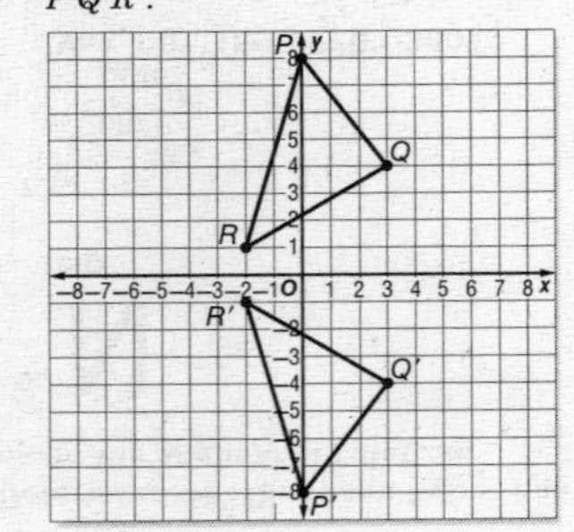

2. Reflect PQR over the y-axis. Graph $P'Q'R'$.

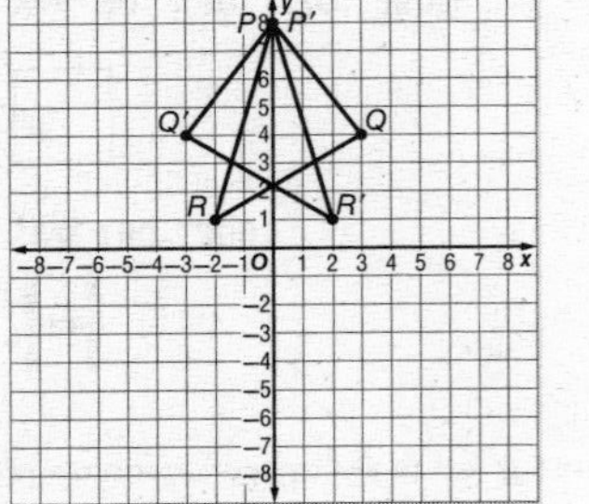

3. Reflect DEF over the x-axis. Graph $D'E'F'$.

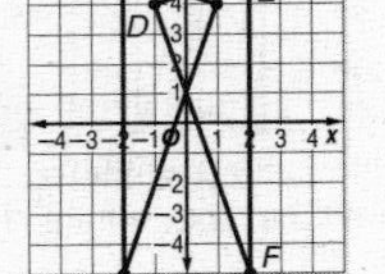

4. Reflect DEF over the y-axis. Graph $D'E'F'$.

A table has vertices of (0, 3), (6, 2), (0, 8), and (−2, 5) on a floor. Find the vertices of the table after each transformation.

5. a reflection over the x-axis
   (0, −3), (6, −2), (0, −8), (−2, −5)

6. a reflection over the y-axis.
   (0, 3), (−6, 2), (0, 8), (2, 5)

A piece of artwork has vertices of (2, 5), (−1, 6) and (0, −7) on a wall. Find the vertices of the table after each transformation.

7. a reflection over the x-axis
   (2, −5), (−1, −6), (0, 7)

8. a reflection over the y-axis
   (−2, 5), (1, 6), (0, −7)

NAME ______________ DATE ________ PERIOD ____

11-10 Study Guide and Intervention
Rotations

- A rotation occurs when a figure is rotated around a point.
- Another name for a rotation is a turn.
- In a rotation clockwise of 90° about the origin, the point (x, y) becomes $(y, -x)$.
- In a rotation clockwise of 180° about the origin, the point (x, y) becomes $(-x, -y)$.
- In a rotation clockwise of 270° about the origin, the point (x, y) becomes $(-y, x)$.

Example 1 **Rotate triangle ABC clockwise 180° about the origin.**

Step 1 Graph triangle ABC on a coordinate plane.

Step 2 Sketch segment AO connecting point A to the origin. Sketch another segment $A'O$ so that the angle between point A, O, and A' measures 180° and the segment is congruent to AO.

Step 3 Repeat for point B (point C won't move since it is at the origin). Then connect the vertices to form triangle $A'B'C'$.

Exercises

Find the coordinates of the image of (2, 4), (1, 5), (1, −3) and (3, −4) under each transformation.

1. a rotation of 90° about the origin
   (4, −2), (5, −1), (−3, −3), (−4, −3)

2. a rotation of 270° about the origin
   (−4, 2), (−5, 1), (3, 1), (4, 3)

Determine whether each figure has rotational symmetry. Write *yes* or *no*. If yes, name the angle(s) of rotation.

3. 
   Yes, 180°, 360°

4. Q
   No

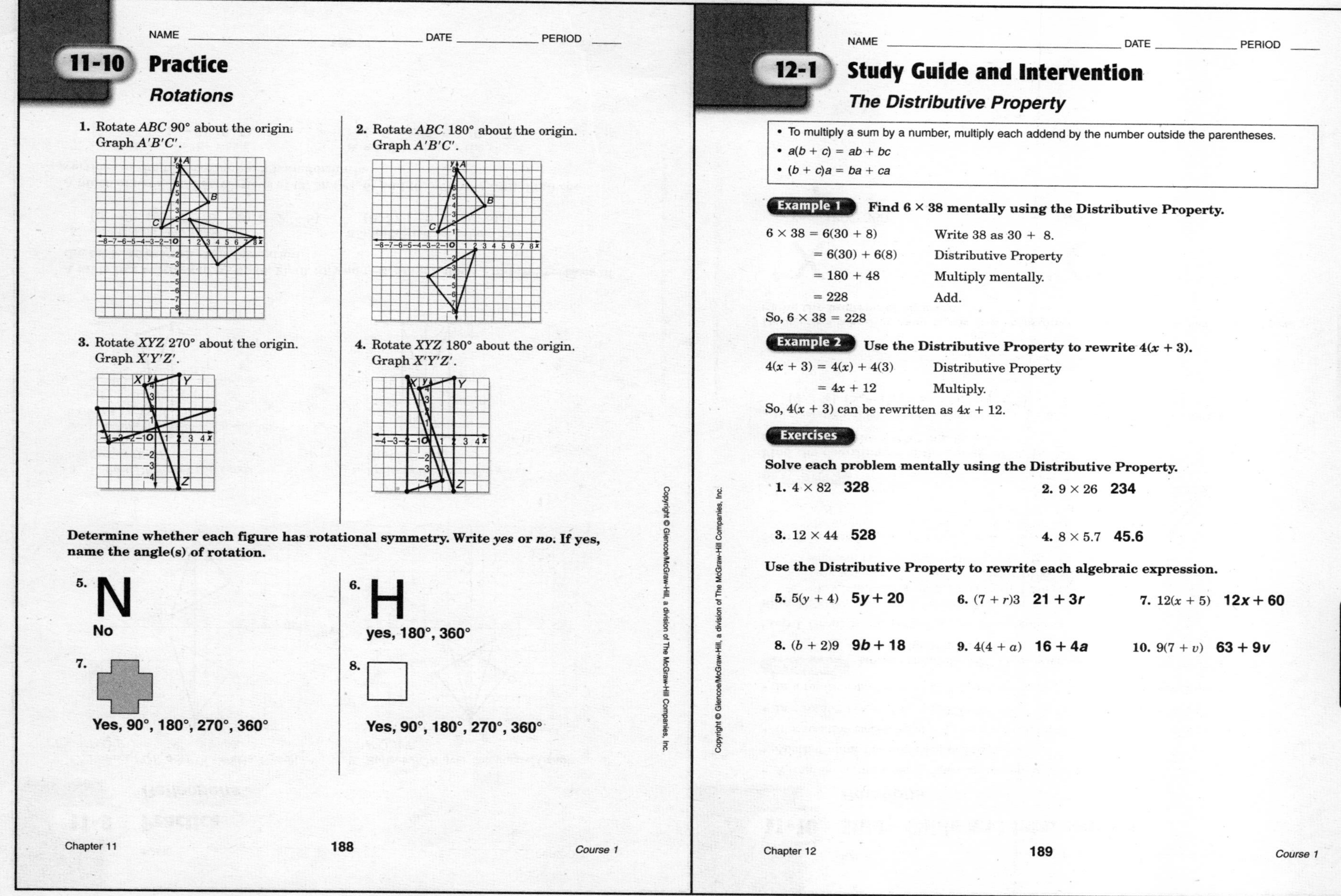

NAME ________________ DATE ________ PERIOD ____

11-10 Practice

Rotations

1. Rotate ABC 90° about the origin. Graph $A'B'C'$.

2. Rotate ABC 180° about the origin. Graph $A'B'C'$.

3. Rotate XYZ 270° about the origin. Graph $X'Y'Z'$.

4. Rotate XYZ 180° about the origin. Graph $X'Y'Z'$.

Determine whether each figure has rotational symmetry. Write *yes* or *no*. If yes, name the angle(s) of rotation.

5. N **No**

6. H **yes, 180°, 360°**

7. **Yes, 90°, 180°, 270°, 360°**

8. **Yes, 90°, 180°, 270°, 360°**

NAME ________________ DATE ________ PERIOD ____

12-1 Study Guide and Intervention

The Distributive Property

- To multiply a sum by a number, multiply each addend by the number outside the parentheses.
- $a(b + c) = ab + bc$
- $(b + c)a = ba + ca$

Example 1 **Find 6 × 38 mentally using the Distributive Property.**

$6 \times 38 = 6(30 + 8)$	Write 38 as 30 + 8.
$= 6(30) + 6(8)$	Distributive Property
$= 180 + 48$	Multiply mentally.
$= 228$	Add.

So, $6 \times 38 = 228$

Example 2 **Use the Distributive Property to rewrite $4(x + 3)$.**

$4(x + 3) = 4(x) + 4(3)$	Distributive Property
$= 4x + 12$	Multiply.

So, $4(x + 3)$ can be rewritten as $4x + 12$.

Exercises

Solve each problem mentally using the Distributive Property.

1. 4×82 **328**
2. 9×26 **234**
3. 12×44 **528**
4. 8×5.7 **45.6**

Use the Distributive Property to rewrite each algebraic expression.

5. $5(y + 4)$ **$5y + 20$**
6. $(7 + r)3$ **$21 + 3r$**
7. $12(x + 5)$ **$12x + 60$**
8. $(b + 2)9$ **$9b + 18$**
9. $4(4 + a)$ **$16 + 4a$**
10. $9(7 + v)$ **$63 + 9v$**

NAME ______________ DATE ________ PERIOD ____

12-1 Practice

The Distributive Property

Solve each problem mentally using the Distributive Property.

1. 8×34 **272**
2. 5×47 **235**
3. 12×51 **612**
4. 8×53 **424**
5. 6×4.4 **26.4**
6. 7×2.9 **20.3**

Use the Distributive Property to rewrite each algebraic expression.

7. $6(n + 4)$ **$6n + 24$**
8. $(2 + r)15$ **$30 + 15r$**
9. $8(s + 5)$ **$8s + 40$**
10. $(b + 8)3$ **$3b + 24$**
11. $5(6 + b)$ **$30 + 5b$**
12. $9(3 + v)$ **$27 + 9v$**
13. $(r - 7)7$ **$7r - 49$**
14. $12(4 - v)$ **$48 - 12v$**
15. $11(3 - s)$ **$33 - 11s$**

For Exercises 16–18, use the table that shows the prices of tickets and various food items at the movie theater.

Item	Price
Ticket	$8.50
Popcorn	$5.25
Soda	$4.00
Candy	$3.75
Nachos	$6.50

16. Four friends each bought a ticket and a bag of popcorn. How much total money did they spend? **$55.00**

17. How much money will the movie theater make if a birthday party of 12 kids each buys a box of candy and a soda but doesn't go see a movie? **$93.00**

18. How much more money will a person spend who buys three orders of nachos than a person who buys three bags of popcorn? **$3.75**

Copyright © Glencoe/McGraw-Hill, a division of The McGraw-Hill Companies, Inc.

NAME ______________ DATE ________ PERIOD ____

12-2 Study Guide and Intervention

Simplifying Algebraic Expressions

- **Commutative Property:** The order which numbers are added or multiplied does not change the sum or the product.
- $a + b = b + a$ or $a \cdot b = b \cdot a$.
- **Associative Property:** The way in which numbers are grouped does not change the sum or the product.
- $(a + b) + c = a + (b + c)$ or $(a \cdot b) \cdot c = a \cdot (b \cdot c)$
- **Like terms** contain the same variables. Ex: $2y$, y, and $7y$ are all like terms, but $4x$ is not.

Example 1 **Simplify the expression $16 + (v + 4)$.**

$16 + (v + 4) = 16 + (4 + v)$ Commutative Property
$= (16 + 4) + v$ Associative Property
$= 20 + v$ Add.

So, $16 + (v + 4)$ in simplified form is $20 + v$.

Example 2 **Simplify the expression $3x + (6 + 2x)$.**

$3x + (6 + 2x) = 3x + (2x + 6)$ Commutative Property
$= (3x + 2x) + 6$ Associative Property
$= 5x + 6$ Combine like terms.

So, $3x + (6 + 2x)$ in simplified form is $5x + 6$.

Exercises

Simplify each expression. Justify each step.

1. $5 + x + 3$
 $= 5 + 3 + x$ Comm. Prop.
 $= 8 + x$ Add.

2. $6 + (x + 4)$
 $= 6 + (4 + x)$ Comm. Prop.
 $= (6 + 4) + x$ Assoc. Prop.
 $= 10 + x$ Add.

3. $(b + 10) + 15$
 $= b + (10 + 15)$ Assoc.
 $= b + 25$ Add.

4. $8x + 5 + 2x$
 $= 8x + 2x + 5$ Assoc. Prop.
 $= 10x + 5$ Combine like terms.

5. $(12 + 2u) + 3$
 $= (2u + 12) + 3$ Comm. Prop
 $= 2u + (12 + 3)$ Assoc. Prop
 $= 2u + 15$ Add.

6. $11p + 8 + 7p$
 $= 11p + 7p + 8$ Comm.
 $= 18p + 8$ Combine like terms.

7. $9x + (4 + 3x)$
 $9x + (3x + 4)$ Comm. Prop.
 $(9x + 3x) + 4$ Assoc. Prop.
 $12x + 4$ Combine like terms.

8. $(8 + 12x) + (2 + 7x)$
 $= (8 + 12x) + (7x + 2)$ Comm. Prop.
 $= 8 + (12x + 7x) + 2$ Assoc. Prop.
 $= 8 + 19x + 2$ Combine like terms.
 $= 8 + 2 + 19x$ Comm. Prop.
 $= 10 + 19x$ Add.

9. $5y + 4 + 7y$
 $= 5y + 7y + 4$ Comm.
 $= 12y + 4$ Combine like terms.

NAME ______________________ DATE ____________ PERIOD _____

12-2 Practice

Simplifying Algebraic Expressions

Simplify each expression. Justify each step.

1. $(7 + x) + 7x$
$= 7 + (x + 7x)$ **Assoc.**
$= 7 + 8x$ **Like terms**

2. $5 \cdot (4 \cdot x)$
$= (5 \cdot 4) \cdot x$ **Assoc.**
$= 20 \cdot x$ **Like terms**

3. $15 + (x + 9)$
$= 15 + (9 + x)$ **Comm.**
$= (15 + 9) + x$ **Assoc.**
$= 24 + x$ **Add.**

4. $(6x + 21) + 14$
$= 6x + (21 + 4)$ **Assoc.**
$= 6x + 25$ **Add.**

5. $3x + 2 + 11x$
$= 3x + 11x + 2$ **Comm.**
$= 14x + 2$ **Like terms**

6. $(x + 13) + 8$
$= x + (13 + 8)$ **Assoc.**
$= x + 21$ **Add.**

7. $(12 + 2x) + 4$
$= (2x + 12) + 4$ **Comm.**
$= 2x + (12 + 4)$ **Assoc.**

8. $8 \cdot (x \cdot 4)$
$= 8 \cdot (4 \cdot x)$ **Comm.**
$= (8 \cdot 4) \cdot x$ **Assoc.**

9. $3(5x)$
$= (3 \cdot 5)x$ **Assoc.**
$= 15x$ **Multiply.**

10. $3x + (7x + 10)$
$= (3x + 7x) + 10$ **Assoc.**
$= 10x + 10$ **Like terms**

11. $5x + (2 + x)$
$= 5x + (x + 2)$ **Comm.**
$= (5x + x) + 2$ **Assoc.**

12. $4 \cdot x \cdot 10$
$= 4 \cdot 10 \cdot x$ **Comm.**
$= 40 \cdot x$ **Multiply.**

13. $(x \cdot 12) \cdot 3$
$= x \cdot (12 \cdot 3)$ **Assoc.**
$= x \cdot 36$ **Multiply.**

14. $14x + 9 + 6x$
$= 14x + 6x + 9$ **Comm.**
$= 20x + 9$ **Like terms**

15. $5x + (24 + 14x)$
$= 5x + (14x + 24)$ **Comm.**
$= (5x + 14x) + 24$ **Assoc.**
$= 19x + 24$ **Like terms**

ALGEBRA **For Exercises 16 through 21, translate each verbal expression into an algebraic expression. Then, simplify the expression.**

16. The sum of three and a number is added to twenty-four.
$(3 + n) + 24$; $n + 27$

17. The product of six and a number is multiplied by nine. **$(6x)9$; $54x$**

18. The sum of 10 times a number and fifteen is added to eleven times the same number.
$(10x + 15) + 11x$; $15 + 21x$

19. Two sets of the sum of a number and eight are added to five times the same number.
$2(x + 8) + 5x$; $7x + 16$

20. Three sets of a sum of a number and four are added to the sum of seven times the same number and thirteen.
$3(x + 4) + (7x + 13)$; $10x + 25$

21. Five friends went to a baseball game. Three of the friends each bought a ticket for x dollars and a soda for $6.00. The other two friends each bought only tickets. Write and simplify an expression that represents the amount of money spent.
$3(x + 6) + 2x$; $5x + 18$

NAME ______________________ DATE ____________ PERIOD _____

12-3 Study Guide and Intervention

Solving Addition Equations

Subtraction Property of Equality If you subtract the same number from each side of an equation, the two sides remain equal.

$$\begin{array}{r} 5 = 5 \\ -3 = -3 \\ \hline 2 = 2 \end{array}$$

Example 1 **Solve $x + 2 = 7$ using models.**

$x + 2 = 7$ — Model the equation.

$x + 2 - 2 = 7 - 2$ — Remove 2 counters from each side of the mat.

$x = 5$ — The counters remaining on the right side of the mat represent the solution or value of x.

The solution is 5. $5 + 2 = 7$ ✓
5 substituted in the original equation is correct.

Example 2 **Solve $b + 3 = 2$.**

$b + 3 = 2$ — Write the equation.
$-3 = -3$ — Subtract 3 from each side to undo the addition of 3 on the left.
$b + 0 = -1$ — Simplify.
$b = -1$

The solution is -1.

Check $b + 3 = 2$ — Write the original equation.
$-1 + 3 \stackrel{?}{=} 2$ — Replace b with -1.
$2 = 2$ ✓ — This sentence is true.

Exercises

Solve each equation. Use models if necessary. Check your solution.

1. $a + 1 = 7$ **6**
2. $3 + b = 8$ **5**
3. $c + 7 = 4$ **−3**
4. $9 = x + 4$ **5**
5. $g + 8 = -2$ **−10**
6. $d + 6 = -5$ **−11**

NAME ______________ DATE ________ PERIOD ____

12-3 Practice

Solving Addition Equations

Solve each equation. Use models if necessary. Check your solution.

1. $9 + d = -5$ **−14**
2. $b + 2 = 6$ **4**
3. $x + (-4) = 1$ **5**
4. $-2 + j = -9$ **−7**
5. $m + (-4) = 9$ **13**
6. $1 = f + (-7)$ **8**
7. $6 + c = 3$ **−3**
8. $8 + y = -9$ **−17**
9. $3 + h = -6$ **−9**
10. $p + (-6) = -4$ **2**
11. $\frac{1}{4} + a = \frac{3}{4}$ $\mathbf{\frac{2}{4} = \frac{1}{2}}$
12. $-\frac{3}{8} + g = \frac{2}{8}$ $\mathbf{\frac{5}{8}}$
13. **ALGEBRA** What is the value of n if $7 + n = 5$? **−2**

THOROUGHBREDS The table shows the earnings of some of the leading horses at Northlands Park. Use the table to answer Exercises 14 and 15.

Horse Earnings at Northlands Park	
Horse	**Earnings**
Sparhawk	$52,800
Griffin's Web	$43,757
Kaylee's Magic	$121,113
Eternal Secrecy	$57,532
Silver Sky	
Huntley's Creek	

14. Sparhawk has earned $8,329 more than Silver Sky. Write and solve an equation to find Silver Sky's earnings.
$x + 8{,}329 = 52{,}800$
$x = 44{,}471$
Silver Sky earned $44,471.

15. Write and solve an equation to find Huntley's Creek's earnings if the total earnings for all the horses is $354,386.
$52{,}800 + 43{,}757 + 121{,}113 + 57{,}532 + 44{,}471 + x = 354{,}386$
$319{,}673 + x = 354{,}386$
$x = 34{,}713$

NAME ______________ DATE ________ PERIOD ____

12-4 Study Guide and Intervention

Solving Subtraction Equations

Addition Property of Equality If you add the same number to each side of an equation, the two sides remain equal.

$$\begin{aligned} 5 &= 5 \\ +3 &= +3 \\ \hline 8 &= 8 \end{aligned}$$

Example 1 **Solve $x - 2 = 1$ using models.**

$x - 2 = 1$ — Model the equation.

$x - 2 + 2 = 1 + 2$ — Add 2 positive counters to each side of the mat.

$x = 3$ — Remove the zero pairs.

The solution is 3.

Example 2 **Solve $b - 3 = -5$.**

$b - 3 = -5$ Write the equation.
$+3 = +3$ Add 3 to each side to undo the subtraction of 3 on the left.
$b + 0 = -2$ Simplify.
$b = -2$

Check $b - 3 = -5$ Write the original equation.
$-2 - 3 \stackrel{?}{=} -5$ Replace b with −2.
$-5 = -5$ ✓ This sentence is true.

Exercises

Solve each equation. Use models if necessary. Check your solution.

1. $a - 2 = 3$ **5**
2. $b - 1 = 7$ **8**
3. $c - 4 = 4$ **8**
4. $-2 = x - 4$ **2**
5. $z - 6 = -3$ **3**
6. $g - 3 = -4$ **−1**
7. $-9 + w = 1$ **10**
8. $v - 8 = 5$ **13**
9. $-7 = y - 5$ **−2**
10. $u - 3 = -4$ **−1**
11. $-2 = t - 9$ **7**
12. $f - 6 = -3$ **3**

NAME ______________________ DATE ____________ PERIOD _____

12-4 Practice

Solving Subtraction Equations

Solve each equation. Use models if necessary. Check your solution.

1. $t - 7 = -19$ **−12**
2. $x - 2 = -5$ **−3**
3. $g - 6 = -2$ **4**
4. $-6 = c - 5$ **−1**
5. $h - 5 = 4$ **9**
6. $8 - j = 5$ **3**
7. $y - (-7) = 7$ **0**
8. $9 = a - 9$ **18**
9. $p - (-3) = 5$ **2**
10. $d - 5 = -9$ **−4**
11. $m - \frac{3}{18} = \frac{11}{18}$ $\mathbf{\frac{7}{9}}$
12. $b - \frac{3}{15} = -1$ $\mathbf{-\frac{4}{5}}$

13. **PARASAILING** A parasailer is attached by a cable to a boat and towed so that the parachute she is wearing catches air and raises her into the air. When the boat slows down to turn back towards the beach the parasailer's chute catches less air and dips 25 meters. She must descend another 45 meters to return to the boat. Write and solve a subtraction equation to find her original height above the boat before the turn.
$x - 25 = 45$
$x = 70$
She was 70 meters above the boat.

14. **ALGEBRA** What is the value of k if $-6 = 9 - k$? **15**

15. The Petrified Forest National Park in Arizona recently expanded their boundaries by 93,533 acres. The original acreage was 125,000. Write and solve a subtraction equation to find the new acreage of the park.
$a - 125{,}000 = 93{,}533$
$a = 218{,}533$ acres

16. A mako shark caught by a rod and reel in Massachusetts Bay weighed 1,324 pounds. This was 103 pounds more than the International Game Fish Association (IGFA) record. What is the IGFA record for a mako shark?
1,221 lbs

NAME ______________________ DATE ____________ PERIOD _____

12-5 Study Guide and Intervention

Solving Multiplication Equations

In a multiplication equation, the number by which a variable is multiplied is called the **coefficient**. In the multiplication equation, $2x = 8$, the coefficient is 2.

Example 1 **Solve $2x = 6$ using models.**

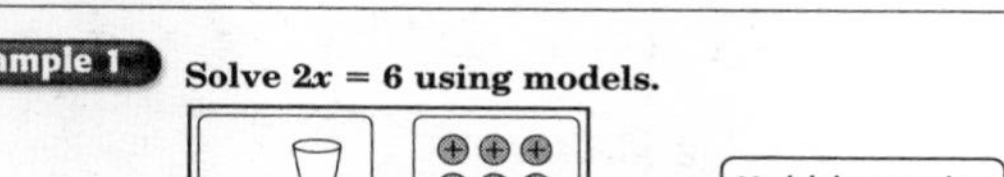

Check $2x = 6$ Write the original equation.
$2(3) \stackrel{?}{=} 6$ Replace x with 3.
$6 = 6$ This sentence is true. ✓

The solution is 3.

Example 2 **Solve $-4b = 12$.**

$-4b = 12$ Write the equation.
$\frac{-4b}{-4} = \frac{12}{-4}$ Divide each side by −4 to get a single positive variable by itself.
$1b = -3$ Simplify.
$b = -3$

Check $-4b = 12$ Write the original equation.
$-4(-3) \stackrel{?}{=} 12$ Replace b with −3.
$12 = 12$ This sentence is true. ✓

The solution is −3.

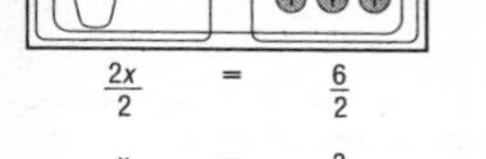

Exercises

Solve each equation. Use models if necessary. Check your solution.

1. $5a = 25$ **5**
2. $7c = 49$ **7**
3. $24 = 6d$ **4**
4. $2x = -8$ **−4**
5. $18 = -9y$ **−2**
6. $-8g = -16$ **2**
7. $18 = -3z$ **−6**
8. $-4w = -36$ **9**
9. $56 = 7v$ **8**
10. $24 = -8f$ **−3**
11. $3u = -27$ **−9**
12. $-42 = 6t$ **−7**

NAME ______________ DATE ________ PERIOD ____

12-5 Practice

Solving Multiplication Equations

Solve each equation. Use models if necessary.

1. $7a = 63$ **9**	**2.** $-14k = 0$ **0**	**3.** $-13w = 39$ **−3**	**4.** $55 = -11x$ **−5**
5. $3v = -42$ **−14**	**6.** $96 = 12f$ **8**	**7.** $-14u = -70$ **5**	**8.** $-3c = 3$ **−1**
9. $15s = -120$ **−8**	**10.** $35q = -5$ $-\frac{1}{7}$	**11.** $-6 = -2y$ **3**	**12.** $-13t = -117$ **9**
13. $72 = -6r$ **−12**	**14.** $0.8b = -1.12$ **−1.4**	**15.** $-2.3g = 7.13$ **−3.1**	**16.** $40 = -1.6m$ **−25**

14. TIME The Russian ice breaker *Yamal* can move forward through 2.3-meter thick ice at a speed of 5.5 kilometers per hour. Write and solve a multiplication equation to find the number of hours it will take to travel 82.5 kilometers through the ice.
$5.5x = 82.5$
$x = 15$ hours

FUNDRAISING A school is raising money by selling calendars for $20 each. Mrs. Hawkins promised a party to whichever of her English classes sold the most calendars over the course of four weeks. Use the table to answer Exercises 15–17.

Mrs. Hawkins' Fundraising Challenge

Class	Number of Calendars Sold
1st Period	60
2nd Period	123
3rd Period	89
4th Period	126

15. Write and solve an equation to show the average number of calendars her 3rd period class sold per week during the four-week challenge.
$4c = 89$
$c = 22.25$

16. How many calendars did the 1st and 2nd period classes sell on average per week? Write and solve a multiplication equation.
$4c = 60 + 123$
$4c = 183$
$c = 45.75$ calendars per week

17. What was the average number of calendars sold in a week by all of her classes? **99.5 calendars**

Copyright © Glencoe/McGraw-Hill, a division of The McGraw-Hill Companies, Inc.

NAME ______________ DATE ________ PERIOD ____

12-6 Study Guide and Intervention

Problem-Solving Investigation: Choose the Best Method of Computation

When solving problems, one strategy that is helpful is to *choose the best method of computation.* After reading a problem you can determine if addition, subtraction, multiplication, or division will be the best method to solve the problem. You may often find that there is more than one method you can use to solve a problem.

You can choose the best method of computation, along with the following four-step problem solving plan to solve a problem.

1 Understand – Read and get a general understanding of the problem.

2 Plan – Make a plan to solve the problem and estimate the solution.

3 Solve – Use your plan to solve the problem.

4 Check – Check the reasonableness of your solution.

Example

SHOPPING At a craft fair, Mia bought a necklace for $6.50, a picture frame for $12.75, and a candle for $4.25. If Mia took $30 to the craft fair, how much money did she have left over?

Understand You know how much Mia spent for each item. You also know how much money she took to the fair. You need to find the amount she has left over.

Plan One method is to add to find the total amount she spent. Then subtract this amount from $30.

Solve Total Mia spent: $6.25 + $12.75 + $4.50 = $23.50

Amount left over: $30.00 – $23.50 = $6.50

So, Mia had $6.50 left over after she bought the three items at the craft fair.

Check Check the result by adding the amount left over, $6.50, with the amount she spent on each of the three items. Since, $6.25 + $12.75 + $4.50 + $6.50 = $30.00, the answer is correct.

Exercise

SPORTS Jeff Gordon won $1,497,150 as the winner of the 2005 Daytona 500. Sterling Marlin won $300,460 as the winner of the 1995 Daytona 500. About how many times more money did Jeff Gordon win than Sterling Marlin?
about 5 times

NAME ______________________ DATE __________ PERIOD ____

12-6 Practice

Problem-Solving Investigation: Choose the Best Method of Computation

Mixed Problem Solving

Choose the method of computation to solve Exercises 1 and 2. Explain your reasoning.

1. **IMMIGRATION** California registered 291,216 immigrants in 2002. New York registered 114,827 immigrants. About how many times greater was the number of immigrants received in California than in New York?
Estimation; 300,000 ÷ 100,000 = 3; California received about three times as many immigrants as New York.

2. **MONEY** Ingrid bought a book for $1.50 and a CD for $5.50 at a flea market. What was the total amount she spent?
Sample answer: mental math; since 0.50 + 0.50 = 1, add $1 + $1 + $5 = $7; Ingrid spent $7.

Use any strategy to solve Exercises 3 and 4. Some strategies are shown below.

Problem-Solving Strategies
• Look for a pattern.
• Use a graph.
• Guess and check.

3. **MONEY** Ilia and Candace went to see a movie. Their tickets were $9.50 a piece. They also bought a large popcorn for $4.00 and two medium drinks for $3.25 each. If they have $10.50 left, how much money did they have originally? **$40.00**

4. **PUMPKINS** Mr. Maldonado figures that he sold an average of 26 pumpkins a day. Use the graph to find how many he sold on Friday. **29 pumpkins**

Pumpkin Sales

Days of Week	M	T	W	Th	F	Sa	Su
Number of Pumpkin Sold	20	11	24	18		43	37

5. **MILEAGE** Mark drove a delivery truck 150 miles on Monday, 63 miles on Tuesday, and 122 miles on Thursday. How many miles did he drive on Wednesday if his average was 106.5 miles per day?
91 mi

6. **WEATHER** The morning outside temperature is −13°F. It rises 10° by midafternoon and drops 4° by evening. What is the outside temperature at the end of the day?
−7°F

Copyright © Glencoe/McGraw-Hill, a division of The McGraw-Hill Companies, Inc.